CHEMICAL PHYSIOLOGY OF ENDOPARASITIC ANIMALS

# Chemical Physiology of
# Endoparasitic Animals

By

Theodor von Brand

*Laboratory of Tropical Diseases, National Institutes of Health, U.S. Public Health Service, Bethesda, Md.*

1952

ACADEMIC PRESS INC., PUBLISHERS

NEW YORK, N. Y.

Campbell & Hall .    Jan. 9, 1956
Biology

Copyright 1952, by

ACADEMIC PRESS INC.

125 East 23rd Street

New York 10, N. Y.

*All Rights Reserved*

# PREFACE

A survey of the parasitological literature shows that the physiological aspects of the field have been developed essentially since the beginning of this century, but that this development has gathered increasing momentum only during the last 10 to 15 years. The purpose of the present book is to review and integrate the relevant literature which, because scattered in many periodicals and contained relatively often in papers dealing primarily with non-physiological topics, is sometimes difficult to locate. As in any other branch of the zoological sciences, physiological studies could be undertaken profitably in parasitology only on the foundations laid by the work of taxonomists, comparative anatomists, cytologists, and embryologists. Peculiar to parasitology are some features that do not play a similar role in other sciences, such as the complicated life cycles of many parasites, their pathological action on the host, the interest inherent in establishing *in vitro* cultures, to name only some of the more important ones. These aspects have occupied the interest of parasitologists for a long time, to the exclusion of physiological work proper.

In addition, physiological studies require a specialized training which the parasitologist, in the past, rarely had an opportunity to acquire. The biochemist, on the other hand, is rarely interested in the specific problems encountered in physiological parasitology. It seems clear that the urgently needed expansion of physiological work in parasitology can be achieved in two ways. Either the young parasitologist of the future will have to acquire a broad foundation in parasitology, physiology, and chemistry, especially biochemistry, or research teams consisting of specialists in these fields will have to be formed. Both ways are slowly developing at present and the future alone will tell which one will lead to more significant findings.

One of the difficulties in training prospective parasitologists in the physiological aspects of the field, or of focusing the interest of the biochemist on parasitological problems, is doubtless the lack of a book that would summarize our knowledge. The present book is an attempt to fill this gap. It is written on a level which should be readily understandable to a graduate student with some preliminary training in both parasitology and biochemistry. The literature has been quoted extensively in the hope that the book may be of use also to the investigator interested in some particular phase of parasite physiology.

As the title indicates, the book deals with the physiological relationships of endoparasitic animals. This term has been interpreted broadly, incorporating such forms as *Sacculina*, which lives with only part of its body inside the host, and also the free-living stages of endoparasites. True ectoparasites, especially most ectoparasitic arthropods, such as fleas or lice,

have not been considered, but a few ectoparasitic worms and crustacea have
been mentioned in such cases where findings made with them help to clarify
our views concerning the physiological activities of endoparasites.

The writer is greatly indebted to Dr. W. H. Wright for his stimulating
interest in the progress of this work and for reviewing Chapter 20, to Drs.
E. Bueding, E. Weinbach, and P. Weinstein for reviewing the entire
manuscript, to Mr. J. Bozicevich, Dr. M. F. Jones, and Dr. E. G. Reinhard
for reading respectively Chapters 7, 6, and 19, and to Mrs. M. O. Nolan
for help in taxonomic questions. All have been most helpful. It is, however,
almost unavoidable that in a book of this kind some errors remain or some
serious ommissions are committed, despite all possible attempts at accuracy.
The writer takes full responsibility for these and will be grateful if they are
pointed out to him. The writer's thanks are also due Drs. C. H. Brown,
E. Bueding, O. Harnisch, J. Oliver-Gonzalez, Z. Suzuoki, and A. D. Welch
for permitting the use of unpublished material, and to Drs. E. B. Cram,
L. J. Olivier, E. G. Reinhard, and C. W. Rees for the loan of books and
reprints.

*Bethesda, Maryland*                                    THEODOR VON BRAND

# CONTENTS

vii

## PART III

### CHEMICAL HOST-PARASITE RELATIONSHIPS

# Part I
# CHEMICAL COMPOSITION OF ENDOPARASITES

CHAPTER 1

## DRY MATTER AND INORGANIC SUBSTANCES

### I. DRY MATTER

The available determinations of the dry substance of parasites as recorded in Table 1 show rather wide variations between different species. This is correlated with the varying content of inorganic substances, proteins, carbohydrates, and fat which will be discussed in subsequent sections. It should be kept in mind that, while the determinations on helminths offer no technical difficulties and the results obtained can therefore be considered as accurate, those concerning parasitic protozoa, especially trypanosomes and malarial parasites, yield only tentative figures. It is nearly impossible to gain true wet weight figures of these organisms since no practical way exists of freeing them completely from adhering medium. The usual procedure of packing the protozoa down by vigorous centrifugation probably causes rather considerable errors.

Some figures of the dry weight of various organ systems are available for nematodes and one acanthocephalid worm (Table 2). Taking the relative bulk of the various systems into account, it becomes apparent that most of the dry matter is concentrated in the body wall. Hobson, Hobson, Bernacca, and Stephenson (no date) subdivided the body wall of *Ascaris* into cuticle, contractile part of the muscle layer plus hypodermis, and noncontractile part of the muscle layer. They found approximately the same percentage of dry substance in each (27.05, 24.84, and 25.26% respectively).

Similar determinations, for obvious reasons, cannot be carried out with flat worms. In tapeworms, variations along the proglottid chain may occur. Smorodincev and Bebesin (1935) found respectively 13.55, 13.57, and 16.15% dry substance in the neck region, the middle region, and the posterior region of *Taenia saginata*.

The fluid contained in the cysts of larval tapeworms is relatively poor in dry substance. An average value of 1.56% has been reported for *Cysticercus tenuicollis*, 1.78% for *Coenurus cerebralis* (Schopfer, 1932), and for *Echinococcus granulosus* different authors give figures centering around 1.3% (Mazzocco, 1923; Lemaire and Ribère, 1935).

1

## II. Inorganic Substances

### A. Quantitative Considerations

The available quantitative date (Table 1) show that in most analyzed parasites the amount of inorganic substances varies between 0.6 and 1.1% of the fresh substance and about 5 to 10% of the dry substance. Exceptions occur among the cestodes where in some cases excessively high values have been found; for example, 41% of the dry substance in the scolices of *Cysticercus tenuicollis* (Schopfer, 1932). This, undoubtedly, is due to the accumulation of calcareous corpuscles in their tissues.

The qualitative analysis of the ash of some helminths (Table 3) shows that the same components are found in free-living organisms.

The question of whether the amount of inorganic substances present in parasites depends upon the type of host has hardly been approached as yet. It is known that the freezing point depression of cestode and nematode tissues from marine fishes is considerably greater than that from comparable parasites occurring in fresh water fishes or terrestrial mammals. *Bothriocephalus sp.* and *Proleptus obtusus*, both from the selachian *Scylliorhinus*, showed freezing point depressions of $-2$ and $-2.41°C$ respectively while that of the trout-inhabiting *Eubothrium crassum* was $-0.933°C$ (Schopfer, 1932) and that of trematodes, cestodes, and nematodes taken from terrestrial vertebrates varied between about $-0.6$ and $-1.1°C$ (Vialli, 1923, 1926; Schopfer, 1927, 1932). It is not known, however, to what extent these differences were due to differences in the amount of inorganic substances. Before drawing premature conclusions it should be remembered that the isotonicity with sea water shown by the blood of poikilosmotic fishes like selachians is largely due to an accumulation of urea rather than of chlorides.

Some data probably significant in this direction because they indicate the impossibility of generalizations are known from the fluids of some parasites. The inorganic constituents of the celomic fluid of ascarids and the cystic fluid of some larval tapeworms have been studied repeatedly (Table 4). The relatively small concentration of chlorides in ascarids is especially noteworthy, an observation already made in 1865 by Marcet. Chlorides are here, from a quantitative standpoint, certainly not of prime importance for the total molecular concentration. Their contribution has variously been estimated to lie between 12 (Schopfer, 1932) and 36% (Duval and Courtois, 1928). These latter investigators showed that bicarbonates are of considerable importance in this respect; they found 58 ml of total carbon dioxide in 100 ml of body fluid. Chlorides, bicarbonates, and amino nitrogen (60 mg/100 ml fluid) accounted for 68% of the total molecular concentration in the case of *Parascaris*. In the fluid of larval tapeworms, on the other hand, the chlorides account for a much higher proportion of the total molecular concentration. In *Cysticercus tenuicollis*, for example, they amounted to 66.8% of the total (Schopfer, 1932). The hemocele fluid of *Gasterophilus* larvae resembles that of ascarids by its low chloride content, accounting for only 7% of the total base. Organic acids (succinic, citric, and lactic acids) account here for 22% (Levenbook, 1950).

The other components listed in Table 4 require little comment with the exception of the uncommonly high sulfur concentration found by Mazzocco (1923) in *Echinococcus*. Schopfer (1932) assumes Mazzocco's value to be in error and the case certainly deserves reinvestigation.

## B. Formed Inorganic Deposits

The calcareous corpuscles of cestodes consist of an organic base of unknown constitution and inorganic material. They have been isolated from *Taenia marginata* where they amounted to 4.1% of the fresh or 18.7% of the dry substance (von Brand, 1933). Their inorganic components consisted of CaO 36.13, MgO 17.07, $P_2O_5$ 14.09, and $CO_2$ 33.09%. The function of the calcareous corpuscles is not known. They have variously been regarded as skeletal substances or excretory products, as serving to bind the respiratory carbon dioxide, as due to an excessive uptake of calcium from the food material, or as serving as an alkali reserve. None of these views has an experimental foundation as yet. It is probable that the solution of this problem will come only from a study of tapeworms cultivated *in vitro*.

It has been known for a long time that concretions morphologically somewhat similar to the calcareous corpuscles of the cestodes occur within the excretory system of several trematodes (Claparède, 1858; Fraipont, 1880, 1881). The excretory bladder of metacercariae especially is often completely filled with these structures. Upon exposure to mineral acids they disappear more or less completely with or without the development of carbon dioxide. On the basis of this observation they are assumed to consist of calcium carbonate or calcium phosphate. The excretory nature of these granules can hardly be doubted, but the physiological significance of their formation and excretion is not clear.

Formed inorganic deposits have been reported rather frequently from the intestinal cells of many parasitic nematodes, such as, *Ascaris*, *Parascaris*, *Heterakis*, and others where they usually appear as small, red-brown, weakly birefringent crystals. They had originally been considered as an endproduct of hemoglobin decomposition because of positive iron tests (Askanazy, 1896; Looss, 1905; Fauré-Fremiet, 1913) or had been thought to be zymogen granules (von Kemnitz, 1912). However, Quack (1913) and Chitwood and Chitwood (1938) established the inorganic nature of these granules in the case of *Strongylus equinus* and some other forms and they

TABLE 1. Dry matter and total inorganic substances in some parasites

| SPECIES | DRY MATTER IN PERCENT OF FRESH WEIGHT | INORGANIC SUBSTANCES IN | | AUTHOR |
|---|---|---|---|---|
| | | Percent of fresh weight | Percent of dry weight | |
| PROTOZOA | | | | |
| Trypanosoma equiperdum......... | approx. 18 | | | Reiner, Leonard, and Chao (1932) |
| T. rhodesiense............... | approx. 8 | | | Christophers and Fulton (1938) |
| Plasmodium knowlesi.......... | approx. 5 | | | Christophers and Fulton (1939) |
| Goussia gadi................. | 16 | | | Panzer (1911, 1913) |
| TREMATODES | | | | |
| Paramphistomum cervi......... | 23–30 | | | Lazarus (1950) |
| Fasciola hepatica............. | 17.8; 17.3 | 1.14 | 4.9 | Flury and Leeb (1926); Weinland and von Brand (1926) |
| CESTODES | | | | |
| Diphyllobothrium latum........ | 9.0 | 0.43 | 4.8 | Smorodincev and Bebesin (1936b) |
| Schistocephalus solidus, plerocercoids... | 31.8 | 1.85 | 5.8 | Hopkins (1950) |
| Railletina cesticillus........... | 20.5 | 2.36 | 11.5 | Reid (1942) |
| Dipylidium caninum........... | 20.4 | | | von Brand (1933) |
| Moniezia expansa............. | 9.9; 11.0; 10.1 | 1.11; 1.4 | 9.3; 10.5 | Weinland (1901); von Brand (1933); Wardle (1937a, b) |
| Coenurus cerebralis, scolex..... | 25.3 | 6.9 | 27.4 | Schopfer (1932) |
| membranes..... | 12.4 | 0.5 | 4.1 | Schopfer (1932) |
| Taenia saginata............. | 12.2; 7.8 | 0.65 | 5.3 | Smorodincev, Bebesin, and Pawlowa (1933); von Brand (1933) |
| T. solium.................. | 8.7 | 0.53 | 6.4 | Smorodincev and Bebesin (1936a) |
| T. marginata............... | 23.5 | | | von Brand (1933) |
| T. plicata.................. | 27.5 | 1.22 | | von Brand (1933) |
| Cysticercus tenuicollis, scolex... | 46.6 | 19.2 | 41.1 | Schopfer (1932) |
| membranes... | 17.8 | 0.3 | 1.2 | Schopfer (1932) |

| | | | | |
|---|---|---|---|---|
| **NEMATODES** | | | | |
| Strongylus equinus........ | 15–16 | | | Lazarus (1950) |
| S. vulgaris........ | 17–18 | | | Lazarus (1950) |
| Haemonchus contortus........ | 19–21 | | | Lazarus (1950) |
| Ostertagia circumcincta........ | 19–21 | | | Lazarus (1950) |
| Eustrongylides ignotus, larvae........ | 25 | 1.1 | 4.4 | von Brand (1938) |
| Syphacia obvelata........ | 23 | | | Lazarus (1950) |
| Heterakis spumosa........ | 22 | | | Lazarus (1950) |
| Parascaris equorum........ | 21; 14.8; ♀19.5; ♂22.7 | | | Schimmelpfennig (1903); Flury (1912); Toryu (1933) |
| Ascaris lumbricoides........ | 20.7; 15.0; 19.6; 22.6 | 0.76; 0.78 | 5.1; 4.0 | Weinland (1901); Flury (1912); Smorodincev and Bebesin (1936c); Gurtner (1948) |
| Diroflaria immitis........ | 21.3 | | | von Brand (unpublished) |
| Litomosoides carinii........ | 17.0 | | | Bueding (personal communication) |
| **ACANTHOCEPHALA** | | | | |
| Macracanthorhynchus hirudinaceus........ | ♀18.2; ♂17.8 | 0.58 | 5.0 | von Brand (1940); von Brand and Saurwein (1942) |
| **ARTHROPODS** | | | | |
| Gasterophilus intestinalis, larvae........ | 22.1–37.3 | | | von Kemnitz (1916) |

agree that the crystals give reactions characteristic for $CaSO_4 \cdot 2H_2O$. Ferric iron may also be present, but only adsorbed.

This finding can, however, apparently not be generalized. Rogers (1940) was unable to demonstrate gypsum in the intestine of *Strongylus edentatus* and *Strongylus vulgaris*. He did find relatively large amounts of zinc and sulfur and he considers it as likely that both were combined zinc sulfide, but he could not link this compound definitely to the sphaero crystals. He

TABLE 2.   Dry matter in some organ systems of helminths

| SPECIES | DRY MATTER IN PERCENT OF FRESH SUBSTANCE IN | | | | AUTHOR |
|---|---|---|---|---|---|
| | Body wall | Alimentary canal | Reproductive organs | Body fluid | |
| *Ascaris lumbricoides* | 23.5–25.0 | 27.5 | 25.0–33.3 | 4.0–6.7 | Flury (1912) |
| | 24.2–27.6 | 17.7–22.3 | 17.9–31.3 | 5.8–6.7 | Hobson, Hobson, Bernacca, and Stephenson (no date) |
| *Parascaris equorum* | 25.0 | 24.9 | 24.0–27.4 | 8.3 | Flury (1912) |
| *Macracanthorhynchus hirudinaceus* | 16.0–17.5 | | 21.9–24.8 | 3.5–3.9 | von Brand (1939) |

TABLE 3.   Inorganic substances occurring in the bodies of some helminths

| SPECIES | K | Na | Mg | Ca | Fe | Al | Cu | Mn | PO₄ | SO₄ | Si | Cl | CO₃ | AUTHOR |
|---|---|---|---|---|---|---|---|---|---|---|---|---|---|---|
| *Cysticercus fasciolaris* | * | * | * | * | | | | | * | * | | | | Salisbury and Anderson (1939) |
| *Ascaris lumbricoides* | * | * | * | * | * | * | 0 | 0 | * | * | * | * | * | Flury (1912); Smorodindev and Bebesin (1936c) |
| *Macracanthorhynchus hirudinaceus* | * | * | * | * | * | * | * | * | * | * | * | * | * | von Brand (1939); von Brand and Saurwein (1942) |

* = substance found; 0 = substance not found; blank = no data available.

demonstrated also small amounts of copper, silver, and iron in the intestine of these two worms and his analyses of the host's intestinal mucosa made it very likely that all metals found in the parasite's intestine were derived from this source.

Finally it may be noted that granules giving positive iron tests are not restricted to nematodes; they were also observed in the intestinal cells of male *Schistosoma japonicum*, although lacking in the female, and in those of *Paragonimus ringeri*. The derivation of these granules both in these cases and in those of some nematodes is obscure and Hsü (1938a, b, c) could not correlate them with the amount of blood taken in by the parasites.

TABLE 4. Inorganic constituents of some parasite fluids

| SPECIES | MATERIAL | INORGANIC COMPONENTS IN MMOL PER LITER | | | | | | | | | | | AUTHOR |
|---|---|---|---|---|---|---|---|---|---|---|---|---|---|
| | | K | Na | Mg | Ca | Fe | Zn | Cu | Cl | S | P | Si | |
| *Cysticercus tenuicollis* | Cyst fluid | * | | 2.1 | 1.2 | | | | 120 | 2.0 | 1.9 | | Schopfer (1925, 1926b, 1932) |
| | | | | | | | | | 121 | | | | Moniez (1880) |
| *Echinococcus granulosus* | Cyst fluid | | | | | | | | 86 | | | | Moniez (1880) |
| | | | | | 2.2 * | | | | 102 | | | | Lemaire and Ribère (1935) |
| | | 9.6 | 171 | 1.5 | 0.9 * | | | | 115 | 44 | 4.0 | * | Mazzocco (1923) |
| | | | | | | | | | 98 | | | | Codounis and Polydorides (1936) |
| *Parascaris equorum* | Body fluid | | | | | | | | 62 | | | | Flury (1912) |
| | | | | | | | | | 21 | | | | Schopfer (1924, 1926a) |
| | | | | | | | | | 58 | | | | Duval and Courtois (1928) |
| *Ascaris lumbricoides* | Body fluid | 23.5 | 119 | 4.95 | | 0.13 | 0.14 | 0.02 | 55 | | 12.0 | | Rogers (1945) |
| | | 24.6 | 129 | 4.9 | 5.9 | | | | 53 | | 17.0 | | Hobson, Stephenson, and Eden (no date) |
| *Gasterophilus intestinalis* larvae | Body fluid | 11.5 | 175 | 4.7 | 2.8 | | 0.14 | 0.09 | 15 | 3.0 | 2.2 | | Levenbook (1950) |

* = element present, but no quantitative data available.

While there is thus no convincing evidence that the deposition of corpusculate inorganic material in helminths is due to the breakdown of hemoglobin, such evidence has been presented in fairly definite form for the pupae of *Gasterophilus intestinalis*. Beaumont (1948) has shown that the hemoglobin of the red organ is completely destroyed during pupation and that an unusually large amount of granules giving iron reactions is then deposited within the intestinal cells, but their exact chemical composition has not been established. It may also be mentioned that iron-positive granules have been found in the oenocytes of the larvae (Dinulescu, 1932).

## C. Experimental and Pathological Inorganic Deposits

The formation of inorganic deposits in parasites can be achieved experimentally in a more or less physiological way. Von Kemnitz (1912) related that upon injection of calcium hydroxide into ascarids, structures appeared in the lateral lines that bore a considerable similarity to the calcareous corpuscles of cestodes. Another method employed was to offer the parasites iron-containing compounds such as iron saccharate or iron lactate and to study by histochemical methods the appearance of inorganic iron deposits. In *Opalina ranarum* Kedrowsky (1931) found the iron within the so called segregation apparatus, a structure of doubtful morphological identity, whereas in *Ascaris* the iron was exclusively adsorbed by the Golgi apparatus of the intestinal cells (Hirsch and Bretschneider, 1937).

Pathological calcium deposits occur in nature frequently in cases of long-lasting parasitism. One has to distinguish here between two possibilities, although on occasion both are realized simultaneously. On the one hand, the host tissues in the vicinity of the parasites may become calcified, such as the walls of the bile ducts in old *Fasciola* infections, or the capsule surrounding the *Trichinella* larvae. On the other hand the parasites themselves may become calcified, as is, for example, well known for filarial worms. It is very likely that this second process sets in only after the parasites have died. This has been assumed by Boehm (1908) in cases where *Trichinella* larvae themselves calcify and by Otto and von Brand (1941) in that of calcified *Capillaria hepatica* specimens.

Experimentally, the calcification phenomena could be speeded up very considerably by the administration of excessive doses of irradiated ergosterol or of parathormone to the host. Almost invariably these experimental calcifications were confined to the host tissues, the only possible exception being some doubtful calcium reactions within schistosome eggs (von Brand *et al.*, 1933; Wantland, 1934, 1936; Wantland *et al.*, 1936; Otto and von Brand, 1941; von Brand *et al.*, 1933, 1938).

## D. Intimate Distribution of Ash Constituents

Very little is known about the intimate localization of inorganic substances within the tissues of parasites when they do not appear as definite granules. Some measure of success has been achieved by means of microincineration procedures as applied to some species of parasitic protozoa. Scott and Horning (1932) and Horning and Scott (1933) have studied *Opalina* and *Nyctotherus* in this way. They found ash deposits in the myonemes, cilia, and basal granules of both species but in other respects the species differed considerably. The nuclei of the opalinids were practically ash-free, while the nuclear apparatus of *Nyctotherus* contained considerable amounts of inorganic material. In the cytoplasm of the former species the inorganic substances formed especially dense deposits consisting chiefly of calcium oxide in the "vegetative granules." In the latter species ash rich in probably sodium formed a fine network throughout the cytoplasm. In the cytopharynx of *Nyctotherus* crystals containing silica were observed and it was also characteristic that the wall of the food vacuoles was rich in inorganic material, the ash consisting in this latter case of variable proportions of calcium and iron. MacLennan and Murer (1934) incinerated several *Trichonympha* species and found most of the mineral ash, consisting chiefly of calcium compounds, in the neuromotor system, the regions of active absorption, the nucleus, and some cytoplasmic granules. The chromatin was especially rich in iron.

### LITERATURE

Askanazy, M. (1896). *Deut. Arch. klin. Med.* **57**: 104–117.
Beaumont, A. (1948). *Compt. rend. soc. biol.* **142**: 1369–1371.
Boehm, J. (1908). *Z. Fleisch-u. Milchhyg.* **18**: 319–324.
von Brand, T. (1933). *Z. vergleich. Physiol.* **18**: 562–596.
von Brand, T. (1938). *J. Parasitol.* **24**: 445–451.
von Brand, T. (1939). *J. Parasitol.* **25**: 329–342.
von Brand, T. (1940). *J. Parasitol.* **26**: 301–307.
von Brand, T., Holtz, F., and Vogel, H. (1933). *Z. Parasitenk.* **6**: 308–322.
von Brand, T., Otto, G. F., and Abrams, E. (1938). *Am. J. Hyg.* **27**: 461–470.
von Brand, T., and Saurwein, J. (1942). *J. Parasitol.* **28**: 315–318.
Chitwood, B. G., and Chitwood, M. B. (1938). *Proc. Helminthol. Soc. Wash.* **5**: 16–18.
Christophers, S. R., and Fulton, J. D. (1938). *Ann. Trop. Med. Parasitol.* **32**: 43–75.
Christophers, S. R., and Fulton, J. D. (1939). *Ann. Trop. Med. Parasitol.* **33**: 161–170.
Claparède, E. (1858). *Z. wiss. Zoöl.* **9**: 99–105.
Codounis, A., and Polydorides, J. (1936). *Compt. rend. III. congr. intern. pathol. comp.* **2**: 195–202.
Dinulescu, G. (1932). *Ann. sci. nat. Zool.* **15**: 1–183.
Duval, M., and Courtois, A. (1928). *Compt. rend. soc. biol.* **99**: 1952–1953.
Fauré-Fremiet, E. (1913). *Compt. rend. soc. biol.* **74**: 567–569.
Flury, F. (1912). *Arch. exptl. Path. Pharmakol.* **67**: 275–392.

Flury, F., and Leeb, F. (1926). *Klin. Wochschr.* **5:** 2054–2055.
Fraipont, J. (1880). *Arch. biol.* **1:** 415–456.
Fraipont, J. (1881). *Arch. biol.* **2:** 1–40.
Gurtner, H. (1948). *Z. Hyg. Infektionskrankh.* **128:** 423–439.
Hirsch, G. C., and Bretschneider, L. H. (1937). *Protoplasma* **29:** 9–30.
Hobson, Hobson, Bernacca, and Stephenson (no date). Unpublished experiment. Quoted in Hobson, A. D. (1948). *Parasitology* **38:** 183–227.
Hobson, Stephenson, and Eden (no date). Unpublished experiment. Quoted in Hobson, A. D. (1948). *Parasitology* **38:** 183–277.
Hopkins, C. A. (1950). *J. Parasitol.* **36:** 384–390.
Horning, E. S., and Scott, G. H. (1933). *J. Morphol.* **54:** 389–397.
Hsü, H. F. (1938a). *Bull. Fan Mem. Inst. Biol. Zool. Ser.* **8:** 121–132.
Hsü, H. F. (1938b). *Bull. Fan Mem. Inst. Biol. Zool. Ser.* **8:** 347–366.
Hsü, H. F. (1938c). *Bull. Fan Mem. Inst. Biol. Zool. Ser.* **8:** 403–406.
Kedrowsky, B. (1931). *Z. Zellforsch. u. mikroskop. Anat.* **13:** 1–81.
von Kemnitz, G. (1912). *Arch. Zellforsch.* **7:** 463–603.
von Kemnitz, G. (1916). *Z. Biol.* **67:** 129–244.
Lazarus, M. (1950). *Australian J. Sci. Research* **B3:** 245–250.
Lemaire, G., and Ribère, R. (1935). *Compt. rend. soc. biol.* **118:** 1578–1579.
Levenbook, L. (1950). *Biochem. J.* **47:** 336–346.
Looss, A. (1905). *Records School Med. Cairo* **3:** 1–158.
MacLennan, R. F., and Murer, H. K. (1934). *J. Morphol.* **56:** 231–239.
Marcet, W. H. (1865). *Proc. Roy. Soc. London* **14:** 69–70.
Mazzocco, P. (1923). *Compt. rend. soc. biol.* **88:** 342–343.
Moniez, R. L. (1880). Thèse, Lille.
Otto, G. F., and von Brand, T. (1941). *Am. J. Hyg.* **34D:** 13–17.
Panzer, T. (1911). *Z. physiol. Chem.* **73:** 109–127.
Panzer, T. (1913). *Z. physiol. Chem.* **86:** 33–42.
Quack, M. (1913). *Arch. Zellforsch.* **11:** 1–50.
Reid, W. M. (1942). *J. Parasitol.* **28:** 319–340.
Reiner, L., Leonard, C. S., and Chao, S. S. (1932). *Arch. intern. pharmacodynamie* **43:** 186–198.
Rogers, W. P. (1940). *J. Helminthol.* **18:** 103–116.
Rogers, W. P. (1945). *Parasitology* **36:** 211–218.
Salisbury, L. F., and Anderson, R. J. (1939). *J. Biol. Chem.* **129:** 505–517.
Schimmelpfennig, G. (1903). *Arch. wiss. u. prakt. Tierheilk.* **29:** 332–376.
Schopfer, W. H. (1924). *Actes soc. helv. sci. nat.* **105:** 188–189.
Schopfer, W. H. (1925). *Actes soc. helv. sci. nat.* **106:** 157–158.
Schopfer, W. H. (1926a). *Parasitology* **18:** 277–282.
Schopfer, W. H. (1926b). *Compt. rend. soc. phys. hist. nat. Genève* **43:** 64–67.
Schopfer, W. H. (1927). *Compt. rend. soc. phys. hist. nat. Genève* **44:** 4–7.
Schopfer, W. H. (1932). *Revue suisse zool.* **39:** 59–194.
Scott, G. H., and Horning, E. S. (1932). *J. Morphol.* **53:** 381–388.
Smorodincev, I., and Bebesin, K. W. (1935). *Biochem. Z.* **276:** 271–273.
Smorodincev, I., and Bebesin, K. W. (1936a). *J. Biochem.* **23:** 19–20.
Smorodincev, I., and Bebesin, K. W. (1936b). *J. Biochem.* **23:** 21–22.
Smorodincev, I., and Bebesin, K. W. (1936c). *J. Biochem.* **23:** 23–25.
Smorodincev, I., Bebesin, K. W., and Pawlowa, P. I. (1933). *Biochem. Z.* **261:** 176–178.
Toryu, Y. (1933). *Science Repts. Tôhoku Imp. Univ. Fourth Ser.* **8:** 65–74.
Vialli, M. (1923). *Rend. ist. lombardo sci.* **56:** 935–938.

Vialli, M. (1926). *Arch. fisiol.* **23:** 577–596.

Wantland, W. W. (1934). *Proc. Soc. Exptl. Biol. Med.* **32:** 438–444.

Wantland, W. W. (1936). *J. Parasitol.* **22:** 537.

Wantland, W. W., Hausen, C., and Feeney, R. E. (1936). *J. Parasitol.* **22:** 538.

Wardle, R. A. (1937a). *Can. J. Research* **D15:** 117–126.

Wardle, R. A. (1937b). In: Manitoba Essays. 60th Anniv. Commem. Vol. Univ. Manitoba, pp. 338–364.

Weinland, E. (1901). *Z. Biol.* **41:** 69–74.

Weinland, E., and von Brand, T. (1926). *Z. vergleich. Physiol.* **4:** 212–285.

CHAPTER 2

# CARBOHYDRATES

## I. Simple Carbohydrates

There is no information available as to the occurrence of the simple carbohydrates in parasitic protozoa and the evidence concerning the extent of storage and the chemical nature of such sugars in metazoan parasites is scanty and somewhat contradictory. Weinland (1901b) and Schulte (1917), respectively, reported a glucose content of 1.6 and 0.9% of the fresh weight in *Ascaris lumbricoides*, while Foster (1865) and von Brand (1934) could detect only traces of reducing sugars in the same parasite. It is possible that in the experiments of the former authors some polysaccharide became hydrolyzed during the analytical procedures. This possibility is also not excluded in the case of *Cysticercus fasciolaris* where Salisbury and Anderson (1939) found about 1% of the dry substance consisting of a reducing sugar.

It is, however, certain that the body fluids of helminths contain reducing sugars and it is quite possible that this may be a universal occurrence both in parasitic worms and arthropods since carbohydrates are in most cases transported from one part, of the body to another in the form of carbohydrates of low molecular weight. Specifically, reducing sugar expressed as glucose has been determined as 0.15% of the fresh weight of the body fluid in the case of *Parascaris* (Fauré-Fremiet, 1913), as 0.22% in that of *Ascaris* (Rogers, 1945), and as 0.05% in that of the female *Macracanthorhynchus* (von Brand, 1940). Reducing sugars have also been found regularly in the fluid of larval tapeworm cysts. In *Echinococcus granulosus* the newer data vary between 0.03 and 0.04% (Mazzocco, 1923; Lemaire and Ribère, 1935), but in liver hydatids somewhat higher values, up to 0.1% have been observed (Codounis and Polydorides, 1936). In *Cysticercus fasciolaris* fluid 0.14% has been found (Schopfer, 1932).

It should be realized that the finding of a reducing sugar in a parasite does not necessarily indicate that glucose is involved. In the case of *Gasterophilus* larvae fructose has been identified as the only fermentable sugar of the hemolymph (Levenbook, 1947, 1950).

## II. Glycogen and Paraglycogen

### A. Chemical Considerations

The most widely distributed polysaccharide of parasites is unquestionably glycogen. It is a highly dextrorotatory compound built up by glucoside

12

radicals linked in the 1:4-$\alpha$ manner; upon hydrolysis by mineral acids it yields D-glucose. It is readily water soluble and gives a mahogany-red-brown color when treated with iodine. Paraglycogen is closely related to glycogen (Buetschli, 1885; Maupas, 1886); it gives the same color when treated with iodine and also yields glucose upon acid hydrolysis. It occurs, however, in the form of granules which, in contrast to glycogen, are sparingly soluble in cold water, are birefringent, and are resistant to saliva digestion.

Glycogen has been described from parasitic protozoa, mesozoa, helminths, and arthropods. Whether it is, in all cases, exactly identical chemically with vertebrate glycogen remains to be studied. The optical rotation of some parasite glycogens (Table 5) is very similar to that of pure mammalian

TABLE 5. Optical rotation of parasite glycogens

| GLYCOGEN FROM | $[\alpha]_D$ | AUTHOR |
| --- | --- | --- |
| *Fasciola hepatica* | +201.2 | Oesterlin and von Brand (1934) |
| *Moniezia expansa* | +187; +187.5; +194 | Weinland (1901a); Oesterlin and von Brand (1934); Abdel-Akher and Smith (1951) |
| *Ascaris lumbricoides* | +189; +196; +194 | Weinland (1901a); Baldwin and King (1942); Abdel-Akher and Smith (1951) |
| *Macracanthorhynchus hirudinaceus* | +187.5 | von Brand and Saurwein (1942) |
| *Gasterophilus intestinalis*, larvae | +192.6 | von Kemnitz (1916) |

glycogen, the $[\alpha]_D$ of which has been determined as +196.6 by Gatin-Gruzewska (1906).

The only parasite glycogen studied intensively from the chemical standpoint is that of *Ascaris lumbricoides*. It has about the same unit chain length (12 to 13 units) as mammalian glycogen but has apparently a somewhat smaller molecular weight (Baldwin and King, 1942; Bell, 1944; Halsall *et al.*, 1947; Bell *et al.*, 1948; Bell, 1948). The heat of combustion of *Ascaris* glycogen has been determined to be 4212 and 4125 cal/g by Emery and Benedict (1911) and Schulte (1917), respectively.

It is probable that glycogen is deposited in most cases as such in the cells. In tapeworms, however, evidence has been presented that at least part of the polysaccharide is bound to proteins. Kent and Macheboeuf (1947) isolated two electrophoretically homogeneous nitrogen-containing substances from *Moniezia expansa*. One of these, baerine, contained 60% glycogen, the other, moniezine, 11%.

The paraglycogen so far described has been only from protozoa. The term was coined originally by Buetschli (1885) for the polysaccharide granules of gregarines. In later years it became customary to use it with reference to those organisms such as coccidia, rumen- and many other parasitic ciliates, that store a polysaccharide difficult to dissolve in water. Whether future chemical analysis will uphold the validity of this procedure is somewhat questionable (von Brand, 1935). Insolubility in cold water in microscopic preparations seems hardly a sufficient criterion for differentiation. Panzer (1913), in any event, by chemical procedure isolated a very easily water soluble substance which probably was a polysaccharide from the coccidium, *Goussia gadi*. In those ciliates, like *Nyctotherus*, where the polysaccharide appears in the form of well defined granules (Armer, 1944) there may be more justification for a separation from glycogen.

## B. Quantitative Aspects

No quantitative polysaccharide determinations are available for parasitic protozoa or mesozoa. Data obtained with more or less specific histochemical procedures (iodine, Best's carmine, or Bauer's stain) make it very probable that great variations in glycogen and paraglycogen content occur in different species. Smaller or larger stores of polysaccharide have thus been found in parasitic amoebae (Kuenen and Swellengrebel, 1913, 1917; Dobell, 1919; Morita, 1938), gregarines (Buetschli, 1885), coccidia (Giovannola, 1934; Edgar *et al.*, 1944; Lillie, 1947), trichomonads (Stewart, 1938), some species of *Trypanoplasma* (Keysselitz, 1906; Schindera, 1922), and many parasitic ciliates (Westphal, 1934; Hungate, 1943; Armer, 1944). No glycogen, on the other hand, has been found in trypanosomes and malarial parasites (Krijgsman, 1936; Lillie, 1941). As to mesozoa, Nouvel's (1929, 1931) work has demonstrated the occurrence of significant amounts of glycogen in various stages of their life cycle.

The glycogen content of a relatively large number of parasitic worms has been determined quantitatively, but few such data are available for endoparasitic arthropods. A survey of Table 6 makes it likely that a certain correlation between habitat and glycogen content can be seen, at least in broad outlines. The parasites living in oxygen-poor habitats or in habitats with periodic oxygen deficiencies (stomach) regularly have a high glycogen content. Apparent exceptions, such as the adult *Ancylostoma caninum* or the adult *Trichinella spiralis* can be explained on the assumption that they do not lead a predominantly anaerobic life in nature. The hookworms can get significant amounts of oxygen from the ingested host blood; the trichinae probably directly from the intestinal mucosa.

No clear cut correlation, however, exists in the case of parasites living in surroundings with moderate to high oxygen tensions, *i.e.*, in the case of tissue parasites. Some, like the filariae, are characterized by a relatively low glycogen content while others, such as *Cysticercus fasciolaris* or larval

*Eustrongylides ignotus*, contain at least as much glycogen as the large intestinal helminths. The subsequent fate of the worms may be of importance in this connection. The adults of both species are relatively large organisms and may lead a predominantly anaerobic life, although this is by no means certain for *Eustrongylides*.

Sexual differences in glycogen content have been described from several species. The females of *Schistosoma mansoni* (Bueding and Koletsky, 1950) and of *Macracanthorhynchus hirudinaceus* (von Brand, 1940) contain less glycogen than the males. In nematodes, the data are somewhat contradictory. According to Smorodincev and Bebesin (1936), Toryu (1933), and Reid (1944), respectively, the females of *Ascaris*, *Parascaris*, and *Ascaridia* store more glycogen than the males while, on the other hand, von Brand (1937) and Ro (1939) found more glycogen in male than female *Ascaris*.

So far no evidence has been produced that seasonal variations in glycogen content occur in parasitic worms although such variations are quite evident in many free-living invertebrates, *e.g.*, planariae and snails. It must be emphasized, however, that sufficient data to exclude them are available only for parasites of warmblooded hosts, and these live the year round under uniform conditions. A study of intestinal parasites of cold blooded hosts would seem an interesting project, the more so since glycogen has been found only during the winter but not during the summer in the protozoan parasite *Cryptobia helicis* (Dubosq and Grassé, 1933). Hopkins (1950) recently reported that the glycogen content of *Schistocephalus solidus* plerocercoids, which live in the body cavity of fish, do not show seasonal variations in glycogen content.

Considerable variations in glycogen content apparently take place during the life history of helminths. Although no strictly quantitative data are available, the morphological studies of Axmann (1947) have shown that the primary sporocysts of schistosomes contained no discernible amounts of glycogen, and secondary sporocysts but little, whereas the free-living stages, miracidia and cercariae, contained relatively large polysaccharide stores. On the contrary, the free-living stages of hookworms and of *Nippostrongylus* were found to be practically glycogen-free or to contain at the most very small amounts (Busch, 1905; Payne, 1923; Giovannola, 1936). Nor was any glycogen found in the blood-inhabiting microfilariae of *Acanthocheilonema perstans* (Brault and Loeper, 1904b) while the larvae of *Trichinella spiralis*, in contrast to the adults, contain appreciable amounts of polysaccharide (Giovannola, 1936).

Many larval nematodes migrate through the body of the host before settling down at their final destination and during this migration they appear to increase their glycogen stores (Stepanow-Grigoriew and Hoeppli, 1926; Giovannola, 1936). The attempt to link the migration and polysac-

TABLE 6. Glycogen content of parasitic worms and arthropods

| SPECIES | GLYCOGEN IN PERCENT OF | | HABITAT | AVAILABILITY OF SIGNIFICANT AMOUNTS OF OXYGEN | AUTHOR |
|---|---|---|---|---|---|
| | Fresh weight | Dry weight | | | |
| **TREMATODES** | | | | | |
| Schistosoma mansoni | | ♂14–29 ♀3–5 | Bloodstream | Yes | Bueding and Koletsky (1950) |
| Fasciola hepatica | 3.1; 3.7 | 15; 21 | Bile ducts | No | Flury and Leeb (1926); Weinland and von Brand (1926) |
| **CESTODES** | | | | | |
| Diphyllobothrium latum | 1.9 | 20 | Intestine | No | Smorodincev and Bebesin (1936) |
| Ligula intestinalis | | 34 | Body cavity | ? | Markov (1939) |
| Schistocephalus solidus, plerocercoids | 16.2 | 51 | Body cavity | ? | Hopkins (1950) |
| Eubothrium rugosum | | 23 | Intestine | ? | Markov (1939) |
| Triaenophorus nodulosus | | 14 | Intestine | ? | Markov (1939) |
| Railletina cesticillus | 6.5 | 32 | Intestine | No | Reid (1942) |
| Moniezia expansa | 2.7; 3.2 | 24; 32 | Intestine | No | Weinland (1901a); von Brand (1933); Wardle (1937) |
| M. denticulata | 1.6 | 19 | Intestine | No | von Brand (1933) |
| Taenia saginata | 7.4 | 60 | Intestine | No | Smorodincev and Bebesin (1936) |
| T. solium | 2.2 | 25 | Intestine | No | Smorodincev and Bebesin (1936) |
| T. marginata | 6.7 | 28 | Intestine | No | von Brand (1933) |
| T. plicata | 1.6 | 6 | Intestine | No | von Brand (1933) |
| Cysticercus fasciolaris | | 28 | Liver | ? | Salisbury and Anderson (1939) |
| **NEMATODES** | | | | | |
| Strongylus vulgaris | 3.5 | | Intestine | ? | Toryu (1933) |
| Ancylostoma caninum | 1.6 | | Intestine | Yes | von Brand and Otto (1938) |
| Ascaridia galli | 3.6–4.7 | | Intestine | ? | Reid (1945a, b) |
| Eustrongylides ignotus, larvae | 6.9 | 28 | Various organs | Yes | von Brand (1938) |

| | | | | | |
|---|---|---|---|---|---|
| *Paruscaris equorum*.......... | 2.1; 3.8 | 10; 23 | Intestine | No | Schimmelpfennig (1903); Toryu (1933) |
| *Ascaris lumbricoides*.......... | 5.3–8.7 | 24–24 | Intestine | No | Weinland (1901a); Flury (1912); Smorodincev and Bebesin (1936); von Brand (1937) |
| *Dirofilaria immitis*.......... | 1.9 | 10 | Heart | Yes | von Brand (1950) |
| *Litomosoides carinii*.......... | 0.8 | 5 | Pleural cavity | Yes | Bueding (1949) |
| *Dipetalonema gracilis*.......... | 0.2 | | Abdominal cavity | Yes | von Brand (1950) |
| ACANTHOCEPHALA | | | | | |
| *Macracanthorhynchus hirudinaceus*... | 1.1; 2.3 | 8; 13 | Intestine | No | von Brand (1939; 1940) |
| ARTHROPODS | | | | | |
| *Gasterophilus intestinalis*, larvae..... | 5.0–9.0 | 14–31 | Stomach | Variable | von Kennitz (1916); Dinulescu (1932) |
| *Gasterophilus nasalis*, larvae.......... | 2.9–9.4 | | Stomach, duodenum | Variable | Dinulescu (1932) |
| *Gasterophilus haemorrhoidalis*, larvae.......... | 3.0–4.6 | | Stomach | Variable | Dinulescu (1932) |
| *Gasterophilus inermis*, larvae......... | 8.9 | | Rectum | No | Dinulescu (1932) |

charide accumulation to the need for glycogen for a subsequent life in anaerobic habitats (Pintner, 1922) does not, however, appear well founded.

In acanthocephala, the studies of Miller (1943) showed that the acanthor of *Macracanthorhynchus hirudinaceus* lost all its polysaccharide upon liberation from the egg shell. Glycogen reappeared in traces only after 22 days development. It increased from then on progressively until the fully developed acanthella contained relatively large amounts.

Similarly, in endoparasitic arthropods a dependency of the glycogen content on the stage of the life cycle has been reported. The polysaccharide stores of *Gasterophilus* larvae increase progressively until they reach a maximum in the pre-pupal stage (Dinulescu, 1932).

*C. Distribution of Glycogen and Paraglycogen in the Body of Parasites*

Two ways of studying the distribution of polysaccharide in the body of organisms exist. One is the quantitative determination by chemical methods. It is feasible only where organs, or at least organ systems, can be isolated and can therefore readily be used in nematodes or acanthocephala of suitable size, but not in flatworms where all the organs are embedded in the parenchyma. The second way is the use of histochemical methods which have the advantage of allowing the investigation of small organisms and give an insight into the intimate distribution of polysaccharide within a given cell type but have the drawback of being under the best of circumstances only semi-quantitative.

*1. Protozoa.* The polysaccharides may occur spread throughout the body without definite localization, as in the case of the trophozoites of intestinal amoebae (Armer, 1944; Lillie, 1947) or in *Trichomonas foetus* (Stewart, 1938). In other protozoa the polysaccharide usually has a definite location. In binucleate *Endamoeba* cysts a large glycogen vacuole is located more or less centrally between the two nuclei (Dobell and O'Connor, 1921), whereas in the *Iodamoeba* cyst it is found eccentrically at the pole opposite the nuleus (von Brand, 1932) in most cases. In gregarines the paraglycogen granules occur primarily within the deutomerite (Giovannola, 1934) whereas in the trophozoites of *Nyctotherus* they frequently form a bean-shaped mass between the anterior end of the body and the macronucleus (Armer, 1944). In a third group the glycogen storage is largely, though not exclusively, confined to definite organelles. The best examples are the rumen ciliates where the complicated skeletal plates are the chief storage places for the polysaccharide (Schulze, 1924; Trier, 1926; Weineck, 1931; Westphal, 1934).

*2. Parasitic worms.* A few quantitative analyses of various body regions of helminths have been carried out (Table 7) which indicate that in the species studied by far the greatest part of the total glycogen is deposited in the tissues of the body wall.

Many histochemical glycogen studies have been reported from a variety of nematodes (Busch, 1905; von Kemnitz, 1912; Fauré-Fremiet, 1913; Quack, 1913; Martini, 1916; Toryu, 1933; Giovannola, 1935; Hirsch and Bretschneider, 1937), trematodes (Ortner-Schoenbach, 1913; Prenant, 1922; Kajiro, 1927; Wilmoth and Goldfisher, 1945; Fernando, 1945; Axmann, 1947), cestodes (Brault and Loeper, 1904a, b; Busch, 1905; Ortner-Schoenbach, 1913; Smyth, 1949), and acanthocephala (von Brand, 1939, 1940; Bullock, 1949).

These studies can be summarized briefly as follows. The cuticle is generally glycogen-free. The subcuticle is an important storage place in nematodes, especially its enlargement along the lateral lines, and in acantho-

TABLE 7. Glycogen content of various organ systems of helminths

| | ORGAN SYSTEM | | | | | | | | | | | |
|---|---|---|---|---|---|---|---|---|---|---|---|---|
| SPECIES | Body wall | | Intestine | | Uterus | | Ovaries and eggs | | Male reproductive system | | Body fluid | |
| | A | B | A | B | A | B | A | B | A | B | A | B |
| *Parascaris equorum*[a] | | | | | | | | | | | | |
| ♂ | 4.9 | 96 | 0.6 | 2 | | | | | 0.5 | 2 | | |
| ♀ | 5.8 | 66 | 0.6 | 2 | 1.6 | 9 | 6.5 | 23 | | | | |
| *Macranthorhynchus hirudinaceus*[b] | | | | | | | | | | | | |
| ♀ | 1.5 | 80 | | | | | 0.9 | 12 | | | 0.2 | 8 |

A = Percent of fresh substance.
B = Percent of total glycogen.
[a] After Toryu (1933).
[b] After von Brand (1939).

cephala where the glycogen is deposited not only along the subcuticular fibers but also within the lacunar system. In practically all worms studied the muscles contained large amounts of glycogen. In nematodes it is characteristic that the glycogen occurs not so much in the contractile parts of the muscle fibers, but in the large plasmatic bulbs of the cells. Similarly, in acanthocephala the noncontractile parts of the cells are the main storage place. The corresponding conditions are more difficult to study in flatworms, since the muscle cells are embedded in dense parenchyma. It appears likely that the glycogen is deposited primarily in the latter rather than in the muscle cells proper. These, however, seem to contain at least some polysaccharide. The parenchyma cells of flatworms are, in general, very rich in glycogen, especially those located in the suckers.

The intestinal cells occasionally are rich in glycogen in nematodes, while those of flukes are usually found glycogen-free. The nerve cells of nematodes, trematodes, and cestodes do not contain polysaccharide, but distinct glycogen granules have been encountered within the nerve cells of acanthocephala.

The reproductive systems of various groups of helminths are so different that their glycogen relationships have to be taken up separately and only the main points can be mentioned. In trematodes and cestodes the ovarian eggs contain no, or but little glycogen. In the composite uterine eggs conditions are variable. In some forms they contain large amounts of polysaccharide, in others only small ones. These differences are probably correlated to similar differences in the vitellaria. *Fasciola* and *Fascioloides*, for example, have appreciable glycogen stores both in the mature vitellarian cells and the uterine eggs. The vitellaria of schistosomes, on the other hand, are glycogen-free and their uterine eggs contain only little polysaccharide. The male reproductive system of flatworms is, in general, glycogen-poor, although in most cases the mature sperms give a distinctly positive glycogen reaction.

In nematodes, the oocytes contain little glycogen, the oogonia a very large amount, which is decreased somewhat in mature eggs. This is due, at least in part, to the formation of the chitinous layer of the egg shell. In the male system the spermatocytes are glycogen-free while spermatids and mature sperms contain some polysaccharide. In so far as the accessory organs are concerned it may be mentioned that the bursa is quite rich in glycogen.

In acanthocephala, the floating ovaries and the young embryos are poor in glycogen, but the mature embryo contains large amounts of polysaccharide in the region of the "Embryonalkern," which appears to be not all glycogen. The testes and the cement glands contain but little glycogen.

*3. Endoparasitic arthropods.* Hardly any information as to the distribution of glycogen in their bodies is available. It has been reported (von Kemnitz, 1916) that the giant cells making up the red organ of *Gasterophilus* larvae are especially rich in glycogen.

## III. Chitin

Chitin is a complex polysaccharide which yields glucosamine and acetic acid upon acid hydrolysis. It forms the exoskeleton of endoparasitic arthropods, fulfilling the same function as in free-living ones. Von Kemnitz (1916) determined the chitin content of *Gasterophilus intestinalis* larvae as 1.38 to 3.12% of the fresh or 5.13 to 8.98% of the dry substance.

In other groups of parasites chitin occurs but sporadically. The egg shell proper of so many species of nematodes consists of this polysaccharide that it is probably a general occurrence (see Krakow, 1892; Jammes and Martin, 1910; Fauré-Fremiet, 1912, 1913; Schulze, 1924; Wottge, 1937; Chitwood, 1938; Jacobs and Jones, 1939). In acanthocephala the innermost egg membrane has been recognized as chitin (von Brand, 1940). While the chitin of worm eggs gives quite typical reactions, it differs somewhat from arthropod chitin in optical properties (Schmidt, 1936), and by its greater elasticity (von Brand, 1940; Pick, 1947). It has been claimed that the lining of the stoma and esophagus of *Strongylus edentatus* is chitinous (Immink, 1924) but the more recent studies of Chitwood (1938) on the corresponding structures of *Strongylus equinus* cast considerable doubt on this observation.

In so far as parasitic protozoa are concerned, chitin has been reported twice; once as forming the spore capsule of *Nosema apis* (Koehler, 1921) and again, tentatively, as constituting the cuticle of the ciliates *Cycloposthium bipalmatum* and *Ophryoscolex sp.* (Schulze, 1924). A reinvestigation of these cases would be desirable.

## IV. POLYSACCHARIDES OF UNKNOWN CONSTITUTION

Besides glycogen, relatively large amounts of a polysaccharide of unknown constitution have been found in *Litomosoides carinii* (Bueding, 1949). Small amounts of a polysaccharide that withstands diastase digestion and yields, upon acid hydrolysis, a substance giving reactions similar to those given by galactose have been isolated from *Macracanthorhynchus hirudinaceus* (von Brand and Saurwein, 1942). No final identification was possible; it may have been galactogen.

Several authors have isolated immunologically active polysaccharide fractions from a variety of parasitic worms (Campbell, 1936, 1937, 1939; Melcher and Campbell, 1942; Melcher, 1943; Oliver-Gonzalez, 1944; Oliver-Gonzalez and Torregrosa, 1944) and protozoa (Senekjie, 1941; Muniz and De Freitas, 1944). At least in the case of the worms the yield was so large that the assumption of the polysaccharide having been mainly glycogen seems unavoidable (Baldwin and King, 1942). These latter authors pointed to the improbability of glycogen as such being antigenic. They think it possible that the antigen may have been present as an impurity in the glycogen fraction, or else that some active prosthetic group was attached to the glycogen. The whole question urgently needs further clarification especially in view of the previously mentioned findings of Kent and Macheboeuf (1947) indicating the occurrence of chemical combinations between glycogen and proteins. It is improbable that glycogen was involved in the case of the parasitic protozoa tested: Leishmanias, leptomonads, *Trypanosoma cruzi* and *Endotrypanum schaudinni*. As mentioned above the trypanosomidae do not appear to store glycogen.

### LITERATURE

Abdel-Akher, M., and Smith, F. (1951). *J. Am. Chem. Soc.* **73**: 994–996.
Armer, J. M. (1944). *J. Parasitol.* **30**: 131–142.

Axmann, M. C. (1947). *J. Morphol.* **80**: 321–343.

Baldwin, E., and King, H. K. (1942). *Biochem. J.* **36**: 37–42.

Bell, D. J. (1944). *J. Chem. Soc.* **1944**: 473–476.

Bell, D. J. (1948). *Biol. Revs. Cambridge Phil. Soc.* **23**: 256–266.

Bell, D. J., Gutfreund, H., Cecil, R., and Ogston, A. G. (1948). *Biochem. J.* **42**: 405–408.

von Brand, T. (1932). *Z. Parasitenk.* **4**: 753–775.

von Brand, T. (1933). *Z. vergleich. Physiol.* **18**: 562–596.

von Brand, T. (1934). *Z. vergleich. Physiol.* **21**: 220–235.

von Brand, T. (1935). *Ergeb. Biol.* **12**: 161–220.

von Brand, T. (1937). *J. Parasitol.* **23**: 68–72.

von Brand, T. (1938). *J. Parasitol.* **24**: 445–451.

von Brand, T. (1939). *J. Parasitol.* **25**: 329–342.

von Brand, T. (1940). *J. Parasitol.* **26**: 301–307.

von Brand, T. (1950). *J. Parasitol.* **36**: 178–192.

von Brand, T., and Otto, G. F. (1938). *Am. J. Hyg.* **27**: 683–689.

von Brand, T., and Saurwein, J. (1942). *J. Parasitol.* **28**: 315–318.

Brault, A., and Loeper, M. (1904a). *J. physiol. et pathol. gén.* **6**: 295–301.

Brault, A., and Loeper, M. (1904b). *J. physiol. et pathol. gén.* **6**: 503–512.

Bueding, E. (1949). *J. Exptl. Med.* **89**: 107–130.

Bueding, E., and Koletsky, S. (1950). *Proc. Soc. Exptl. Biol. Med.* **73**: 594–596.

Buetschli, O. (1885). *Z. Biol.* **21**: 603–612.

Bullock, W. L. (1949). *J. Morphol.* **84**: 201–225.

Busch, P. W. C. M. (1905). Dissertation, Utrecht.

Campbell, D. H. (1936). *J. Infectious Diseases* **59**: 266–280.

Campbell, D. H. (1937). *J. Parasitol.* **23**: 348–353.

Campbell, D. H. (1939). *J. Infectious Diseases* **65**: 12–15.

Chitwood, B. G. (1938). *Proc. Helminthol. Soc. Wash.* **5**: 68–75.

Codounis, A., and Polydorides, J. (1936). *Compt. rend. III. congr. intern. pathol. comp.* **2**: 195–202.

Dinulescu, G. (1932). *Ann. sci. nat., Zool.* **15**: 1–183.

Dobell, C. (1919). The Amoebae Living in Man. Bale and Danielsson, London.

Dobell, C., and O'Connor, F. W. (1921). The Intestinal Protozoa of Man. Bale and Danielsson, London.

Dubosq, O., and Grassé, P. (1933). *Arch. zool. exptl. gén.* **73**: 381–621.

Edgar, S. A., Herrick, C. A., and Fraser, L. A. (1944). *Trans. Am. Microscop. Soc.* **63**: 199–202.

Emery, A. G., and Benedict, F. G. (1911). *Am. J. Physiol.* **28**: 301–307.

Fauré-Fremiet, E. (1912). *Bull. soc. zool. France* **37**: 83–84.

Fauré-Fremiet, E., (1913). *Arch. anat. microscop.* **15**: 435–757.

Fernando, W. (1945). *J. Parasitol.* **31**: 185–190.

Flury, F. (1912). *Arch. exptl. Path. Pharmakol.* **67**: 275–392.

Flury, F., and Leeb, F. (1926). *Klin. Wochschr.* **5**: 2054–2055.

Foster, M. (1865). *Proc. Roy. Soc. London* **14**: 543–546.

Gatin-Gruzewska, Z. (1904). *Arch. ges. Physiol.* **102**: 569–591.

Giovannola, A. (1934). *Arch. Protistenk.* **83**: 270–274.

Giovannola, A. (1935). *Arch. ital. sci. med. colon.* **16**: 430–436.

Giovannola, A. (1936). *J. Parasitol.* **22**: 207–218.

Halsall, T. G., Hirst, E. L., and Jones, J. K. N. (1947). *J. Chem. Soc.* **1947**; 1399–1400.

Hirsch, G. C., and Bretschneider, L. H. (1937). Cytologia, Tokyo. Fujii Jubilee Volume, 424–436.

Hopkins, C. A. (1950). *J. Parasitol.* **36**: 384–390.

Hungate, R. E. (1943). *Biol. Bull.* **84**: 157–163.

Immink, B. D. C. M. (1924). *Arch. anat., histol. et embryol.* **3**: 281–326.

Jacobs, L., and Jones, M. F. (1939). *Proc. Helminthol. Soc. Wash.* **6**: 57–60.

Jammes, L., and Martin, A. (1910). *Compt. rend.* **151**: 250–251.

Kajiro, Y. (1927). *Trans. Jap. Path. Soc.* **17**: 213–214.

von Kemnitz, G. (1912). *Arch. Zellforsch.* **7**: 463–603.

von Kemnitz, G. (1916). *Z. Biol.* **67**: 129–244.

Kent, N., and Macheboeuf, M. (1947). *Compt. rend.* **225**: 602–604.

Keysselitz, G. (1906). *Arch. Protistenk.* **7**: 1–174.

Koehler, A. (1921). *Zool. Anz.* **53**: 84–87.

Krakow, N. P. (1892). *Z. Biol.* **29**: 177–198.

Krijgsman, B. J. (1936). *Z. vergleich. Physiol.* **23**: 663–711.

Kuenen, W. A., and Swellengrebel, N. H. (1913). *Zentr. Bakt. Parasitenk. Abt. I. Orig.* **71**: 378–410.

Kuenen, W. A., and Swellengrebel, N. H. (1917). *Geneesk. Tijdschr. Nederland. Indië* **57**: 496–506.

Lemaire, G., and Ribère, R. (1935). *Compt. rend. soc. biol.* **118**: 1578–1579.

Levenbook, L. (1947). *Nature* **160**: 465.

Levenbook, L. (1950). *Biochem. J.* **47**: 336–346.

Lillie, R. D. (1947). *J. Lab. Clin. Med.* **32**: 76–88.

Markov, G. S. (1939). *Compt. rend. acad. sci. U.R.S.S.* **25**: 93–96.

Martini, E. (1916). *Z. wiss. Zoöl.* **116**: 142–543.

Maupas, E. (1886). *Compt. rend.* **102**: 120–123.

Mazzocco, P. (1923). *Compt. rend. soc. biol.* **88**: 342–343.

Melcher, L. R. (1943). *J. Infectious Diseases* **73**: 31–39.

Melcher, L. R., and Campbell, D. H. (1942). *Science* **96**: 431–432.

Miller, M. A. (1943). *J. Morphol.* **73**: 19–41.

Morita, Y. (1938). *J. Oriental Med.* **28**: No.' 3: 38 (English summary).

Muniz, J., and De Freitas, G. (1944). *Rev. brasil. biol.* **4**: 421–438.

Nouvel, H. (1929). *Bull. soc. zool. France* **54**: 124–128.

Nouvel, H. (1931). *Arch. zool. exptl. gén. Notes et rev.* **71**: 53–61.

Oesterlin, M., and von Brand, T. (1934). *Z. vergleich. Physiol.* **20**: 251–254.

Oliver-Gonzalez, J. (1944). *J. Infectious Diseases* **74**: 81–84.

Oliver-Gonzalez, J., and Torregrosa, M. V. (1944). *J. Infectious Diseases* **74**: 173–177.

Ortner-Schoenbach, P. (1913). *Arch. Zellforsch.* **11**: 413–449.

Panzer, T. (1913). *Z. physiol. Chem.* **86**: 33–42.

Payne, F. K. (1923). *Am. J. Hyg.* **3**: 547–597.

Pick, F. (1947). *Compt. rend. soc. biol.* **141**: 983–986.

Pintner, T. (1922). *Sitzber. Akad. Wiss. Wien. Math.-naturw. Klasse, Abt. I.* **131**: 129–138.

Prenant, M. (1922). *Arch. morphol.* **5**: 1–474.

Quack, M. (1913). *Arch. Zellforsch.* **11**: 1–50.

Reid, W. M. (1942). *J. Parasitol.* **28**: 319–340.

Reid, W. M. (1944). *J. Parasitol.* **30** Suppl.: 12.

Reid, W. M. (1945a). *Am. J. Hyg.* **41**: 150–155.

Reid, W. M. (1945b). *J. Parasitol.* **31**: 406–410.

Ro, M. (1939). *Acta Japon. Med. Tropical.* **1**: 29–36.

Rogers, W. P. (1945). *Parasitology* **36**: 211–218.

Salisbury, L. F., and Anderson, R. J. (1939). *J. Biol. Chem.* **129**: 505–517.

Schimmelpfennig, G. (1903). *Arch. wiss. u. prakt. Tierheilk.* **29**: 332–376.

Schindera, M. (1922). *Arch. Protistenk.* **45**: 200-240.

Schmidt, W. J. (1936). *Z. Zellforsch. u. Mikroskop. Anat.* **25**: 181-203.

Schopfer, W. H. (1932). *Rev. suisse zool.* **39**: 59-194.

Schulte, H. (1917). *Arch. ges. Physiol.* **166**: 1-44.

Schulze, P. (1924). *Z. Morphol. Ökol. Tiere* **2**: 643-666.

Senekjie, H. A. (1941). *J. Hyg.* **34**: 63-66.

Smorodincev, I., and Bebesin, K. (1936). *Compt. rend. acad. sci. U.R.S.S. N.S.* **2**: 189-191.

Smyth, J. D. (1949). *J. Exptl. Biol.* **26**: 1-14.

Stepanow-Grigoriew, J., and Hoeppli, R. (1926). *Arch. Schiffs-u. Tropen-Hyg.* **30**: 577-585.

Stewart, H. M. (1938). *Am. J. Hyg.* **28**: 80-84.

Toryu, Y. (1933). *Science Repts. Tôhoku Imp. Univ. Fourth Ser.* **8**: 65-74.

Trier, H. J. (1926). *Z. vergleich. Physiol.* **4**: 305-330.

Wardle, R. A. (1937). *Can. J. Research* **D15**: 117-126.

Weineck, E. (1931). *Jena. Z. Naturw.* **65**: 739-750.

Weinland, E. (1901a). *Z. Biol.* **41**: 69-74.

Weinland, E. (1901b). *Z. Biol.* **42**: 55-90.

Weinland, E., and von Brand, T. (1926). *Z. vergleich. Physiol.* **4**: 212-285.

Westphal, A. (1934). *Z. Parasitenk.* **7**: 71-117.

Wilmoth, J. H., and Goldfisher, R. (1945). *J. Parasitol.* **32** Suppl.: 22.

Wottge, K. (1937). *Protoplasma* **29**: 31-59.

# CHAPTER 3

# LIPIDS

## I. Quantitative Considerations

The term "lipids" includes true fats (triglycerol esters of fatty acids), waxes, sterols, and other higher alcohols, as well as phospho- and glyco-lipids. In crude "fat" determinations all these constituents are usually measured together as the sum of the substances extractable by ether, alcohol, chloroform, or similar solvents. Few quantitative data exist for parasitic protozoa and arthropods whereas more are available for helminths (Table 8). A survey of these figures shows that the amount of lipids in parasites is fairly variable. There is no evidence that the habitat has any influence on the degree of lipid accumulation, which may or may not be due to the fact that so far very few forms have been analyzed for the various lipid fractions. In contrast to polysaccharides, the physiological function of various lipids may be quite different from each other. It is possible that future research may reveal some hitherto unsuspected relationship between one or the other lipid fraction and some peculiarities of the habitat. One such relationship, the occurrence of higher fatty acids as metabolic end-products in some parasitic worms leading *in vivo* a predominantly anaerobic life, will be dealt with in greater detail in a later section.

## II. Lipid Fractions

The few analyses of parasite "fats" available (Table 9) make it evident that all the usual lipid fractions occur. Some of the more interesting points will be emphasized in the following paragraphs.

### A. Phospholipids

Only one phospholipid has been studied in greater detail from the chemical standpoint. Lesuk and Anderson (1941) isolated from *Cysticercus fasciolaris* a mono-amino-mono-phosphatide which, upon analysis, proved to be a hydrolecithin, essentially dipalmitolecithin. The main constituents isolated by hydrolysis were palmitic acid, glycerophosphoric acid, and choline. It should be emphasized that this finding is rather unusual since hydro-lecithin usually does not occur in animal tissues.

Most other phospholipid fractions isolated from helminths obviously were mixtures of various substances, but few attempts at further fractionation have been reported. Tötterman and Kirk (1939) could separate a cephalin

TABLE 8.  Lipid content of some parasites

| SPECIES | LIPIDS IN PERCENT OF | | AUTHOR |
| | Fresh substance | Dry substance | |
|---|---|---|---|
| PROTOZOA | | | |
| Trypanosoma lewisi | | 3.3 | Ikejiani (1947) |
| T. equiperdum | | 18.6 | Ikejiani (1947) |
| T. evansi | | 60 | Kligler and Olitzki (1936) |
| Plasmodium knowlesi | | 28.8 | Morrison and Jeskey (1947) |
| Goussia gadi | 3.6 | 22.0 | Panzer (1913) |
| TREMATODES | | | |
| Fasciola hepatica | 2.4; 1.9 | 13.3; 12.2 | Flury and Leeb (1926); Weinland and von Brand (1926) |
| CESTODES | | | |
| Diphyllobothrium latum | 1.5; 1.6 | | Smorodincev and Bebesin (1936b); Tötterman and Kirk (1939) |
| Railletina cesticillus | 3.2 | 15.5 | Reid (1942) |
| Moniezia expansa | 3.4 | 30.1 | von Brand (1933) |
| M. denticulata | 1.3 | 16.2 | von Brand (1933) |
| Taenia solium | 1.4 | | Smorodincev and Bebesin (1936a) |
| T. saginata | 1.2; 1.4 | 15.0 | Smorodincev et al. (1933); von Brand (1933) |
| T. marginata | 1.1 | 4.9 | von Brand (1933) |
| T. plicata | 9.1 | 33.1 | von Brand (1933) |
| Cysticercus fasciolaris | | 11.9 | Salisbury and Anderson (1939) |
| NEMATODES | | | |
| Ascaris lumbricoides | 1.1–1.8 | 10.9 | Weinland (1901); Flury (1913); Schulte (1917); von Brand (1934b); Smorodincev and Bebesin (1936c, d) |
| Eustrongylides ignotus, larvae | 1.1 | 4.4 | von Brand (1938) |
| ACANTHOCEPHALA | | | |
| Macracanthorhynchus hirudinaceus | 1.0; 1.5; 2.1 | | von Brand (1939, 1940) |
| ARTHROPODS | | | |
| Gasterophilus intestinalis, larvae | 5.2 | 16.2 | von Kemnitz (1916) |
| Peltogaster paguri | | 26.6 | Reinhard and von Brand (1944) |

and a lecithin fraction from *Diphyllobothrium latum*. Rogers and Lazarus (1949) found lecithin, cephalin, and sphingomyelin as components of the phospholipids isolated from the intestine and hemocele fluid of *Ascaris*

TABLE 9.  Lipid fractions isolated from some parasites

FRACTIONS IN PERCENT OF TOTAL LIPIDS

| SPECIES | Phos-phatids | Unsaponi-fiable matter | Saturated | Unsatu-rated | Hydroxy | Glycerol | Soaps | AUTHOR |
|---|---|---|---|---|---|---|---|---|
| | | | | Fatty acids | | | | |
| Plasmodium knowlesi | | 16–32 | 36 | 41 | | | Approx. 20 | Morrison and Jeskey (1947) |
| Goussia gadi | | 35.8 | 48.7 (Saturated–Unsaturated) | | | | 16 | Panzer (1913) |
| Fasciola hepatica | 30 | 19 | 4 | 12 | | 2 | | von Brand (1928) |
| Diphyllobothrium latum | 13 | 17 | 5 | 65 | | | | Faust and Tallqvist (1907) |
| | 31 | 35 | | | | | | Tötterman and Kirk (1939) |
| Moniezia expansa | 15.2 | 7.0 | 8.1 | 51.3 | 14.0 | 4.3 | | von Brand (1933) |
| | 6.6 | 24.7 | 30.9 | 34.1 | | 2.4 | | Flury (1912) |
| Ascaris lumbricoides | | 26 | 65 (Saturated–Unsaturated) | | | 8.8 | | Schulz and Becker (1933) |
| Eustrongylides ignotus, larvae | 25.8 | 16.9 | 7.4 | 22.4 | | 1.9 | | von Brand and Winkeljohn (1945) |
| Macracanthorhynchus hirudina-ceus | 27 | 24 | 2 | 32 | | 2 | | von Brand (1939) |

*lumbricoides*, but only the two former fractions in the ovary. The cephalin fraction could be subdivided into an ethanolamine- and a serine-containing phospholipid.

In so far as parasitic protozoa are concerned, no true quantitative figures are available. Moraczewski and Kelsey (1948) identified phospholipid as one of the constituents of the lipid fractions of the blood stream form of *Trypanosoma equiperdum*, finding 4.14 μg. phospholipid phosphorus in 100 million flagellates.

## B. Glycolipids

It is somewhat surprising that glycolipids have been reported so far only from cestodes. Lesuk and Anderson (1941) studied the cerebroside fraction of *Cysticercus fasciolaris* which proved to be essentially a hydrophrenosin, yielding galactose, phrenosinic acid (that is, probably a mixture of α-hydroxyacids), and dihydrosphingosine upon hydrolysis. This last finding especially is interesting since all other hitherto known cerebrosides contain sphingosine instead. A cerebroside containing 47% fatty acid esters, 32% sphingosine, and 21.7% galactose has been isolated from *Moniezia expansa* (Kent *et al.*, 1948), and Tötterman and Kirk (1939) found a relatively large cerebroside fraction in *Diphyllobothrium latum*.

## C. Unsaponifiable Fraction

The unsaponifiable material of *Goussia gadi* has been reported as consisting essentially of cholesterol although a certain amount of other unidentified higher alcohols was also found (Panzer, 1913). Cholesterol is also the main unsaponifiable material occurring in *Plasmodium knowlesi* (Morrison and Jeskey, 1947).

In worms, the unsaponifiable material of *Fasciola hepatica*, *Moniezia expansa*, *Cysticercus fasciolaris*, and *Macracanthorhynchus hirudinaceus* gave sterol reactions (von Brand, 1928, 1933, 1939; Salisbury and Anderson, 1939). Whether true cholesterol was present cannot be decided definitely at present. Melting points and color reactions were not always entirely in agreement with those of cholesterol. It is well to remember in this connection that the sterols are quite varied in several invertebrate groups, for example the sponges. The exact identification of the sterols occurring in parasites is definitely a desirable problem for future investigation.

In nematodes certain higher alcohols other than cholesterol seem to predominate. Definite chemical information is available only for one of them, ascaryl alcohol. It was found independently by Flury (1912) and Fauré-Fremiet (1913) and restudied by Schulz and Becker (1933). Its probable formula is $C_{33}H_{68}O_4$, but little is known about its structure. It has been established that the compound has only two hydroxyl groups; the two remaining oxygen atoms are probably present in form of ether linkages. Fauré-Fremiet (1913) stated that ascaryl alcohol occurs only in the female reproductive cells of *Ascaris* and *Parascaris*. More recent studies, however, have shown it to be present also in male ascarids (von Brand and Winkeljohn, 1945). The physiological function of the substance is unknown. It seems to replace cholesterol in ascarids, since this latter substance seems to occur only in very small amounts in these worms.

Whether ascaryl alcohol occurs also in other parasitic worms is questionable. It is interesting to note in this connection that Bondouy (1910) reported the absence of cholesterol in *Strongylus equinus*. The unsaponifiable material of larval *Eustrongylides ignotus* could be divided into two fractions, one having a melting point close to that of cholesterol, the other close to ascaryl alcohol. The identity of either fraction however has not yet been established beyond doubt (von Brand and Winkeljohn, 1945).

## D. Fatty Acids

In parasites, just as in most other animals, a large fraction of the fatty acids is bound to glycerol, cholesterol, or other higher alcohols. To what extent free fatty acids occur hardly is known at present.

Lower volatile fatty acids have been found in abundance in *Ascaris* and *Parascaris* ether extracts (Schimmelpfennig, 1903; Flury, 1912). In *Ascaris* for example, they amounted to 31% of the total fat. In *Parascaris* the predominant volatile acid seems to be butyric acid.

Among the higher fatty acids the unsaturated acids predominate in most hitherto studied parasites, oleic acid being the only definitely identified member of this group. It has been found in *Diphyllobothrium latum*, *Ascaris lumbricoides*, and *Fasciola hepatica* (Faust and Tallqvist, 1907; Flury, 1912; von Brand, 1928) and may occur in *Plasmodium knowlesi* (Morrison and Jeskey, 1947). The probability of the occurrence of other unsaturated acids is evident considering that the iodine numbers of the fatty acids of *Goussia gadi* (Panzer, 1913) and *Taenia saginata* (Smorodincev and Bebesin, 1939) are 116 and 168 respectively, that is, higher than that of oleic acid.

Palmitic and stearic acids are the only saturated higher fatty acids identified with any degree of probability in the above worms while only the latter has been found in *Plasmodium knowlesi*. In *Moniezia expansa* higher hydroxy acids have been found. Their identity has not yet been established and there may be some doubt whether they occur as such, or as constituents of the cerebroside mentioned previously (von Brand, 1933; Oesterlin and von Brand, 1934).

## E. Soaps

The occurrence of soaps in relatively large amounts in some parasites is rather curious. There is little information available concerning their chemical constitution but some indications exist that the fatty acids of the soaps may differ qualitatively or in their relative proportions from those of the glycerides. Panzer (1913) found the iodine number of the fatty acids bound as soaps lower than that of the other fat fractions in *Goussia gadi* and von Brand (1928) reported the relatively low iodine number of 30 for the fatty acids isolated from the soaps of *Fasciola hepatica*. In addition to the parasites listed in Table 9, the occurrence of soaps has been demonstrated qualitatively in *Strongylus equinus* (Bondouy, 1910).

### III. MORPHOLOGICAL OBSERVATIONS AND OCCURRENCE OF LIPIDS IN VARIOUS ORGANS

The occurrence of fatty materials in parasites has been studied frequently by means of more or less specific staining methods, *e.g.*, osmic acid, Sudan III, and others. In evaluating these observations it must be kept in mind that all staining procedures show only a part, often only a small fraction, of the lipids extractable by chemical methods. It must be realized that negative observations, such as those by Armer (1944) on parasitic protozoa of cockroaches do not indicate the actual absence of lipids. Despite their limitations, morphological fat data are of physiological interest in many cases because they permit the study of organisms or organs not available in sufficient quantity for chemical analysis. In view of the great differences in fat deposition in various groups of parasites, they will be taken up separately.

### A. Parasitic Protozoa

No attempt has been made to collect all the morphological fat data scattered throughout the protozoological literature. Even a cursory survey sufficed to show that fat droplets have been reported from many parasitic protozoa. They have been encountered especially frequently and apparently in fairly great abundance in myxosporidia (Cohn, 1896; Doflein, 1898; Erdmann, 1917; Petruschewsky, 1932), coccidia, and gregarines (Joyet-Lavergne, 1926; Gurwitsch, 1927; Daniels, 1938). It is of interest that in the latter group sexual differences have been observed, the female of an encysted pair having more lipids than the male. Fat droplets seem on the whole less frequent in parasitic amoebas and flagellates (Sassuchin, 1928, 1930), but they occur with greater regularity and greater abundance in some, although not all, parasitic ciliates (Cheissin, 1930; Kedrowsky, 1931). In the case of *Opalina ranarum* a seasonal fat cycle has been recorded, a large accumulation of fat occurring in fall which almost completely disappeared towards the end of winter.

## B. Parasitic Worms

The distribution of lipids in various body regions or organs has been studied but rarely by chemical methods. In addition to the data shown in Table 10, the work of Smorodincev and Bebesin (1935) has shown that in *Taenia saginata* the head and neck region has a fat content of 3.05% of the fresh weight, while the respective figures for the middle region of the strobila and for the gravid segments were 1.55 and 1.25% respectively. More data are available that were gathered by staining procedures and these will be reviewed in the following paragraphs.

*1. Cestodes.* The fat distribution has been studied by Schiefferdecker (1874), Brault and Loeper (1904), Arndt (1922), Pintner (1922), Coutelen (1931), von Brand (1933), and Smyth (1947, 1949). Quite generally, the

TABLE 10. Distribution of lipids in various organ systems of helminths

| SPECIES | LIPIDS IN PERCENT OF FRESH SUBSTANCE OCCURRING IN | | | AUTHOR |
|---|---|---|---|---|
| | Body wall | Body fluid | Reproductive organs | |
| *Ascaris lumbricoides* | 1.0 | | 4.0–6.3 | Flury (1912) |
| *Macracanthorhynchus hirudinaceus* | 1.3 | 0.2 | 1.9 | von Brand (1939) |

parenchyma was the most important storage place. Most other organs contained either no or only little demonstrable fat. Lipid droplets were found, however, in the eggs where they usually were not located within the embryo itself but between the latter and the egg shell. In some instances, for example *Dipylidium caninum*, large fat droplets occurred in the lumen of the uterus.

Of special interest, because of its bearing on the interpretation of the significance of fat deposits, is the observation that at least in two cases, *Echinococcus granulosus* and *Moniezia expansa*, fat droplets were found within the lumen of the excretory system. This indicates that some "fat" fraction is a metabolic endproduct rather than an energy reserve. It is also probable that a part at least of the parenchymal fat is unexcreted metabolic waste. Of interest in this connection is Smyth's (1949) observation that the plerocercoid larva of *Ligula intestinalis* produces large amounts of cytoplasmic fat during starvation under aseptic conditions. The view that fat deposits may represent waste products is not as unorthodox as may appear at first glance. Fats are undoubtedly much less toxic than many other excreta. Furthermore, tapeworm segments are only ephemereal structures. The excretion of relatively nontoxic metabolic endproducts is there-fore much less important than in organisms with a longer life span.

It is true that this view has been questioned because of the observation of Smorodincev and Bebesin (1935) that the anterior regions of the tape-worms contain more fat than the posterior ones. However, the figures of these authors are percentage figures which do not take into account the fact that the proglottids become progressively larger. If the actual amounts of fat in the single proglottids were compared, an increase in fat content as postulated by the above theory probably would be revealed. Another criticism has been based on Reid's (1942) observation that the fat content of *Railletina cesticillus* was the same in worms taken from fed and starved chickens although the parasites occurring in the latter had lost most of their glycogen. These experiments, however, hardly have a bearing on the problem, since it is quite possible that the starving tapeworms could keep up their normal metabolic rate from their endogenous glycogen. It must also be realized that the metabolic processes in various species need not to be identical; we will presently see differences in fat excretion in trematodes.

*2. Trematodes.* Only *Fasciola hepatica* has been studied in detail (Prenant, 1922; von Brand and Weinland, 1924; Vogel and von Brand, 1933; Stephen-son, 1947). In adult liver flukes only few fat droplets occurred in any organ, with the exception of the excretory system. Numerous fat droplets were found embedded in the wall of the smaller excretory vessels while they were freely floating in the lumen of the larger ones. Their expulsion through the excretory pore could be observed under the microscope. Microchemical tests indicated that the droplets did not contain cholesterol, cholesterides, or lipines, but that they were probably triglycerides containing possibly some unsaturated fatty acid. The absence of cholesterol is especially note-worthy because it indicates that no simple excretion of exogenous fat taken up with the food is involved. The environment of the flukes is very rich in cholesterol and the occurrence of this compound in the droplets would be expected if food lipids were involved. It is quite obvious that we are dealing with the excretion of fat originating in the body of the worms themselves, presumably, as will be shown later, from their carbohydrate metabolism.

This fat excretion can be demonstrated only in the adult liver fluke; its developmental stages, miracidia, rediae, and cercariae, show some fat droplets within the tissues but they are never found in the excretory system.

The fat distribution in *Fasciola* does not represent a pattern characteristic for other trematodes. In adult *Dicrocoelium lanceatum* no fat excretion could be demonstrated by morphological methods (von Brand, 1934a) despite the fact that it lives in exactly the same habitat as *Fasciola*. A comparative study of more fluke species in this respect would be very desirable. Other differences in fat distribution between various species also have been observed. There is no indication that the vitellaria of *Fasciola* contain cholesterol esters whereas these have been found in abundance in those of *Gorgodera cygnoides* as well as in its eggs (Schmidt, 1930).

3. *Nematodes.* The adults of *Ascaris lumbricoides* and *Parascaris equorum* have been investigated to some extent (von Kemnitz, 1912; Fauré-Fremiet, 1913; Mueller, 1929; Hirsch and Bretschneider, 1929). The general aspects of fat deposition were similar in both species, the subcuticula, especially the chords, and the plasma bulbs of the body wall muscles being the most important storage places. Fat droplets also were found within the ganglion cells, the intestinal cells, and various structures of the reproductive tracts. Of special interest is the observation that the vitelline membrane of the eggs is lipid in nature, as first recognized by Fauré-Fremiet (1913) and since substantiated for these and other nematode species by various authors (Zawadowsky, 1928; Wottge, 1937; Chitwood, 1938; Jacobs and Jones, 1939). The exact chemical nature of this membrane has not yet been established unequivocally. Some authors consider it as consisting mainly of ascaryl alcohol, others call it cholesterol, or more generally a sterol membrane. Timm (1950) recently isolated the membrane substance and concluded, chiefly on the basis of melting point and mixed melting points, that it consists of myricyl palmitate.

Various other adult and larval nematodes have been studied in more or less detail by Payne (1922, 1923), Cort (1925), Giovannola (1935, 1936), Rogers (1939, 1940), Chitwood and Jacobs (1938), Chitwood and Chitwood (1938), and Weinstein (1949). One of the most interesting observations was the finding that fat in some instances accumulated not only within the cells of the intestine but also in the lumen of the gut. The fat content of the larvae was found to be a good indicator of the physiological age of hookworm larvae. Reduction in fat content and activity paralleled each other rather closely. Some correlation with infectivity also existed but a minority of the larvae was still infective when the fat reserves were exhausted completely.

4. *Acanthocephala.* The occurrence of lipid droplets in the vessels of the lacunar system of some species has been mentioned by Saefftigen (1885), Hamann (1891), and Meyer (1931). More details were presented by von Brand (1939) and Bullock (1949). The subcuticula contained relatively large amounts of fat in all species studied whereas specific differences occurred in respect to the muscles. Those of *Macracanthorhynchus* contained but little fat while those of *Echinorhynchus*, *Neoechinorhynchus*, and *Pomphorhynchus* did show marked accumulations. Some fat droplets were seen in the cells of the nervous and the male reproductive system. In the female reproductive system, the germ balls were especially rich in fat, as were some

of the other structures, such as the vaginal glands. Histochemical tests showed that phospholipids, though not completely lacking in the other organs, were especially plentiful in the subcuticula, having a tendency to accumulate around the lacunae. Cholesterol and cholesterol esters, on the other hand, were found essentially limited to the inner layer of the subcuticula.

## C. Endoparasitic Arthropods

Morphological fat data are available only for *Peltogaster paguri* (Reinhard and von Brand, 1944). The root system of the parasite, which permeates the liver of the host, always contained some fat but it was not seen in the bulbous tips of the roots which presumably are the main places of absorption. The external sacs of the parasites showed variable conditions depending upon the age of the parasites. The smallest, that is, the youngest sacs were fat-free while the eggs and developing embryos of mature specimens were extremely rich in fat. Fully developed free-swimming nauplii, which do not feed, again showed a decrease in fat content.

### LITERATURE

Armer, J. M. (1944). *J. Parasitol.* **30:** 131–142.
Arndt, W. (1922). *Verhandl. deut. zool. Ges.* **1922:** 76–78.
Bondouy, T. (1910). Thèse, Paris.
von Brand, T. (1928). *Z. vergleich. Physiol.* **8:** 613–624.
von Brand, T. (1933). *Z. vergleich. Physiol.* **18:** 562–596.
von Brand, T. (1934a). *Ergeb. Biol.* **10:** 37–100.
von Brand, T., (1934b). *Z. vergleich. Physiol.* **21:** 220–235.
von Brand, T., (1938). *J. Parasitol.* **24:** 445–451.
von Brand, T. (1939). *J. Parasitol.* **25:** 329–342.
von Brand, T. (1940). *J. Parasitol.* **26:** 301–307.
von Brand, T. (1941). *Proc. Soc. Exptl. Biol. Med.* **46:** 417–418.
von Brand, T., and Weinland, E., (1924). *Z. vergleich. Physiol.* **2:** 209–214.
von Brand, T., and Winkeljohn, M. I. (1945). *Proc. Helminthol. Soc. Wash.* **12:** 62–65.
Brault, A., and Loeper, M. (1904). *J. phys. et pathol. gén.* **6:** 503–512.
Bullock, W. L. (1949). *J. Morphol.* **84:** 201–226.
Cheissin, E. (1930). *Arch. Protistenk.* **70:** 531–618.
Chitwood, B. G. (1938). *Proc. Helminthol. Soc. Wash.* **5:** 68–75.
Chitwood, B. G., and Chitwood, M. B. (1938).    *Proc. Helminthol. Soc. Wash.* **5:** 16–18.
Chitwood, B. G., and Jacobs, L. (1938). *J. Wash. Acad. Sci.* **28:** 12–13.
Cohn, L. (1896). *Zool. Jahrb.* **9:** 227–272.
Cort, W. W. (1925). *Am. J. Hyg.* **5:** 49–89.
Coutelen, F. R. (1931). *Ann. parasitol. humaine et comparée* **9:** 97–100.
Daniels, M. I. (1938). *Quart. J. Microscop. Sci.* **80:** Part II.: 293–320.
Doflein, F. (1898). *Zool. Jahrb. Abt. Anat.* **11:** 281–350.
Erdmann, R. (1917). *Arch. Protistenk.* **37:** 276–326.
Fauré-Fremiet, E. (1913). *Arch. anat. microscop.* **15:** 435–757.
Faust, E. S., and Tallqvist, T. W. (1907). *Arch. exptl. Path. Pharmakol.* **57:** 367–385.
Flury, F. (1912). *Arch. exptl. Path. Pharmakol.* **67:** 275–392.

Flury, F., and Leeb, F. (1926). *Klin. Wochschr.* **5**: 2054–2055.

Giovannola, A. (1935). *Arch. ital. sci. med. colon.* **16**: 430–436.

Giovannola, A. (1936). *J. Parasitol.* **22**: 207–218.

Gurwitsch, B. M. (1927). *Arch. Protistenk.* **59**: 369–372.

Hamann, O. (1891). *Jena. Z. Naturw.* **25**: 113–231.

Hirsch, G. C., and Bretschneider, L. H. (1937). Cytologia, Tokyo. Fujii Jubilee Vol., pp. 424–436.

Ikejiani, O. (1947). *Am. J. Hyg.* **45**: 144–149.

Jacobs, L., and Jones, M. F. (1939). *Proc. Helminthol. Soc. Wash.* **6**: 57–60.

Joyet-Lavergne, P. (1926). *Arch. anat. microscop.* **22**: 1–17.

Kedrowsky, B. (1931). *Z. Zellforsch. mikroskop. Anat.* **12**: 666–714.

von Kemnitz, G. (1912). *Arch. Zellforsch.* **7**: 463–603.

von Kemnitz, G. (1916). *Z. Biol.* **67**: 129–244.

Kent, N., Macheboeuf, M., and Neiadas, B. (1948). *Experientia* **4**: 193–194.

Kligler, I. J., and Olitzki, L. (1936). *Ann. Trop. Med. Parasitol.* **30**: 287–291.

Lesuk, A., and Anderson, R. J. (1941). *J. Biol. Chem.* **139**: 457–469.

Meyer, A. (1931). *Z. Zellforsch. mikroskop. Anat.* **14**: 255–265.

Moraczewski, S. A., and Kelsey, F. E. (1948). *J. Infectious Diseases* **82**: 45–51.

Morrison, D. B., and Jeskey, H. A. (1947). *Federation Proc.* **6**: 279.

Mueller, J. F. (1928–29). *Z. Zellforsch. mikroskop. Anat.* **8**: 361–403.

Oesterlin, M., and von Brand, T. (1934). *Z. vergleich. Physiol.* **20**: 251–254.

Panzer, T. (1913). *Z. physiol. Chem.* **86**: 33–42.

Payne, F. K. (1922). *Am. J. Hyg.* **2**: 254–263.

Payne, F. K. (1923). *Am. J. Hyg.* **3**: 547–583.

Petruschewsky, G. K. (1932). *Arch. Protistenk.* **78**: 542–556.

Pintner, T. (1922). *Sitzber. Akad. Wiss. Wien. Math.-naturw. Klasse, Abt. I*, **131**: 129–138.

Prenant, M. (1922). *Arch. morphol.* **5**: 1–474.

Reid, W. M. (1942). *J. Parasitol.* **28**: 319–340.

Reinhard, E. G., and von Brand, T. (1944). *Physiol. Zoöl.* **17**: 31–41.

Rogers, W. P. (1939). *J. Helminthol.* **17**: 195–202.

Rogers, W. P. (1940). *J. Helminthol.* **18**: 183–192.

Rogers, W. P., and Lazarus, M. (1949). *Parasitology* **39**: 302–314.

Saefftigen, A. (1885). *Morphol. Jahrb.* **10**: 120–171.

Salisbury, L. F., and Anderson, R. J. (1939). *J. Biol. Chem.* **129**: 505–517.

Sassuchin, D. (1928). *Arch. Protistenk.* **64**: 71–92.

Sassuchin, D. (1930). *Arch. Protistenk.* **70**: 681–686.

Schiefferdecker, P. (1874). *Jena. Z. Naturw.* **8**: 458–487.

Schimmelpfennig, G. (1903). *Arch. wiss. prakt. Tierheilk.* **29**: 332–376.

Schmidt, W. J. (1930). *Zool. Jahrb. Abt. allg. Zool. Physiol.* **47**: 249–258.

Schulte, H. (1917). *Arch. ges. Physiol.* **166**: 1–44.

Schulz, F. N., and Becker, M. (1933). *Biochem. Z.* **265**: 253–259.

Smorodincev, I. A., and Bebesin, K. W. (1935). *Biochem. Z.* **276**: 271–273.

Smorodincev, I. A., and Bebesin, K. W. (1936a). *J. Biochem.* **23**: 19–20.

Smorodincev, I. A., and Bebesin, K. W. (1936b). *J. Biochem.* **23**: 21–22.

Smorodincev, I. A., and Bebesin, K. W. (1936c). *J. Biochem.* **23**: 23–25.

Smorodincev, I. A., and Bebesin, K. W. (1936d). *Compt. rend. acad. sci. U.R.S.S. N.S.* **2**: 189–191.

Smorodincev, I. A., and Bebesin, K. W. (1939). *Bull. soc. chim. biol.* **21**: 478–482.

Smorodincev, I. A., Bebesin, K. W., and Pawlowa, P. I. (1933). *Biochem. Z.* **261**: 176–178.

Smyth, J. D. (1947). *Biol. Revs.* **22:** 214–238.
Smyth, J. D. (1949). *J. Exptl. Biol.* **26:** 1–14.
Stephenson, W. (1947). *Parasitology* **38:** 140–144.
Timm, R. W. (1950). *Science* **112:** 167–168.
Tötterman, G., and Kirk, E. (1939). *Nord. Med.* **3:** 2715–2716.
Vogel, H., and von Brand, T. (1933). *Z. Parasitenk.* **5:** 425–431.
Weinland, E. (1901). *Z. Biol.* **42:** 55–90.
Weinland, E., and von Brand, T. (1926). *Z. vergleich. Physiol.* **4:** 212–285.
Weinstein, P. P. (1949). *J. Parasitol.* **35** Suppl.: 14.
Wottge, K. (1937). *Protoplasma* **29:** 31–59.
Zawadowsky, M. (1928). *Trans. Lab. Exptl. Biol. Zoo-Park Moscow* **4:** 201–206.

# CHAPTER 4

## PROTEINS

### I. Quantitative Considerations

A series of quantitative nitrogen determinations has been done on parasites, especially helminths. If these figures are multiplied by one of the conventional factors, 6.25 or 6.41, the approximate protein content can be calculated (Table 11). It should be realized that at present some doubt as to the validity of this procedure must remain, since very little is known about the nitrogen percentage of parasite protoplasm. Serious doubts have been raised, especially in the case of the cestodes, by Reid (1942) since he assumes, on the basis of Salisbury and Anderson's (1939) and Eisenbrandt's (1938) data, that the nonprotein fraction of the total nitrogen is unusually high. While this may well be so, Eisenbrandt's (1938) data are hardly detailed enough to deduce such a relationship; they can also be interpreted as being due to the use of varying amounts of material for extraction purposes.

### II. Nitrogenous Fractions

The chemical entities constituting the proteins of parasites are very imperfectly known. Some fractionations have been carried out with nematodes and cestodes (Table 12). The resulting fractions have, in general, been attributed to one of the conventional protein groups chiefly on the basis of their solubilities, and in appropriate cases, their phosphorus and sulfur content. Whether this procedure was entirely justified in all cases is open to some doubt.

The proteins of tapeworms, especially *Moniezia expansa*, and to a lesser extent *Taenia saginata*, recently have been studied by Kent (1947) and Kent and Macheboeuf (1947a, b, c). Their analytical procedures and findings are summarized in Table 13. The most unusual result is the observation that practically none of the protein fractions was obtained as such, but that they occurred either in combination with glycogen, cerebrosides, or bile acids. Bueding (1949), however, has pointed out that the Pettenkofer reaction which the above authors used to identify the bile acids is not specific enough to make the presence of bile salts certain. Of the various fractions isolated, only baerine and moniezine are considered by Kent (1947) as definite chemical compounds because they behaved

37

TABLE 11.  Protein content (N × 6.25) of some parasites

| SPECIES | PROTEIN IN PERCENT OF DRY SUBSTANCE | AUTHOR |
|---|---|---|
| TREMATODES | | |
| Fasciola hepatica.............. | 58 | Weinland and von Brand (1926) |
| CESTODES | | |
| Diphyllobothrium latum....... | 60 | Smorodincev and Bebesin (1936b) |
| Schistocephalus solidus, plero- | | |
| cercoids................... | 36 | Hopkins (1950) |
| Railletina cesticillus........... | 36 | Reid (1942) |
| Moniezia expansa............. | 36; 30 | von Brand (1933); Wardle (1937) |
| Taenia saginata.............. | 33 | Smorodincev et al. (1933) |
| T. solium.................... | 46 | Smorodincev and Bebesin (1936a) |
| Cysticercus fasciolaris........ | 31 | Salisbury and Anderson (1939) |
| NEMATODES | | |
| Ascaris lumbricoides.......... | 54; 54; 48 | Weinland (1901); Flury (1912); Smorodincev and Bebesin (1936c) |
| ACANTHOCEPHALA | | |
| Macracanthorhynchus hirudina- | | |
| ceus...................... | 70 | von Brand (1939) |
| ARTHROPODS | | |
| Gasterophilus intestinalis, lar- | | |
| vae....................... | 43 | von Kemnitz (1916) |

TABLE 12.  Protein fractions isolated from the bodies of parasitic worms

| PROTEIN FRACTION | Diphyllobothrium latum[a] | Taenia saginata[b] | Strongylus equinus[c] | Ascaris lumbricoides[d] |
|---|---|---|---|---|
| Peptones................. | | | | × |
| Albumins............... | × | × | × | × |
| Globulins............... | × | × | | × |
| Albumoses.............. | | × | × | × |
| Purine bases............ | | | × | × |
| Nucleoproteins.......... | | × | | |
| Mucin.................. | | | × | |
| Keratin................. | | × | | |
| Elastin................. | | × | | |
| Collagen................ | | × | | |
| Reticulin............... | | × | | |

[a] Faust and Tallqvist (1907).
[b] Smorodincev and Pawlowa (1936).
[c] Bondouy (1910).
[d] Flury (1912).

homogeneously during electrophoresis. These two substances proved to be very resistant to tryptic digestion, not more than 37% of their amino acid nitrogen being liberated. The combination with cerebrosides or bile

TABLE 13. Fractionation of 28 gm *Moniezia expansa* (after Kent, 1947)

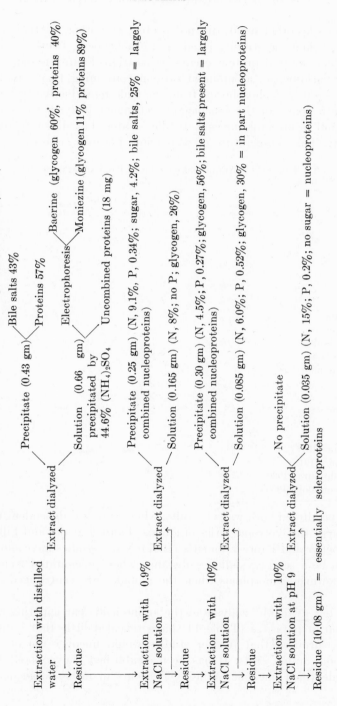

Extraction with distilled water → Precipitate (0.43 gm) → Bile salts 43%; Proteins 57%

Extract dialyzed → Residue; Solution (0.66 gm) precipitated by 44.6% (NH₄)₂SO₄ → Electrophoresis → Baerine (glycogen 60%, proteins 40%); Moniezine (glycogen 11% proteins 89%); Uncombined proteins (18 mg)

Extraction with 0.9% NaCl solution → Precipitate (0.25 gm) (N, 9.1%, P, 0.34%; sugar, 4.2%; bile salts, 25% = largely combined nucleoproteins)

Extract dialyzed → Solution (0.165 gm) (N, 8%; no P; glycogen, 26%)

Residue → Extraction with 10% NaCl solution → Precipitate (0.30 gm) (N, 4.5%; P, 0.27%; glycogen, 56%; bile salts present = largely combined nucleoproteins)

Extract dialyzed → Solution (0.085 gm) (N, 6.0%; P, 0.52%; glycogen, 30% = in part nucleoproteins)

Residue → Extraction with 10% NaCl solution at pH 9 → No precipitate

Extract dialyzed → Solution (0.035 gm) (N, 15%; P, 0.2%; no sugar = nucleoproteins)

Residue (10.08 gm) = essentially scleroproteins

acids, on the other hand, did not protect the other fractions but rather enhanced their digestibility (Kent and Macheboeuf, 1949).

Another unusual protein occurs in ascarids. Fauré-Fremiet (1913) isolated ascaridine, an albuminoid protein containing 17.5% nitrogen, but neither sulfur nor phosphorus, from the male reproductive system. Ascaridine is the basis of the conspicuous refringent body of the sperms. The compound is insoluble in cold distilled water, but dissolves suddenly at 50–51°C. This temperature of dispersion, however, is not a fixed point.

TABLE 14.　Amino acids isolated from some parasites

| AMINO ACID | Moniezia expansa[a] | Ascaris lumbricoides[b] | Ascaris lumbricoides[c] | Gasterophilus intestinalis[d] LARVAL HEMOLYMPH |
|---|---|---|---|---|
| Glycine.......... | | X | X | X |
| Alanine.......... | X | | X | X |
| Valine........... | X | X | X | X |
| Serine........... | | X | X | X |
| Leucine......... | X | X | X | X |
| Isoleucine....... | X | | X | X |
| Tyrosine........ | | X | X | X |
| Phenylalanine... | | | X | X |
| Aspartic acid.... | X | X | X | X |
| Glutamic acid... | X | | X | X |
| Lysine........... | | X | X | X |
| Arginine........ | X | X | X | X |
| Histidine........ | X | X | X | X |
| Proline.......... | | | X | X |

[a] Kent (1947).
[b] Flury (1912).
[c] Yoshimura (1930).
[d] Levenbook (1950).

It can be altered both ways by salts, whose action is dependent upon their position in the lyotropic series of anions (Fauré-Fremiet and Filhol, 1937). Champétier and Fauré-Fremiet's (1937) X-ray studies have shown ascaridine to be a semi-crystalline substance when precipitated from solution. It is, however, amorphous when the globules are centrifuged and desiccated.

The few available analyses of the amino acids participating in the constitution of parasites (Table 14) have revealed little that is unusual. It can be surmised that further studies would uncover the occurrence of additional amino acids. It has been established (Levenbook, 1950) that an unidentified phenolic amino acid occurs in rather large quantities in the hemolymph of *Gasterophilus intestinalis* larvae. It may be important for the darkening of the cuticle.

Some protein fractions have been correlated with a greater or lesser degree of probability with certain morphological structures and this will now be reviewed briefly. It should be emphasized that all identifications are of a preliminary nature; the exact chemical constitution of the compounds involved has not yet been established in any case.

## A. *Scleroproteins*

The capsule of the spores of *Goussia gadi* does not contain chitin, carbohydrates, or nucleoproteins. After hydrolysis the following amino acids were identified with some degree of probability: Lysine, histidine, arginine, tyrosine, glutamic acid, and glycine. It may consist of a keratin- or elastin-like albuminoid (Panzer, 1911, 1913). A study of the cyst wall of *Endamoeba histolytica*, *Endolimax nana*, and *Giardia lamblia* led to an essentially similar conclusion (Kofoid *et al.*, 1931).

The cuticle of nematodes is a complicated structure consisting of several layers. The older investigations by Sukatschoff (1899), Reichard (1902), and Flury (1912) showed that the inner layers of the cuticle were digestible by pepsin and were dissolved readily by KOH, while the outer layer proved much more resistant. Analyses of the cuticle showed a high nitrogen and sulfur content (Flury, 1912; Magath, 1919; Mueller, 1929). These and related tests led to the tentative conclusion that a keratin-like substance was present at least in the outer layer. The cuticle of *Ascaris* was then studied in more detail by Chitwood (1936). He demonstrated rather conclusively that only the external cortical layer was built by a keratin-like substance. The conclusion that a true keratin is present cannot be drawn, however. Brown (1949) states that keratin, that is, a protein with molecules cross-linked by cystine bridges, probably occurs only in vertebrates. In invertebrates, most skeletal proteins seem to belong to the general type of collagen, which may be rendered more resistant by tanning. Brown (1950, and personal communication) found —S—S-bonding in the external cortical layer of *Ascaris* and *Proleptus obtusus*, and obtained evidence of polyphenols which usually are the precursors of tanning.

Chitwood (1936) also found another member of the collagen group which he named ascarogelatin and which seems to be derived from a substance called ascarocollagen. It corresponded to the internal cortical and fibril layers. Finally, the matrix layer consisted of a fibroid for which he proposed the name matricin. In a later paper, Chitwood (1938) stated that a keratin-like substance also occurred in the cortical layer of the cuticle and the esophageal and cloacal lining of several other parasitic nematodes. The spicules, on the other hand, consisted at least in part of collagen.

The hooks of cestodes do not contain chitin (Dollfus, 1942). They seem to consist of a scleroprotein (Crusz, 1947).

Whether a substance similar to that contained in the external cortical layer in nematodes occurs in the cuticle of acanthocephala is not yet known. Possibly suggestive is Mueller's (1929) finding that the cuticle of *Macracanthorhynchus* contains 14.78% nitrogen and 0.564% sulfur.

The egg shells of trematodes, considered in the early days as chitinous (Thomas, 1883), are derived from the granules of the vitelline cells. Stephenson (1947) has found that the egg shells of *Fasciola* give all the reactions of sclerotin, a quinone-tanned protein. He found indications that the vitellarian granules contained both the proteins and polyphenols involved in sclerotin formation. The occurrence of one of the components, catechol, within the vitelline cells of trematodes and cestodes had already become known through Vialli's (1933) studies.

## B. Glycoproteins

Chitwood (1936), with some probability, identified a mucoid as a constituent of the cuticle of *Ascaris*, but he could not correlate it with any definite morphological structure. Glycoproteins may also be present in the spicules of parasitic nematodes, the albuminous layer of the egg shell of *Ascaris*, and they seem to constitute the operculae of the eggs of *Dioctophyme renale* (Chitwood, 1938).

## C. Protein Reserves

Proteins are not usually deposited as reserve material in higher animals, while in lower forms, especially free-living protozoa, such deposits have been observed rather frequently. Some observations exist indicating the occurrence of reserve proteins also in parasites. Joyet-Lavergne (1926) described granules from the cytoplasm of coccidia and gregarines which gave a positive Millon test and which also proved to contain phosphorus. Whether he was dealing in part at least, with volutin is not quite clear.

Volutin, which appears to consist of free nucleic acid, is apparently a reserve substance for the nucleus. It accumulates especially in protozoa undergoing rapid nuclear divisions, such as coccidia and trypanosomes (Reichenow, 1929).

Volutin does not occur in metazoa and to what extent protein reserves are deposited in the bodies of multicellular parasites is difficult to decide. There is some justification to look upon the previously mentioned vitellarian granules of flatworms in this light. The only other definite information is due to Chitwood and Jacobs (1938). They observed that the globules deposited in the intestinal cells of *Agamermis decaudata* during parasitic development and used up during the adult free-living existence gave, at least in part, the reactions characterizing a conjugated fatty acid-protein.

## LITERATURE

Bondouy, T. (1910). Thèse, Paris.

von Brand, T. (1933). *Z. vergleich. Physiol.* **18:** 562–596.

von Brand, T. (1939). *J. Parasitol.* **25:** 329–342.

Brown, C. H. (1949). *Exptl. Cell Research, Suppl.* **1:** 351–355.

Brown, C. H. (1950). *Nature* **165:** 275.

Bueding, E. (1949). *Physiol. Revs.* **29:** 195–218.

Champétier, G., and Fauré-Fremiet, E. (1937). *Compt. rend.* **204:** 1901–1903.

Chitwood, B. G. (1936). *Proc. Helminthol. Soc. Wash.* **3:** 39–49.

Chitwood, B. G. (1938). *Proc. Helminthol. Soc. Wash.* **5:** 68–75.

Chitwood, B. G., and Jacobs, L. (1938). *J. Wash. Acad. Sci.* **28:** 12–13.

Crusz, H. (1947). *J. Parasitol.* **33:** 87–98.

Dollfus, R. P. (1942). *Arch. mus. natl. hist. nat.* Paris. Ser. 6, **19:** 52–53.

Eisenbrandt, L. L. (1938). *Am. J. Hyg.* **27:** 117–141.

Fauré-Fremiet, E. (1913). *Compt. rend. soc. biol.* **74:** 1407–1409.

Fauré-Fremiet, E., and Filhol, J., (1937). *J. chim. phys.* **34:** 444–451.

Faust, E. S., and Tallqvist, T. W. (1907). *Arch. exptl. Path. Pharmakol.* **57:** 367–385.

Flury, F. (1912). *Arch. exptl. Path. Pharmakol.* **67:** 275–392.

Hopkins, C. A. (1950). *J. Parasitol.* **36:** 384–390.

Joyet-Lavergne, P. (1926). *Arch. anat. microscop.* **22:** 1–128.

von Kemnitz, G. (1916). *Z. Biol.* **67:** 129–244.

Kent, F. N. (1947). *Bull. soc. neuchateloise sci. nat.* **70:** 85–108.

Kent, F. N., and Macheboeuf, M. (1947a). *Compt. rend.* **225:** 539–540.

Kent, F. N., and Macheboeuf, M. (1947b). *Compt. rend.* **225:** 602–604.

Kent, F. N., and Macheboeuf, M. (1947c). *Schweiz. Z. Path. u. Bakt.* **10:** 464–469.

Kent, F. N., and Macheboeuf, M. (1949). *Schweiz. Z. Path. u. Bakt.* **12:** 81–84.

Kofoid, C. A., McNeil, E., and Kopac, M. J. (1931). *Proc. Soc. Exptl. Biol. Med.* **29:** 100–103.

Levenbook, L. (1950). *Biochem. J.* **47:** 336–346.

Magath, T. B. (1919). *Trans. Am. Microscop. Soc.* **38:** 49–170.

Mueller, J. F. (1929). *Z. Zellforsch. u. Mikroskop. Anat.* **8:** 362–403.

Panzer, T. (1911). *Z. physiol. Chem.* **73:** 109–127.

Panzer, T. (1913). *Z. physiol. Chem.* **86:** 33–42.

Reichard, A. (1902). Dissertation, Frankfurt (not seen).

Reichenow, E. (1929). Lehrbuch der Protozoenkunde. Ed. 5., Fischer, Jena.

Reid, W. M. (1942). *J. Parasitol.* **28:** 319–340.

Salisbury, L. F., and Anderson, R. J. (1939). *J. Biol. Chem.* **129:** 505–517.

Smorodincev, I. A., and Bebesin, K. W. (1936a). *J. Biochem.* **23:** 19–20.

Smorodincev, I. A., and Bebesin, K. W. (1936b). *J. Biochem.* **23:** 21–22.

Smorodincev, I. A., and Bebesin, K. W. (1936c). *Compt. rend. acad. sci. U.R.S.S.* [N.S.] **2:** 189–191.

Smorodincev, I. A., Bebesin, K. W., and Pawlowa, P. I. (1933). *Biochem. Z.* **261:** 176–178.

Smorodincev, I. A., and Pawlowa, P. I. (1936). *Ann. parasitol. humaine et comparée* **14:** 489–494.

Stephenson, W. (1947). *Parasitology* **38:** 128–139.

Sukatschoff, B. (1899). *Z. wiss. Zoöl.* **66:** 377–406.

Thomas, A. P. (1883). *Quart. J. Microscop. Soc.* **23:** 99–133.

Vialli, M. (1933). *Boll. zool. Napoli* **4:** 135–138.

Wardle, R. A. (1937). In: Manitoba Essays. 60th Anniv. Commem. Vol. Univ. Manitoba, pp. 338–364.

Weinland, E. (1901). *Z. Biol.* **42:** 55–90.

Weinland, E., and von Brand, T. (1926). *Z. vergleich. Physiol.* **4:** 212–285.

Yoshimura, S. (1930). *J. Biochem., Japan* **12:** 27–34.

CHAPTER 5

# MISCELLANEOUS PHYSIOLOGICALLY ACTIVE SUBSTANCES

## I. INTRODUCTORY REMARKS

The occurrence of substances that most probably play a role in the chemical reactions of the parasites will be discussed in this chapter. The role of such substances, like vitamins, is well established for vertebrates and for some invertebrate forms but is not yet fully understood in the case of parasites. It is, therefore, more convenient to discuss them under the general heading of chemical composition rather than in connection with metabolism, where the few known facts about vitamins as growth factors will be mentioned. Other physiologically-active compounds, such as digestive and glycolytic enzymes, or anti-enzymes will be considered at appropriate places in later sections.

## II. VITAMINS

Few determinations of the vitamin content of parasites have been reported so far and they all concern the water-soluble vitamins only. In view of the high fat content of many parasites an extension of these studies to the fat-soluble vitamins appears desirable.

Quantitative microbiological assays of some members of the vitamin B complex were done by Chance and Dirnhuber (1949) who used *Fasciola hepatica*, *Moniezia benedeni*, *Ascaris lumbricoides*, and various stages of *Nippostrongylus muris*. They found that these worms contained thiamine, nicotinic acid, pantothenic acid, and riboflavin in amounts somewhat smaller than occurred in the liver of the respective hosts. On the other hand, more pyridoxine was found in the parasites than in the host's liver. They think that a correlation with the high rate of egg production may exist, since pyridoxine is involved in the processes leading to protein synthesis. Varying amounts of nicotinic acid and of thiamine also have been reported from the hydatid fluid (Latif and El Kordy, 1946). It does seem probable that the rumen ciliates contain vitamin B. Manusardi (1931) showed that the feeding of these ciliates to pigeons can cure beriberi but the amounts necessary were very large. It is possible that the ciliates did not actually synthesize the vitamin, but that it was derived from ingested bacteria.

Vitamin C (ascorbic acid) has been found in the muscles, reproductive organs, and intestine of *Parascaris equorum*, the respective amounts being

45

70, 80, and 110 $\mu$g/gm fresh substance (Giroud and Rakoto-Ratsimamanga, 1936), and in the body fluid of *Ascaris lumbricoides* (Rogers, 1945). Histological studies (Hill and Smyth, 1944; Smyth *et al.*, 1945) confirmed the predominant localization within the intestinal cells in the case of *Toxocara canis*. In the trematode *Opistioglyphe ranae*, on the contrary, these authors found the gut cells vitamin-free; surprisingly, the greatest amounts were seen within the walls of the excretory vessels. Similarly, dense deposits of vitamin C were observed in the protoplasmatic lining of the smaller excretory vessels of *Fasciola hepatica*. Fairly large amounts also occurred in the submuscular layer of the body wall, but only small deposits were encountered in other organs (Stephenson, 1947).

Great variations in vitamin C content apparently occur among parasitic protozoa. Vitamin C granules have been reported from *Trypanosoma equiperdum* (Roskin and Nastiukova, 1941) and in this case the absorption of the vitamin from the host appears likely. It was observed that the number of granules within the parasites increased upon raising the ascorbic acid level of the host's blood by injection of a vitamin solution. *Opalina*, on the other hand, was found to be entirely devoid of vitamin C granules, whereas such granules were found throughout, but confined to, the endoplasm of *Nyctotherus cordiformis* (Smyth *et al.*, 1945).

In evaluating these morphological studies it should be realized that future research may well alter the available picture. Sosa (1949) raised serious doubts as to the specificity of the methods used for the histological demonstration of vitamin C and Glick (1949) pointed out that it has not yet been proven "that the ascorbic acid is attached to a nondiffusible body and that the reaction product could not diffuse, or that the ascorbic acid site has a high affinity for the reaction product."

## III. GLUTATHIONE

The tripeptide glutathione is widely distributed both in animal and plant tissues. Despite many speculations its physiological function is rather obscure. It is assumed to play a role in the oxidation-reduction system of the cells and it does serve as coenzyme for glyoxalase. Hopkins and Morgan (1945) utilized this fact to demonstrate the occurrence of glutathione in *Ascaris* after their attempt to isolate the compound from the worm tissues yielded only very small amounts as a result of technical difficulties. It should be noted that this is the first, and so far the only instance, in which glyoxalase was observed in a parasite.

In parasitic protozoa glutathione has been demonstrated only histochemically, by means of several variations of the nitroprusside reaction. It has thus been found in the flagellate *Trypanosoma equiperdum* (Voegtlin *et al.*, 1923), in the coccidium *Aggregata eberthi*, and in several species of mealworm gregarines (Joyet-Lavergne, 1927). In the trophozoites of the latter it was especially concentrated within the deutomerite and due to similarities in distribution it was assumed that the mitochondrial elements were the carrier of glutathione. In encysted gregarines the nitroprusside-positive substance was dispersed throughout the protoplasm.

## IV. Acetylcholine and Cholinesterase

Acetylcholine is widely distributed in invertebrates and vertebrates where it is commonly liberated to the endings of the parasympathetic nerve fibers. It has on occasion, however, also been found in organisms devoid of a nervous system, such as *Paramaecium*, and some bacteria. Acetylcholine is hydrolyzed by cholinesterase to choline and acetic acid.

Acetylcholine, or at least a substance producing the essential physiological effects of acetylcholine, has been demonstrated directly only in the tapeworms *Taenia crassicollis* and *Dipylidium caninum* in so far as metazoan parasites are concerned (Artemov and Lure, 1941).

Cholinesterase, the demonstration of which makes the presence of acetylcholine very probable, has been reported from *Fasciola hepatica*, *Taenia pisiformis*, and *Cysticercus pisiformis* (Bacq and Oury, 1937; Pennoit-DeCooman, 1940; Pennoit-DeCooman and van Grembergen, 1942). Activity was greatest in the adult tapeworm, where it was found to be about ten times as high as in the larval form or as in *Fasciola*. All values obtained were, however, lower than in free-living invertebrates, such as planarians. There is some doubt as to whether the enzyme occurs in nematodes. Bacq and Oury (1937) did report a strong cholinesterase activity of the *Parascaris* muscle. Baldwin and Moyle (1949), on the other hand, observed in *Ascaris* preparations that the effects of acetylcholine on the muscles are not influenced by previous treatment with eserine and that the effects do not diminish with time. They, therefore, assume the probable absence of cholinesterase.

Bacq (1941), after reviewing the distribution of acetylcholine and cholinesterase in invertebrates and taking into account their reactions to such drugs as eserine, curare, or atropine, comes to the conclusion that the motor nerves of worms in general are cholinergic. Whether future research will uphold this view remains to be seen. Bueding (personal communication) has pointed out that the methods employed by the authors quoted above were not specific enough to prove the presence of a specific acetylcholine esterase since many enzymes, especially lipases, will also split acetylcholine. He found that homogenates of *Schistosoma mansoni* readily hydrolyze acetylcholine and butyrylcholine. Upon dissolving the residue obtained from high speed centrifugation of the homogenates only acetylcholine was split and this reaction was completely inhibited by low concentrations of prostigmine and physostigmine. In this case, therefore, a true acetylcholine esterase was demonstrated. Its activity was somewhat lower than in mammalian brain. The same enzyme was found in filarias and ascarid muscle, but the activity in the latter was quite low.

Acetylcholine has been found so far only in one parasitic protozoon, *Trypanosoma rhodesiense*; it does not occur in *Plasmodium gallinaceum* (Bülbring *et al.*, 1949). The trypanosomes contained from 2.38 to 8.60 $\mu$g acetylcholine/gm fresh weight, and 1 gm acetone-dried flagellates formed 71.5 $\mu$g acetylcholine in 75 minutes at 37°C. The mentioned difference between the two protozoon species is rather surprising. The above authors suggest that it may be correlated with the vigorous motility of the flagellates as contrasted to the sluggish motion of the malarial parasites.

## V. Phosphatases

Phosphatases, enzymes hydrolyzing esters of phosphoric acid, are widely distributed and play an important role in various metabolic processes such as carbohydrate metabolism, bone formation, and others. The phosphatases can be divided into three classes, phosphomonoesterases, phosphodiesterases, and pyrophosphatases (Green and Colowick, 1944). One member of the pyrophosphatases, adenosinetriphosphatase, has been definitely identified in *Trypanosoma equiperdum* and *Trypanosoma hippicum* by Chen (1948) and Harvey (1949) respectively. It appears not to be present in significant amounts in *Plasmodium gallinaceum* (Speck and Evans, 1945). An adenosinetriphosphatase-like enzyme occurs in *Ascaris*. Rogers and Lazarus (1949) found a phosphatase active at pH 7.2 in the muscles of this helminth, and compounds hydrolyzing like ATP and glucose-6-phosphate accumulated when the phosphatase activity was inhibited.

In general, however, it has not yet been possible to connect the occurrence of phosphate-splitting enzymes in parasites with definite metabolic processes, although a connection with the utilization of carbohydrates is in many cases very probable. It has been shown that the phosphatase activities of various parasites are not identical in all cases since the pH optimum of the enzymes has been found to be quite different in different species.

In *Trypanosoma hippicum* an alkaline phosphatase splitting $\alpha$ and $\beta$-glycerophosphates at pH 9.8 was found; it was only slightly activated by magnesium ions (Harvey, 1949). Especially striking are the differences in pH optima reported by Pennoit-DeCooman and van Grembergen (1942) from parasitic flatworms and the fact that each worm had either only an alkaline or an acid phosphatase, but never both at the same time. In free-living flatworms like planarians, on the other hand, both types of enzymes were present simultaneously. Figure 1 shows the curves obtained by the above authors for some parasitic flatworms.

Pennoit-DeCooman and van Grembergen (1942) found that the phosphatase of *Fasciola* was inhibited by sodium fluoride and that it was not

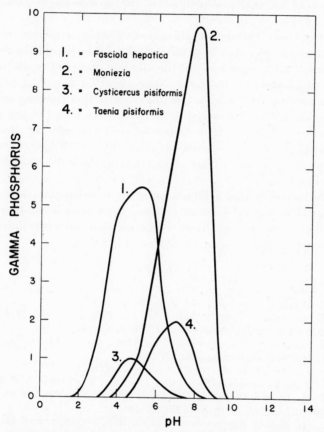

Fig. 1.  pH relationships of phosphatases occurring in helminths (after Pennoit-DeCooman and van Grembergen, 1942).

activated by magnesium, thus showing similarities to the spleen phosphatase of mammals. The phosphatase of adult tapeworms, on the contrary, was activated by magnesium. It was inactivated by dialysis and by potassium cyanide in the presence of magnesium, but it was not inhibited by sodium fluoride (Pennoit-DeCooman and van Grembergen, 1947). It resembled a typical mammalian alkaline phosphatase.

Especially curious is the fact that the pH optimum of the phosphatase occurring in *Cysticercus pisiformis* was distinctly different from that found in the adult form of the same species (Fig. 1). The transition of the acid type of phosphatase, which occurs in the larval stage, to the alkaline type found in the adult must take place abruptly during the life history of the parasite. Pennoit-DeCooman and van Grembergen (1947) did not find even a trace of an acid phosphatase in the scolices or in the youngest proglottids of *Taenia pisiformis*.

Besides the above chemical studies, there are also available some histochemical observations concerning the distribution of phosphatases in parasites. Rogers (1947) found most of the alkaline phosphatase in the cuticle of mature proglottids of *Moniezia*. None occurred in young proglottids, but small amounts were observed in the vicinity of developing eggs. Small granules giving positive phosphatase activity were found in the intestinal cells of *Ascaris*. Bullock (1949) reported that the alkaline phosphatase was restricted to the subcuticula of the trunk of *Echinorhynchus* and *Pomphorhynchus*, but not a trace of the enzyme could be demonstrated in *Neoechinorhynchus*.

A strong histochemical acid phosphatase reaction has been reported from *Endamoeba histolytica* from culture, from amoebas aspirated from the intestinal contents, and from amoebas that invaded the intestinal tissues (Carrera and Changus, 1948; Carrera, 1950).

LITERATURE

Artemov, N. M., and Lure, R. N. (1941). *Bull. acad. sci. U.R.S.S.* **2:** 278–282.
Bacq, Z. M. (1941). *Ann. soc. roy. zool. Belg.* **72:** 181–203.
Bacq, Z. M., and Oury, A. (1937). *Bull. acad. roy. Belg. Classe sci.* **23:** 891–893.
Baldwin, E., and Moyle, V. (1949). *Brit. J. Pharmacol.* **4:** 145–152.
Bülbring, E., Lourie, E. M., and Pardoe, U. (1949). *Brit. J. Pharmacol.* **4:** 290–294.
Bullock, W. L. (1949). *J. Morphol.* **84:** 185–200.
Carrera, G. M. (1950). *Proc. Soc. Exptl. Biol. Med.* **73:** 682.
Carrera, G. M., and Changus, G. W. (1948). *Proc. Soc. Exptl. Biol. Med.* **68:** 610–611.
Chance, M. R. A., and Dirnhuber, P. (1949). *Parasitology* **39:** 300–301.
Chen, G. (1948). *J. Infectious Diseases* **82:** 226–230.
Giroud, A., and Rakoto-Ratsimamanga (1936). *Bull. soc. chim. biol.* **18:** 375–383.
Glick, D. (1949). Techniques of Histo- and Cytochemistry. Interscience Publishers, New York.
Green, A. A., and Colowick, S. P. (1944). *Ann. Rev. Biochem.* **13:** 155–186.
Harvey, S. C. (1949). *J. Biol. Chem.* **179:** 435–453.
Hill, G. R., and Smyth, J. D. (1944). *Nature* **153:** 21.
Hopkins, F. G., and Morgan, E. J. (1945). *Biochem. J.* **39:** 320–324.
Joyet-Lavergne, P. (1927). *Compt. rend.* **184:** 1587–1589.
Latif, N., and El Kordy, M. I. (1946). *J. Roy. Egypt. Med. Assoc.* **29:** 71–75.
Manusardi, L. (1931). *Boll. zool. agrar. e bachicolt., univ. Milano* **4:** 140–148.
Pennoit-DeCooman, E. (1940). Ann. soc. roy. zool. Belg. **71:** 76–77.
Pennoit-DeCooman, E., and van Grembergen, G. (1942). *Verhandel. Koninkl. Vlaam. Acad. Wetenschap. Belg. Klasse Wetenschap.* **4:** No. 6: 7–77.

Pennoit-DeCooman, E., and van Grembergen, G. (1947). *Natuurw. Tijdschr. (Belg.)* **29:** 9–12.

Rogers, W. P. (1945). *Parasitology* **36:** 211–218.

Rogers, W. P. (1947). *Nature* **159:** 374.

Rogers, W. P., and Lazarus, M. (1949). *Parasitology* **39:** 302–314.

Roskin, G., and Nastiukova, O. (1941). *Compt. rend. acad. sci. U.R.S.S.* **33:** 8 (not seen).

Smyth, J. D., Bingley, W. J., and Hill, G. R. (1945). *J. Exptl. Biol.* **21:** 13–16.

Sosa, J. M. (1949). *Exptl. Cell Research, Suppl.* **1:** 402–413.

Speck, J. F., and Evans, E. A. (1945). *J. Biol. Chem.* **164:** 71–96.

Stephenson, W. (1947). *Parasitology* **38:** 140–144.

Voegtlin, C., Dyer, H. A., and Leonard, C. S. (1923). U.S. Pub. Health Service. *Pub. Health Repts.* **38:** 1882–1912.

# CHAPTER 6

# PIGMENTS

## I. General Considerations

Endoparasites, like many other organisms living in the dark, are not usually distinguished by bright colors. Parasitic protozoa are generally colorless and transparent but there are some exceptions. The oocysts of *Eimeria stiedae* are bright yellow, brownish or yellowish oocysts have been described for other coccidia (Reichenow, 1929), and gray, yellowish, brown, or orange tints occur in the trophozoites of gregarines (Doflein, 1916). The endoplasm of several myxosporidia, such as *Leptotheca agilis*, *Chloromyxum leydigi*, *Myxidium lieberkuehni*, and others contains numerous yellow or yellow-brown droplets or granules (Reichenow, 1929), which in some cases at least seem to be only bile droplets ingested by the parasites. Another type of pigmentation, excretory pigmentation, occurs in malarial parasites and this pigment will be discussed in greater detail below.

Representative cases of pigmentation occurring in helminths and endoparasitic arthropods are shown in Table 15. This list could undoubtedly be increased by a closer search through the morphological and taxonomic literature. While it is known that the red or reddish colors of some nematodes, trematodes, and *Gasterophilus* larvae is due to hemoglobin, hardly any data about the other pigments are available. Reactions characteristic for carotene have been obtained in the case of *Arhythmorhynchus comptus* by van Cleave and Rausch (1950).

It is possible that in some instances the pigmentations listed are due simply to the uptake of colored food material by the parasites. This is assumed, for example, for the yellow-reddish color of *Bothriocephalus balaenopterae*, which seems to correspond to the pigment of crustacea consumed by the host (Lönnberg, 1892). Meyer (1933) assumes that this is the general rule in Acanthocephala. He points out that a colored worm like *Pomphorhynchus* rapidly loses its color *in vitro* and that one species, *Bolbosoma brevicolle*, has been found red in the small intestine but white in the large intestine of the same host. Peculiar situations, however, exist that make a dogmatic stand on this question somewhat precarious. Red *Pomphorhynchus* occur together with colorless *Acanthocephalus* or *Echinorhynchus* in the same intestine, and the juvenile *Polymorphus minutus* forms orange-red oils or fats while living in the colorless body fluid of *Gammarus*. It must furthermore be recalled that in *Pomphorhynchus proteus* and other forms, brown or reddish-brown granules occur in the wall of the ligament, the uterine bell, and the uterus (Pagenstecher, 1863; Greeff, 1864) and that brown bodies have been reported from the body cavity of the juvenile *Centrorhynchus* (Meyer, 1933). In these cases, at least, a connection with pigmented food seems not to have been established. With the exception of the above cases it does seem probable that the pigmentations listed in Table 15 are genuine pigmentations, that is, the pigment is the result of metabolic activities of the organisms.

## II. Biological Significance of Pigmentation

The biological significance of pigmentation in endoparasites is in many cases obscure, whether one considers the entire body color or the fact that occasionally special organ systems, such as the excretory tubules of *Loxogenoides bicolor* (Byrd, 1950), are especially heavily pigmented. Sometimes, when due to hemoglobin, the color is only a byproduct of the respiratory needs of the organisms. The dark pigment characteristic for the eye spots of some miracidia, of numerous cercariae, a few adult digenea, or the monogenetic trematodes (Faust, 1918) unquestionably will have the same function as in free-living invertebrates with similar light-sensitive organs. It will insure that the receptors receive light rays only from one direction. It has been assumed that the dark body pigment of *Cercaria monostomi* represents a protection against light when the worms encyst (Wunder, 1932).

Another interesting case is that of *Leucochloridium*. The sporocysts of this trematode have large saccular outgrowths brilliantly colored by blue-green or brown bands. These pulsating sacs extend into the tentacles of infected snails (*Succinea*) which become so distended as to let the colors of the parasitic structures become visible. The colored tentacles of the snails then attract birds, the definitive hosts of the worms, thus ensuring the completion of the life cycle (literature in Wesenberg-Lund, 1931).

## III. Nature of the Parasitic Pigments

### A. Melanin Pigments

The mother substance for melanin, tyrosine, is first oxidized through the mediation of tyrosinase to "dopa" (3,4-dihydroxyphenylalanine). Dopa, or other aromatic compounds with one or more phenolic hydroxyl groups, is then further oxidized to the dark pigment, melanin.

Convincing evidence that such a system is present in parasites has been given by Blacklock *et al.* (1930) and Dinulescu (1932) for the larvae of *Cordylobia anthropophaga* and *Gasterophilus intestinalis* respectively. The

TABLE 15.

TABLE 15. Color of endoparasites after data presented by Dawes (1946), Krull (1933), Wesenberg-Lund (1934), Beaver (1937), Braun (1885), Meyer (1933), Reinhard (1945, 1946), and Dinulescu (1932).

TREMATODES

| SPECIES | COLOR | SPECIES | COLOR |
|---|---|---|---|
| Prosorhynchus aculeatus | Yellowish-brown | Prosotocus confusus | Reddish-yellow |
| Peracreadium genu | Neutral gray | Halipegus ovocaudatus | Reddish |
| Allocreadium transversale | Anteriorly white, posteriorly reddish | Echinostoma revolutum | Rose |
| | | E. spp., rediae | Orange |
| Lepidapedon rachion | Pale yellow | Opisthorchis felineus | Golden red |
| Steringophorus furciger | Bright red | Loxogenoides bicolor | Bright yellow, suckers red |
| Fellodistomum fellis | Dull green, pink suckers | Cercaria ephemera | Parallel lines of dark pigment |
| Rhodotrema ovacutum | Bright red | | |
| Zoogonus viridus | Blotchy blood red | C. imbricata | Brown |
| Azygia lucii | Flesh colored | C. monostomi | Parallel lines of dark pigment |
| Ceratotrema furcolabiatum | Reddish-brown mottled with green | C. diplocotylea | Blackish-brown |
| Phyllodistomum acceptum | Golden red | C. lophocerca | Yellow |
| Opistioglyphe ranae | Yellowish-brown | C. splendens | Brown tail stem |
| Pleurogenes claviger | Greenish-brown | | |

CESTODES

| SPECIES | COLOR | SPECIES | COLOR |
|---|---|---|---|
| Bothriocephalus balaenopterae | Reddish-yellow | Echinobothrium musteli | Dark red ring on neck; broad lateral stripes |
| Calliobothrium coronatum | Red granules in neck | | |
| C. affine | Yellow bothridia | E. typus | Four yellow longitudinal stripes |
| Tetrarhynchus ruficollis | Red neck | E. affine | Yellow pigment in head region |
| T. viridis | Green | | |
| T. spp. | Green caudal appendage | Scolex polymorphus | Two red patches in scolex |

## ACANTHOCEPHALA

| Species | Color | Species | Color |
|---|---|---|---|
| *Polymorphus minutus* | Orange-red | *Arhythmorhynchus fuscus* | Anteriorly white, posteriorly blackish |
| *P. magnus* | Orange-yellow | *Centrorhynchus globocaudatus* | White-yellowish |
| *Corynosoma peposacae* | Orange-yellow | *C. buteonis* | White-yellowish |
| *Bolbosoma turbinella* | Orange-red or white | *Prostorhynchus pigmentatus* | Brown in middle |
| *B. brevicolle* | Red | *Echinorhynchus salmonis* | Yellow-white or gray |
| *B. vasculosum* | Reddish | *E. gadi* | Yellow-white or gray |
| *Diplospinifer serpenticola* | Orange-red | | |
| *Pomphorhynchus proteus* | Red | | |

## NEMATODES

| Species | Color | Species | Color |
|---|---|---|---|
| *Strongylus* spp. | Red | *Dioctophyme renale* | Red |
| *Nippostrongylus muris* | Red | *Eustrongylides ignotus*, larvae | Red |
| *Syngamus trachea* | Red | *Tetrameres americana* | Brilliant red |

## ARTHROPODS

| Species | Color | Species | Color |
|---|---|---|---|
| *Peltogaster naushonensis* | Body pale pink, roots light green | *Gasterophilus meridionalis*, larvae | Yellowish |
| *P. paguri* | Sacs red, apricot, green, or brown depending upon maturity | *C. haemorrhoidalis*, larvae | Pale rose |
| *Paguritherium alatum* | Yellow, hepatopancreas red | *G. nasalis*, larvae | Pale yellow |
| *Gasterophilus inermis*, larvae | Pale yellow | *G. intestinalis*, larvae | Red |
| | | *G. pecorum*, larvae | Blood red |

findings were essentially similar in both cases. Tyrosinase was present in greatest concentration in the hemocele fluid, while various organs contained but little, if any, of the enzyme. The concentration of tyrosinase was greatest in the last pre-pupal instar and only then, in *Cordylobia*, could the presence of tyrosine be demonstrated. The presence of the complete melanin-forming system at this point of the development is biologically understandable since large amounts of the pigment are used during the blackening of the pupal case. It is probable that the system is to some degree also active in the earlier instars since the spines of the second instar *Cordylobia* larva are black. Some indications were obtained to the effect that in these young instars tyrosine is present in a form that does not readily blacken under the influence of the enzyme.

Whether true melanin occurs in other parasitic groups has not yet been proven definitely. The eye spots of larval trematodes should be investigated for the presence of this pigment. Whether the conspicuous black or dark-brown color of many trematode eggs is due to melanin is another open question. It has been demonstrated that polyphenols which could serve as mother substance participate in the formation of the egg shell of *Fasciola* (Stephenson, 1947).

## B. Heme Pigments

Two types of pigments that play a role in the respiratory processes of parasites have been described: hemoglobin and cytochrome.

*1. Hemoglobin.* Hemoglobin has not yet been reported from parasitic protozoa, cestodes, or Acanthocephala. It has been found in the following organisms: trematodes—*Telorchis robustus, Allassostoma magnum, Fasciola hepatica,* and *Dicrocoelium lanceatum* (Wharton, 1941; Stephenson, 1947; van Grembergen, 1949); adult nematodes—*Dioctophyme, Ascaris, Parascaris, Toxocara, Nematodirus, Trichostrongylus, Camallanus, Spirocerca, Strongylus, Nippostrongylus, Haemonchus,* and in the larvae of *Eustrongylides* and *Trichinella* (Aducco, 1889; Flury, 1912; Fauré-Fremiet, 1913; Keilin, 1925; Krueger, 1936; von Brand, 1937; Davey, 1938; Stannard *et al.,* 1938; Wharton, 1938, 1941; Hsü, 1938; Janicki, 1939; Davenport, 1945, 1949a, b, c; Rogers, 1950); and endoparasitic arthropods—various species of *Gasterophilus* larvae (von Kemnitz, 1916; Dinulescu, 1932; Keilin and Wang, 1946).

The hemoglobin is present partly as tissue hemoglobin, or, in nematodes, also dissolved in the body fluid. Occasionally the pigment is especially concentrated in certain body regions. In *Fasciola* (Stephenson, 1947) it is found primarily in the vitellarian region and the vicinity of the anterior uterine coils, in *Gasterophilus* larvae especially within the cells of the red organ.

The properties of the parasite hemoglobins are in some respects different from that of their hosts. The absorption maxima of the oxyhemoglobins are usually somewhat different, the $\alpha$-band of *Nippostrongylus* hemoglobin lies at 5777 Å, for example, while that of rat blood lies at 5767 Å (Davenport, 1949b). In the case of *Ascaris* hemoglobins the absorption intensity is greater in the $\beta$ than in the $\alpha$-band while the reverse holds true in mammalian hemoglobins. The alkaline methemoglobins of *Ascaris*, formed at pH 9, have a strong diffuse band at 537 m$\mu$ and a faint $\alpha$-band at 565 m$\mu$, whereas in mammalians both bands are distinct and of about equal intensity (Davenport, 1949a). The affinity of the nematode and *Gasterophilus* hemoglobins to carbon monoxide is unusually low and the "span," that is, the distance between the $\alpha$-bands of the oxyhemoglobin and carboxy-hemoglobin differ in both cases from that of either vertebrate blood or muscle hemoglobin (Keilin and Wang, 1946; Rogers, 1950).

The oxygen relationships are biologically very significant. The oxygen dissociation curves of the hemoglobin of small nematodes like *Camallanus*, *Nippostrongylus*, or similar forms are very steep (Fig. 2), steeper than those of the hosts (Wharton, 1941; Davenport, 1949b; Rogers, 1950). These worms will thus be able to extract oxygen from very oxygen-poor surroundings, but conversely the oxygen tension of their own tissues will have to be extremely low before the oxygen bound to the pigment will become dissociated. It has been shown, however, that these worms are able to reduce their own hemoglobin if kept anaerobically and the same has been demonstrated for the hemoglobin occurring in the body wall of *Ascaris*. It is very likely, therefore, that in these cases the biological significance of the hemoglobins must be sought in their oxygen carrying capacity.

Whether the same is true for the hemocele hemoglobin of such worms as *Dioctophyme*, *Ascaris*, or *Strongylus* is very questionable. They are extremely resistant to deoxygenation, it being almost impossible to dissociate the oxygen by evacuation. Even sodium hyposulfite deoxygenates these hemoglobins very slowly (Aducco, 1889; Davenport, 1949a, b). Laser (1944) thinks that this hemoglobin of *Ascaris* may be important by eliminating peroxides *via* the peroxidase activity of methemoglobin, while Davenport (1949b) holds it possible that these aberrant hemoglobins are "functionless byproducts of the nutrition of the worms." Further progress in this question will probably depend upon the development of media allowing a true culture or at least a long lasting maintenance *in vitro* of these worms. If only a byproduct of nutrition one would expect the color to disappear with time in hemoglobin-free solutions. In larval *Eustrongylides*, which from a taxonomic standpoint is not far from *Dioctophyme*, the red color is maintained completely unchanged even if the worms are kept up to four years *in vitro* (von Brand and Simpson, 1945). But while the properties of this hemoglobin have not yet been studied in a detailed fashion, some observations seem to indicate that the larvae can utilize the oxygen bound to the hemocele hemoglobin (von Brand, 1942).

The question of the origin of the parasite hemoglobins is difficult to

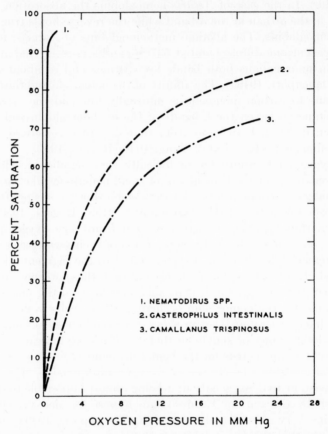

Fig. 2.   Oxygen dissociation curves of parasite hemoglobins (*Nematodirus* after Rogers, 1950; *Gasterophilus* after Keilin and Wang, 1946; *Camallanus* after Wharton, 1941).

answer at the present time. The differences between host and parasite hemoglobins are so pronounced that one certainly cannot think of a direct connection between both. Whether or to what extent parts of the host's pigment are utilized to synthesize that of the parasites is not definitely known. It is obviously a definite possibility in forms that ingest red corpuscles and recently has been advocated strongly for *Gasterophilus* larvae (Beaumont, 1948).

*2. Cytochromes.* The cytochromes are iron-hemoporphyrin compounds that play an exceedingly important part in the respiratory processes of many aerobic organisms. In *Strigomonas fasciculata* Lwoff (1934) found absorption bands tentatively referred to as cytochromes b and c. The culture form of *Trypanosoma cruzi* contains cytochromes a and b, and a cytochrome oxidase which differs in some respects from that occurring in yeast (Baernstein and Tobie, 1951), but no cytochrome oxidase was found in the bloodstream form of *Trypanosoma hippicum* (Harvey, 1949). No cytochrome bands were found in trichomonads (*Trichomonas foetus?*) by Frei *et al.* (1934), but more recently Suzuoki and Suzuoki (1951) described the occurrence of cytochrome b in *Trichomonas foetus*.

In worms, absorption bands similar to those of cytochromes a, b, and c were observed in *Ascaris* (Keilin, 1925), while those for b and c were described from *Moniezia benedeni* and *Fasciola hepatica* (van Grembergen, 1944, 1949) and those for cytochrome c alone have been reported from *Diphyllobothrium latum*, *Triaenophorus lucii* (Friedheim and Baer, 1933), *Allassostoma magnum*, and *Camallanus trispinosus* (Wharton, 1941).

It should be realized, and this has been emphasized by Bueding (1949), that these findings do not necessarily suffice to prove the presence of the cytochrome system in the worms mentioned since the observed absorption spectra could conceivably be due to some other hematin-like pigments. In filarial worms, tests for cytochrome c activity by means of cytochrome oxidase and hydroquinone have failed to give positive results (Bueding, 1949). Bueding and Charms (1951) recently found that *Ascaris* homogenates gave absolutely no cytochrome activity when tested by three different assay methods (ascorbic acid-cytochrome oxidase, hydroquinone-cytochrome oxidase, Keilin-Hartree preparation), nor could they find any cytochrome oxidase activity. In *Schistosoma mansoni* very small but detectable amounts of cytochrome c and cytochrome oxidase occur, but the activity of both was much smaller than would have been expected if the respiratory metabolism would be mediated through the classical cytochrome system.

## C. Flavines

The occurrence of flavines in parasites has been studied only rarely from the quantitative standpoint, although they are an important link of the anaerobic respiratory chain. The values found by Gourevitch (1937) are fairly high as compared with vertebrate tissues (Table 16), but it must be remembered that van Grembergen (1949) recently reported the flavine content of *Fasciola* as only about 1 $\mu$g/gm of fresh tissue. In any event, no parallelism between flavine content and anaerobic faculties seems to exist, since Gourevitch (1937) found even higher values in clearly aerobic invertebrates (*e.g.*, beetles or butterflies) than in the parasites he studied.

## D. Excretory Pigments

The deposition of a dark pigment in the tissue of malaria patients was known long before the parasites were found. Sinton and Ghosh (1934a) who reviewed the history of malarial pigment, mention Lancisi (1717), Stoll (1797), Montfalcon (1824), and others among the earliest workers who described the dark-brown discoloration of liver, spleen, or brain. Before the discovery of the parasites two theories were widely discussed as to the origin of the pigment, the theory of splenic origin (Meckel, 1847; Virchow, 1849) and the theory of hematogenous origin (Planer, 1854). These theories have only historical interest today since the detection of the pigment within the parasites made its derivation from the hemoglobin of the red cells through biological activity of the parasites obvious and this fact became soon generally recognized (*e.g.*, Danilewsky, 1896).

TABLE 16.   Flavine content of parasites (after Gourevitch, 1937)

| SPECIES | μg flavine/ 1 gm fresh tissue |
|---|---|
| *Fasciola hepatica* | 4 |
| *Parascaris equorum*, ♀ | 8.5 |
| ♂ | 12.5 |
| hemocele fluid | <2 |
| ovaries | <2 |
| *Gasterophilus intestinalis*, larvae | 12 |

The pigment of malarial tissues was first regarded as melanin (Meckel, 1847), although the introduction of special names, such as plasmodin (Ross, 1911), or haemo-melanin (Askanazy, 1919) indicates that some differences between true melanin and malarial pigment became evident. Such differences, expecially relating to solubilities and to the bleaching action of oxidizing agents, were emphasized by Brown (1911) and Hueck (1921). Other investigators, such as Carbone (1891), Ascoli (1910), Brown (1911), and Hueck (1921) may be mentioned among the early ones who considered, on the basis of chemical and spectroscopical observations, the malarial pigment as hematin, or at least as a compound closely allied to hematin. In the more recent literature of malariology it is frequently referred to as hemozoin.

The modern era of chemical studies on the malarial pigment goes back to Sinton and Ghosh (1934a, b), Ghosh and Sinton (1934), and Ghosh and Nath (1934). They isolated large numbers of *Plasmodium knowlesi*, extracted the pigment and studied its properties by optical and chemical methods, and reached the conclusion that hemozoin and hematin were identical. Devine and Fulton (1941) pointed out that the data of the above authors did not suffice to differentiate between hematin and hemin chloride. From a study of several derivatives of the *knowlesi* pigment (acid and alkali hematin, hemochromogens, and others), from the properties of the coupling compound between the pigment and globin, and from determinations of the Fe/Cl ratio in crude hemozoin, they concluded that the pigment was hematin. Morrison and Anderson (1942) confirmed this result and in a later paper Devine and Fulton (1942) also identified the pigment of *Plasmodium gallinaceum* as hematin. The most recent investigators of the problem are Rimington *et al.* (1947), who re-studied the pigment of both *Plasmodium knowlesi* and *Plasmodium gallinaceum* because all previous workers had extracted the pigment with dilute alkali which might have altered the compound. They avoided alkali, and a study of the absorption spectra of the pigment itself, the porphyrin derived from it, and of the hemoglobin arrived at by combining the pigment with denatured ox globin, led to the definite conclusion that the malarial pigment of both species was hematin in which the vinyl groups remained intact.

The brown pigment occurring during schistosomiasis in the Kupffer cells of the liver or in mononuclear leucocytes of other organs seems to be identical with that seen within the intestinal ceca of the worms. It has been studied much less than the malarial pigment. Its solubilities are the same as those of the latter and it is assumed that both are identical (Fairley, 1920). The same assumption with but little experimental evidence has been made in regard to the pigment found in the larvae of *Nippostrongylus muris* and in the lung tissues of infected animals (Porter, 1935).

## LITERATURE

Aducco, V. (1889). *Arch. ital. biol.* **11**: 52–69.

Ascoli, V. (1910). *Policlinico (Rome)* **17**: 246–255.

Askanazy, M. (1919). In: Aschoff's Lehrbuch pathologischen Anatomie 4th. ed., Vol. 1, pp. 239 and 257. Fischer, Jena.

Baernstein, H. D., and Tobie, E. J. (1951). *Federation Proc.* **10**: 159.

Beaumont, A. (1948). *Compt. rend. soc. biol.* **142**: 1369–1371.

Beaver, P. C. (1937). *Illinois Biol. Monog.* **15** No. 1: 7–96.

Blacklock, D. B., Gordon, R. M., and Fine, J. (1930). *Ann. Trop. Med. Parasitol.* **24**: 5–54.

Brown, W. H. (1911). *J. Exptl. Med.* **13**: 290–299.

von Brand, T. (1937). *J. Parasitol.* **23**: 316–317.

von Brand, T. (1942). *Biol. Bull.* **82**: 1–13.

von Brand, T., and Simpson, W. F. (1945). *Proc. Soc. Exptl. Biol. Med.* **60**: 368–371.

Braun, M. (1895). Vermes. In: Bronn's Klassen und Ordnungen des Tierreiches. Vol. 4. Abteilung **1b**, pp. 1167–1246. Winter, Leipzig.

Bueding, E. (1949). *Physiol. Revs.* **29**: 195–218.

Bueding, E., and Charms, B. (1951). *Nature* **167**: 149.

Byrd, E. E. (1950). *J. Parasitol.* **36**: 139–144.

Carbone, T. (1891). *Giorn. reale accad. med. Torino* **39**: 901–906.

Danilewsky, —. (1896). *Arch. Russ. Pathol.* **1:** 157 (not seen).
Davenport, H. E. (1945). *Nature* **155:** 516–517.
Davenport, H. E. (1949a). *Proc. Roy. Soc. London* **B136:** 255–270.
Davenport, H. E. (1949b). *Proc. Roy. Soc. London* **B136:** 271–280.
Davenport, H. E. (1949c). *Proc. Roy. Soc. London* **B136:** 281–290.
Davey, D. G. (1938). *Parasitology* **30:** 278–295.
Dawes, B. (1946). The Trematoda. With special reference to British and other European forms. Cambridge Univ. Press, London.
Devine, J., and Fulton, J. D. (1941). *Ann. Trop. Med. Parasitol.* **35:** 15–22.
Devine, J., and Fulton, J. D. (1942). *Ann. Trop. Med. Parasitol.* **36:** 167–170.
Dinulescu, G. (1932). *Ann. sci. nat. Zool.* **15:** 1–183.
Doflein, F. (1916). Lehrbuch der Protozoenkunde. 4th. ed. Fischer, Jena.
Fairley, N. H. (1920). *J. Path. Bact.* **23:** 289–314.
Fauré-Fremiet, E. (1913). *Arch. anat. microscop.* **15:** 435–757.
Faust, E. C. (1918). *Biol. Bull.* **35:** 117–127.
Flury, F. (1912). *Arch. exptl. Path. Pharmakol.* **67:** 275–392.
Frei, W., Riedmueller, L., and Almasy, F. (1934). *Biochem. Z.* **274:** 253–267.
Friedheim, E. A. H., and Baer, J. G. (1933). *Biochem. Z.* **265:** 329–337.
Ghosh, B. N., and Nath, M. C. (1934). *Records Malaria Survey India* **4:** 321–325.
Ghosh, B. N., and Sinton, J. A. (1934). *Records Malaria Survey India* **4:** 43–59.
Gourevitch, M. A. (1937). *Bull. soc. chim. biol.* **19:** 125–129.
Greeff, R. (1864). *Arch. Naturgeschichte* **30:** 361–375.
Harvey, S. C. (1949). *J. Biol. Chem.* **179:** 435–453.
Hsü, H. F. (1938). *Bull. Fan Mem. Inst. Biol., Zool. Ser.* **8:** 347–366.
Hueck, W. (1921). In: Krehl-Marchand's Handb. allg. Pathol. Vol. 3, Part 2 (not seen). Publisher etc. not available.
Janicki, M. J. (1939). *Zool. Poloniae* **3:** 189–223.
Keilin, D. (1925). *Proc. Roy. Soc. London* **98:** 312–339.
Keilin, D., and Wang, Y. L. (1946). *Biochem. J.* **40:** 855–866.
von Kemnitz, G. A. (1916). *Z. Biol.* **67:** 129–244.
Krueger, F. (1936). *Zool. Jahrb., Abt. allg. Zool. Physiol.* **57:** 1–56.
Krull, W. H. (1933). *Trans. Am. Microscop. Soc.* **52:** 47–50.
Lancisi, J. M. (1717). De noxiis paludum effluvis eorumque remediis. Rome (not seen).
Laser, H. (1944). *Biochem. J.* **38:** 333–338.
Lönnberg, E. (1892). *Kgl. Svenska Vetenskapsakad. Handl.* **24:** No. 16: 1–30.
Lwoff, A. (1934). *Zentr. Bakt. Parasitenk. Abt. I. Orig.* **130:** 497–518.
Meckel, H. (1847). *Allgem. Z. Psychiat.* **4:** 198–226.
Meyer, A. (1933). In: Bronn's Klassen und Ordnungen des Tierreiches Vol. 4, Sect. 2, book 2. Akademische. Verlagsgesellschaft, Leipzig.
Montfalcon, —. (1824). Histoire médicale des marais. Paris (not seen).
Morrison, D. B., and Anderson, W. A. D. (1942). *U.S. Pub. Health Service. Pub. Health Repts.* **57:** 90–94.
Pagenstecher, H. A. (1863). *Z. wiss. Zoöl.* **13:** 413–421.
Planer, —. (1854). *Z. Ges. Aerzte (Wien)* Year 1854: 127 and 280 (not seen).
Porter, D. A. (1935). *J. Parasitol.* **21:** 226–228.
Reichenow, E. (1929). Lehrbuch der Protozoenkunde. 5th ed. Fischer, Jena.
Reinhard, E. G. (1942). *Biol. Bull.* **83:** 401–415.
Reinhard, E. G. (1945). *J. Parasitol.* **31:** 198–204.
Reinhard, E. G. (1946). *J. Wash. Acad. Sci.* **36:** 127–131.
Rimington, C., Fulton, J. D., and Sheiman, H. (1947). *Biochem. J.* **41:** 619–622.

Rogers, W. P. (1950). *Australian J. Sci. Research* **B2:** 287–303.

Ross, R. (1911). Prevention of Malaria. London (not seen). Publisher etc. not available.

Sinton, J. A., and Ghosh, B. N. (1934a). *Records Malaria Survey India* **4:** 15–42.

Sinton, J. A., and Ghosh, B. N. (1934b). *Records Malaria Survey India* **4:** 205–221.

Stannard, J. N., McCoy, O. R., and Latchford, W. B. (1938). *Am. J. Hyg.* **27:** 666–682.

Stephenson, W. (1947). *Parasitology* **38:** 128–139.

Stoll, M. (1797). *Ratio Medendi* **1:** 196 (not seen).

Suzuoki, Z., and Suzuoki, T. (1951). *J. Biochem. Japan* **38:** 237–254.

Van Cleave, H. J., and Rausch, R. L. (1950). *J. Parasitol.* **36:** 278–283.

van Grembergen, G. (1944). *Enzymologia* **11:** 268–281.

van Grembergen, G. (1949). *Enzymologia* **13:** 241–257.

Virchow, R. (1849). *Arch. path. Anat. Physiol.* **2:** 587 (not seen).

Wesenberg-Lund, C. (1931). *Kgl. Danske Videnskab. Selskabs Skrifter, Naturvidenskab. math. Afdel.* 9th Raekke **4:** 89–142.

Wesenberg-Lund, C. (1934). *Kgl. Danske Videnskab. Selskabs Skrifter, Naturvidenskab. math. Afdel.* 9th Raekke **5:** 1–223.

Wharton, G. W. (1938). *J. Parasitol., Suppl.* **24:** 21.

Wharton, G. W. (1941). *J. Parasitol.* **27:** 81–87.

Wunder, W. (1932). *Z. Morphol. Ökol. Tiere* **25:** 336–352.

# CHAPTER 7

# TOXIC SUBSTANCES

## I. Introductory Remarks

Animal poisons are defined by Pawlowsky (1927) as substances which, due to their chemical or physical constitution, kill or impair the health of other animals even in small amounts. He is careful to point out that often no sharp delineation can be drawn between a toxin and an innocuous or even a therapeutically active substance, much depending upon dosage, the method of administration, the condition of the receptor, and similar factors. In so far as parasites are concerned, there is little definite information available concerning the occurrence of well defined toxins, that is, substances giving rise to the production of antitoxins, but much more or less convincing evidence for the presence of poisonous substances.

## II. Toxic Substances in Parasitic Protozoa

It is a curious fact that one of the best authenticated cases of toxic substances in parasitic protozoa is that of the sarcosporidia, which are usually harmless *in situ* and possibly do not even belong to the animal kingdom. Pfeiffer (1891) first observed that aqueous or glycerol extracts of the parasites rapidly killed rabbits upon subcutaneous injection. Sarcocystin, as the active principle is called, was then further studied by Laveran and Mesnil (1899), Rievel and Behrens (1904), Teichmann (1910), Teichmann and Braun (1911), Sabrazès and Muratet (1911), Declich (1926), and Sato (1926). It was found that sarcosporidia of different provenience were equally toxic, the only exception being the nontoxic mouse sarcosporidia (Mesnil *et al.*, 1913). Rabbits proved to be much more susceptible to sarcocystin than such totally or nearly nonsusceptible animals as guinea pigs, rats, or mice. Rabbits died rapidly, the chief symptom being a cholera-like diarrhea; there were some indications that sarcocystin acts as a nerve poison. It should be emphasized that the toxic symptoms are not due to bacterial contaminants as has been sometimes assumed, but appear in full force in response to extracts of cysts removed from the host and handled aseptically throughout (Knebel, 1912). The chemical constitution of sarcocystin is unknown. It is heat labile, dialyzable, gives some protein reactions, and has the characteristics of a true toxin since it gives rise to the production of an antitoxin.

A powerful toxin has recently been described from *Toxoplasma* (Weinman and Klatchko, 1950), another organism of rather uncertain taxonomic status. The toxic substance was found in the peritoneal fluid of infected mice and killed both healthy and infected mice very rapidly upon intravenous injection. The toxin was destroyed by the action of trypsin, suggesting that it may be a protein or at least contain a protein fraction essential for its activity. It did not dialyze through a cellophane membrane and was curiously heat resistant for a protein, resisting as it did a 30-minute immersion in a boiling water bath. Its activity was diminished, however, upon autoclaving at 121°C at 15 lbs. pressure.

Whether the African pathogenic trypanosomes contain or produce toxic substances is a controversial question. Some investigators (Laveran, 1913; Laveran and Roudsky, 1913) reported killing mice by the injection of large doses (0.12 to 0.15 gm) of dried *Trypanosoma gambiense* or *Trypanosoma brucei*, while others obtained completely negative results (Braun and Teichmann, 1912; Kligler *et al.*, 1929; Andrews *et al.*, 1930; Fiennes, 1950). These differences may be explained, at least partly, by the observations of Schilling and Rondoni (1913) and Schilling *et al.* (1938). They reported that killed trypanosomes become toxic only 1 hour after death but that the toxic action is again lost after 18 hours storage. This would seem to indicate that an actively toxic principle was obtained only during a certain stage of the autolytic decomposition processes.

Indirect evidence that toxic influences are at work during trypanosomiasis has often been reported. Reichenow (1921) pointed out that the body temperature of infected humans is frequently normal when there are many parasites in the blood but that it usually rises upon the destruction of large numbers of flagellates as a result of antibody formation. This observation corroborates the assumption that the parasites contain endotoxins. On the other hand, the pronounced metabolic disturbances in experimental animals during the later stages of the infection, *e.g.* hypoglycemia or failing gluconeogenesis, are better understood on the basis of exotoxins. Krijgsman (1936) thinks, without any experimental proof, that the latter may be amines. The whole question urgently requires a thorough reinvestigation.

The presence of endotoxins has also been assumed for *Trypanosoma cruzi* on the basis of Roskin and Romanova's (1938), Klyueva and Roskin's (1946) and Coudert and Juttin's (1950) claims of having observed the regression of tumors after injections of extracts from the bloodstream or culture form of the parasite into experimental animals; that is, they assume that the parasites have cancerolytic properties. It must be emphasized, however, that these observations could not be confirmed by numerous other authors (Engel, 1944; Hauschka *et al.*, 1947; Cohen *et al.*, 1947; Spain *et al.*, 1948; Belkin *et al.*, 1949; Talice, 1949).

There is uncertainty as to whether the malarial parasites contain or produce toxins, just as there is for trypanosomes. Although it has been assumed frequently that the release of parasite protein and pigment into the blood stream at the time of sporulation is responsible for the fever paroxysms, all recent reviewers (Young and Coatney, 1941; Manwell, 1941; Kitchen, 1941; Geiman, 1943; Massias, 1948; Maegraith, 1948) point out that no concrete evidence to that effect has ever been produced. In so far as the parasite pigment specifically is concerned, the experiments of Morrison and Anderson (1942) and Anderson and Morrison (1942) have rather conclusively demonstrated that it is directly responsible neither for the paroxysms nor the malarial lesions. Toxic manifestations may occur in malaria, just as in many other parasitic diseases, but whether the metabolism of the parasites directly causes them will probably be decided only upon a study of the pharmacological properties of cultures of malarial parasites. An indirect action *via* formation of auto-intoxicating substances by damaged host cells may have to be considered.

## III. Toxic Substances in Helminths

### A. General Considerations

Symptoms of poisoning are not rare in helminthic infections; loss of weight, nausea and vomiting, convulsions, and other nervous symptoms are described in all textbooks of clinical and veterinary parasitology. Not all these symptoms, obviously, need to have an actual toxic foundation. No further elaboration is necessary for the statement that nervous symptoms following an infection of the brain with a larval tapeworm are probably primarily due to a mechanical action on the nervous tissues. It should also be realized that it is sometimes difficult to differentiate between genuinely toxic and psychologically induced symptoms. If such symptoms become apparent only after a patient has learned that he harbors an immensely long tapeworm, one will be inclined to ascribe them to the second possibility.

Another difficulty is the differentiation between direct verminous intoxication, that is, intoxication due to chemical compounds present in or excreted by the worms, and an indirect action. The toxic symptoms often appearing in trichinosis during the period of migration can, for example, hardly be ascribed solely or even primarily to a poisonous influence of the worms. The flooding of the body with the degeneration products of the destroyed muscle fibers, *i.e.*, an auto-intoxication, is probably the most important factor here. Guanidine retention may be responsible in this specific case (Harwood *et al.*, 1937).

That cases of true verminous intoxication occur, for example, sometimes in heavy *Ascaris* infections, cannot be doubted; the symptoms usually disappear rapidly upon removal of the worms. There are exceptions, however. Moennig (1937) states that sheep heavily infected with *Oesophagosto-mum columbianum* sometimes die weeks after the worms have been expelled, indicating, in his opinion "a marked toxic derangement of the physiological processes of the host which are not easily overcome."

## B. *Toxic Substances in Flatworms*

Liver rot, produced by *Fasciola hepatica,* is in part due to the traumatic destruction of liver tissue, in part to the action of the parasite's proteolytic, lipolytic, and amylolytic enzymes on the host tissues, in part to the toxic action of the excreta of the flukes, and, finally, in part to the absorption of autolysis products of dying worms (Flury and Leeb, 1926) but the differential importance of these factors cannot be assessed at present. Experimentally, some authors have found that extracts of liver flukes have a certain toxicity to animals (Albanese, 1906; Guerrini, 1908) and that the injection of the worms' excreta leads to local edema, inflammation, fever, and anemia (Flury and Leeb, 1926) while Mandoul (1939a) considers *Fasciola* extracts nontoxic. The reason for this difference of opinion seems to be that it is impossible to produce acute poisoning with extracts, but that chronic intoxications are possible (Deschiens and Poirier, 1950). No toxic action has been observed after injection of extracts of *Watsonius watsoni* (Deschiens, 1940) but an ether-soluble hemolysin has been reported from *Schistosoma japonicum* (Yagi, 1910).

Tapeworms are usually harmless to their hosts *in vivo.* Nevertheless there are frequent reports that the injection of aqueous, glycerol, or trichloracetic extracts results in toxic symptoms (Mingazzini, 1901; Pomella, 1912; Bedson, 1913; Mandoul, 1939b; Deschiens and Poirier, 1947a, 1949; and others). It is extremely probable that such extracts do not contain a single well-defined "toxin" but a group of substances with more or less poisonous properties. According to Pawlowsky (1927), they have the characteristics of neurotoxic, hemolytic, and eosinophilotoxic substances and, like the trematode extracts, are less potent than those prepared from nematodes (Deschiens, 1942). It has recently been shown that a trichloracetic extract from *Taenia saginata* brought about symptoms best explained by assuming that it had a histamine-like action, or else that it liberated histamine in the body (Deschiens and Poirier, 1947a), but no similar substance seems to occur in *Moniezia* or *Fasciola* (Mandoul, 1939c).

Two tapeworms need special consideration, *Diphyllobothrium latum* and *Echinococcus granulosus.* It is well known that the former is sometimes associated with an anemia indistinguishible from pernicious anemia, but possibly the worm is only the trigger that sets off a sequence of events culminating in pernicious anemia in predisposed persons only (Birkeland, 1932). The assumption of Faust and Tallqvist (1907) that oleic acid stored in the parasites' body, released upon disintegration of proglottids, and absorbed by the host, causes the anemia due to its hemolytic properties is by no means proven. It has, however, been strengthened to some extent by the observation of Wardle and Green (1941) who found that the unsaturated fatty acids of *Moniezia* led to the sharpest decline in red cell count of all the lipid fractions tested (see also Chapter 17).

The question of whether or not the hydatid fluid of *Echinococcus granulosus* contains toxic substances is difficult to answer unequivocally. It is of course well known that fatalities occur upon the rupture of cysts, or under other conditions when larger amounts of cyst fluid reach the tissues of the host. But in these cases the picture is invariably that of anaphylactic shock; the host had obviously become sensitized over a period of time by some substance or substances reaching him from the parasite. Whether the injection of *Echinococcus* fluid into nonsensitized animals gives rise to frankly toxic symptoms is rather controversial. The toxicity is certainly not very pronounced, large amounts of fluid being necessary to kill an animal. When symptoms appear, they are those of shock, like lowering of the blood pressure, accelerated pulse, deep depression, and so on (Giusti and Hug, 1923). Repeated injections of a trichloracetic extract of the hydatid fluid leads to a chronic intoxication which is less severe than if unaltered fluid is used (Deschiens and Poirier, 1948).

It is well known that some parasitic infections are not rarely associated with the appearance of malignant growths; for example liver sarcoma in infections with *Cysticercus fasciolaris* (Bullock and Curtis, 1924) and it is of special interest that Dunning and Curtis (1946) produced multiple peritoneal sarcoma in rats by means of injections of washed, ground larvae of *Taenia taeniaformis*. Just what compound in the worms was responsible for the sarcoma is unknown but there were some indications that the active agent is associated with the calcareous corpuscles. Tissue extracts of helminths, both flatworms and roundworms, have, on the whole, little influence when used on tissue cultures; certainly no pronounced toxicity has been found (Rix and Laas, 1936; Hoeppli, 1935, 1948).

## C. Toxic Substances in Roundworms

The older and rather voluminous literature on toxicity of roundworms has been summarized by Fredericq (1910) and Schwartz (1921a) and need not be reviewed in detail here. Some of the earlier views, such as the assumption that hookworm anemia is due to a toxin elaborated by the worms (De Langen, 1922), are considered obsolete today. It is nevertheless evident that the injection of tissues, tissue extracts, or residues of tissue extracts of various nematodes, especially *Strongylus*, *Ascaris*, *Parascaris*, and *Dirofilaria*, are frequently damaging to experimental animals and may even be lethal (Ashcroft, 1914; Simonin, 1920; Schwartz, 1923; Bozice-vich and Hutter, 1944). It also has been reported that the injection of body fluid of ascarids is toxic (Sakaguchi, 1928; Read, 1931). But even with these materials some investigators got essentially negative results (Ransom et al., 1924; Vanni, 1938; Eisenbrandt, 1942). Such differences may be at least partly explained by the recent observation of Masquelier and Bailenger (1949) that the hemolytic properties of Ascaris extracts become evident only after partial bacterial decomposition.

The symptoms elicited by the injection of nematode tissues, or fractions therefrom, are often due to sensitization. It is well known that persons working with ascarids (Goldschmidt, 1910; Ransom et al., 1924; Jones and Kingscote, 1935), or animals sensitized with Ascaris tissues (Coventry, 1929; Moraes, 1932) develop an allergy. Sprent (1949) pointed out that sensitization to Ascaris protein may be brought about not only by ascarids but also by other nematodes and that an unsuspected hypersensitivity of the experimental animals may explain some of the above contradictions. Deschiens (1948), on the other hand, maintains that anaphylactic shock and true verminous intoxication, though giving an essentially similar complex of symptoms, must be considered as separate entities. He remarks that all guinea pigs are killed by approximately equal doses of Parascaris extract whereas it is difficult to conceive that all would have been sensitized in equal manner by other parasites that were accidentally present. Sprent (1949) does concede, especially on the basis of Shimamura and Fujii's (1917), Macheboeuf and Mandouls's (1939), and Rocha e Silva and Grana's (1946a, b) studies that biologically active substances occur in ascarids, though possibly only as a result of partial protein breakdown during preparation "but whether they are active in the absence of previous sensitization has not yet been conclusively established." Sprent (1950) did get toxic effects by injecting large amounts of supernatant fluid from centrifuged Ascaris pulp into nonsensitized, worm-free guinea pigs, and this toxicity was apparently due to proteins. Guinea pigs sensitized with Ascaris body fluid or infected with the larvae of Ascaris lumbricoides, Parascaris equorum, and Trichinella spiralis, or adults of Paraspidodera were hypersensitive to various worm fractions, both proteins and polysaccharides being possibly involved. It is obvious that cases of severe clinical human Ascaris intoxications, such as the recent case of Breuer (1950), can be explained by the theory of sensitization, perhaps followed by absorption of protein degradation products of dead worms.

The chemical nature of the toxic substances in roundworms is rather obscure. Bondouy (1908) isolated an alkaloid-like substance with strongly hemolytic properties from Strongylus equinus, but this finding requires confirmation.

The irritating action of ascarids on mucous membranes is, according to Flury (1912), caused primarily by aldehydes formed during the metabolism of the parasites. For the other toxic phenomena ascribed to *Ascaris* or *Parascaris* nitrogen-containing substances have usually been made responsible. An albumose-peptone fraction has been incriminated by Shimamura and Fujii (1917), polypeptides by Macheboeuf and Mandoul (1939), or a proteose fraction by Rocha e Silva and Grana (1946a). Deschiens and Poirier (1947b) have shown that the acute intoxication of guinea pigs by trichloracetic (that is, protein-free) extracts of *Ascaris* has the character of a histamine shock which can be counteracted by synthetic antihistaminics such as aminopyridines. They were, however, not able to demonstrate the occurrence of significant amounts of histamine within the worms and assume therefore that the active substance is not histamine proper but a related compound. This view has been confirmed by Rocha e Silva *et al.* (1946) and Gurtner (1948) and has been amplified by the observation of Deschiens (1948) that 1 ml of celomic fluid of *Ascaris* contains only 2 $\mu$g histamine, that is, the amount of celomic fluid required to kill guinea pigs contains only about 1.2% of a lethal histamine dose. The pathological lesions produced by extracts of *Parascaris equorum*, *Taenia saginata*, or hydatid fluid bear a rather striking resemblance to those found in subacute histamine poisoning (Deschiens and Poirier, 1949).

### D. Toxic Substances in Acanthocephala

It has been observed that dogs infected with *Oncicola canis* exhibited toxic symptoms simulating rabies (Parker, 1909), and in a human *Moniliformis moniliformis* infection some phenomena of possibly toxic origin (diarrhea, humming in the ears) have been described (Grassi and Calandruccio, 1888) but on the whole there is very little evidence that acanthocephala contain or produce normally toxic substances. A slight hemolytic activity of *Macracanthorhynchus hirudinaceus* was reported by Schwartz (1921b).

### IV. Toxic Substances in Endoparasitic Arthropods

Some evidence exists that *Sacculina* is toxic to its host. Lévy (1923) has shown that extracts of the parasite paralyze and kill noninfected crabs and the possibility has to be considered that toxic influences are at least in part responsible for the metabolic disturbances shown by the host (Reinhard and von Brand, 1944).

The degree to which truly toxic substances occur in endoparasitic arthropod larvae is a matter of some doubt. It has been shown rather conclusively (Brodersen, 1919; Jensen, 1919) that the crushing of a *Hypoderma* larva within the skin of cattle leads to a feverish disease ("Rosenfeber" of the Danish authors). It is, however, probable that this effect is simply an anaphylactic reaction. Small laboratory animals are but slightly sensitive of *Hypoderma* extracts (Roubaud and Pérard, 1924).

A similar uncertainty exists in the case of the *Gasterophilus* larvae. It has been claimed that a toxic substance, oestrin, is extractable from these parasites and that it is responsible for the pernicious anemia of horses (Seyderhelm and Seyderhelm, 1914; Seyderhelm, 1918) but this latter view is definitely incorrect (van Es and Schalk, 1918; du Toit, 1920; Marxer, 1920). Extracts of the larvae certainly may kill horses, or at least produce transitory toxic symptoms (Zibordi, 1920, du Toit, 1920, and others), but this again seems to be mainly due to sensitization by a previous infection, that is, anaphylaxis (van Es and Schalk, 1918; Cameron, 1922). It is nevertheless possible that larval extracts contain poisonous substances under some circumstances. De Kock (1919) and Roubaud and Pérard (1924) observed a certain toxicity of such extracts towards small laboratory animals that hardly could have been sensitized beforehand. As in some previously mentioned cases, there is a possibility that only degradation products of the larval proteins are active, and the observation of Roubaud and Pérard (1924) that only nonsterile extracts were effective points in this direction. *Gasterophilus* larvae also seem to contain a hemolytic substance (Weinberg, 1908). It is not produced by the salivary glands the secretion of which only prevents the coagulation of blood without hemolyzing it. Ingested blood hemolyzes only in the intestine of the larvae after clotting (Dinulescu, 1932).

There are only very vague indications that toxic substances produced by the parasites may be responsible, partly or wholly, for some of the symptoms like itching, inflammation, papules on the skin, and so on that occur in infections with chiggers, scabies mites, and similar parasites. It may be mentioned that Bosnic (1919) observed skin irritation in horses after the application of extracts of *Sarcoptes scabiei*.

## LITERATURE

Albanese, G. (1906). *Giorn. reale soc. e. accad. vet. Ital.* **55:** 597–602 and 627–632.
Anderson, W. A. D., and Morrison, D. B. (1942). *Arch. Path.* **33:** 677–686.
Andrews, J., Johnson, C. M., and Dormal, V. J. (1930). *Am. J. Hyg.* **12:** 381–400.
Ashcroft, L. S. (1914). *Compt. rend. soc. biol.* **77:** 442–444.
Bedson, S. P. (1913). *Ann. inst. Pasteur* **27:** 682–699.
Belkin, M., Tobie, E. J., Kahler, J., and Shear, M. J. (1949). *Cancer Research* **9:** 560.
Birkeland, I. W. (1932). *Medicine* **11:** 1–139.
Bondouy, T. (1908). *Compt. rend.* **147:** 928–930.
Bosnic, L. (1919). *Wien. tierärztl. Monatsschr.* **6:** 169–177.
Bozicevich, J., and Hutter, A. M. (1944). *Am. J. Trop. Med.* **24:** 203–208.
Braun, H., and Teichmann, E. (1912). Versuche zur Immunisierung gegen Trypanosomen. Jena. (not seen). Publisher not available.

Breuer, H. (1950). *Med. Klinik* **45:** 173–174.

Brodersen, L. (1919). *Maanedsskr. Dyrlaeg.* **31:** 321–323.

Bullock, F. D., and Curtis, M. R. (1924). *J. Cancer Research* **8:** 446–481.

Cameron, A. E. (1922). *J. Am. Vet. Med. Assoc.* **62:** 332–342.

Cohen, A. L., Borsook, H., and Dubnoff, J. W. (1947). *Proc. Soc. Exptl. Biol. Med.* **66:** 440–444.

Coudert, J., and Juttin, P. (1950). *Compt. rend. soc. biol.* **144:** 847–849.

Coventry, F. A. (1929). *J. Preventive Med.* **3:** 43–62.

Declich, M. (1926). *Nuova vet.* **4:** 210–213.

De Langen, C. D. (1922). *Dutch Ind. Med. Civ. Serv.* **4:** 304–316. (not seen).

De Kock, G. (1919). *Union S. Africa, Dept. Agr., Rept. Director Vet. Services Animal Ind., Onderstepoort* No. 5 and 6: 649–694.

Deschiens, R. (1940). *Bull. soc. path. exotique* **33:** 396–400.

Deschiens, R. (1942). *Bull. soc. path. exotique* **35:** 115–122.

Deschiens, R. (1948). *Ann. inst. Pasteur* **75:** 397–410.

Deschiens, R., and Poirier, M. (1947a). *Compt. rend. soc. biol.* **141:** 988–989.

Deschiens, R., and Poirier, M. (1947b). *Compt. rend.* **224:** 689–690.

Deschiens, R., and Poirier, M. (1948). *Compt. rend. soc. biol.* **142:** 435–436.

Deschiens, R., and Poirier, M. (1949). *Bull. soc. path. exotique* **42:** 70–75.

Deschiens, R., and Poirier, M. (1950). *Compt. rend. soc. biol.* **144:** 1345–1346.

Dinulescu, G. (1932). *Ann. sci. nat., Zool.* **15:** 1–183.

Dunning, W. F., and Curtis, M. R. (1946). *Cancer Research* **6:** 668–670.

Eisenbrandt, L. L. (1942). *J. Parasitol. Suppl.* **28:** 22.

Engel, R. (1944). *Klin. Wochschr.* **23:** 127–129.

Faust, E. S., and Tallqvist, T. W. (1907). Arch. exptl. Path. Pharmakol. **57:** 367–385.

Fiennes, R. N. T. W. (1950). *Ann. Trop. Med. Parasitol.* **44:** 42–54.

Flury, F. (1912). *Arch. exptl. Path. Pharmakol.* **67:** 275–392.

Flury, F., and Leeb, F. (1926). *Klin. Wochschr.* **5:** 2054–2055.

Fredericq, L. (1912). In: Winterstein's Handbuch der vergleichenden Physiologie. Vol. 2, part 2: 1–256. Fischer, Jena.

Geiman, Q. M. (1943). *New Engl. J. Med.* **229:** 283–290 and 324–332.

Giusti, L., and Hug, E. (1923). *Compt. rend. soc. biol.* **88:** 344–346.

Goldschmidt, R. (1910). *Münch. med. Wochschr.* **57:** 1991–1993.

Grassi, G. B., and Calandruccio, S. (1888). *Zentr. Bakt. Parasitenk.* **3:** 521–525.

Guerrini, G. (1908). *Clin. vet.* **31:** 529–538.

Gurtner, H. (1948). *Z. Hyg. Infektionskrankh.* **128:** 423–439.

Harwood, P. D., Spindler, L. A., Cross, S. X., and Cutler, J. T. (1937). *Am. J. Hyg.* **25:** 362–371.

Hauschka, T. S., Saxe, L. H., and Blair, M. (1947). *J. Natl. Cancer Inst.* **7:** 189–197.

Hoeppli, R. (1935). *Acta Path. Microbiol. Scand.* **12:** 281–289.

Hoeppli, R. (1948). *Proc. 4th Intern. Congr. Trop. Med. Malaria* **2:** 992–995.

Jensen, C. O. (1919). *Maanedsskr. Dyrlaeg.* **31:** 324–326.

Jones, T. L., and Kingscote, A. A. (1935). *Am. J. Hyg.* **22:** 406–413.

Kitchen, S. F. (1941). *Pub. Am. Assoc. Advanc. Sci.* **No. 15:** 41–46.

Kligler, I. J., Geiger, A., and Comaroff, R. (1929). *Ann. Trop. Med. Parasitol.* **23:** 325–335.

Klyueva, N. G., and Roskin, G. (1946). *Am. Rev. Soviet Med.* **4:** 127–129.

Knebel, M. (1912). *Zentr. Bakt. Parasitenk. I. Abt. Orig.* **66:** 523–524.

Krijgsman, B. J. (1936). *Z. vergleich. Physiol.* **23:** 663–711.

Laveran, C. L. A. (1913). *Bull. soc. path. exotique* **6:** 693–698.

Laveran, C. L. A., and Mesnil, F., (1899). *Compt. rend. soc. biol.* **51:** 311–314.

Laveran, C. L. A., and Roudsky, D. (1913). *Bull. soc. path. exotique* **6:** 176–181.

Lévy, R., (1923). *Bull. soc. zool., France* **48:** 291–294.

Macheboeuf, M., and Mandoul, R. (1939). *Compt. rend. soc. biol.* **130:** 1032–1034.

Maegraith, B. (1948). Pathological Processes in Malaria and Blackwater Fever. Thomas, Springfield, Ill.

Mandoul, R. (1939a). *Compt. rend. soc. biol.* **132:** 128.

Mandoul, R. (1939b). *Compt. rend. soc. biol.* **130:** 1035–1036.

Mandoul, R. (1939c). *Ann. parasitol. humaine et comparée* **17:** 187–192.

Manwell, R. D. (1941). *Pub. Am. Assoc. Advanc. Sci.* No. **15:** 30–40.

Marxer, A. (1920). *Z. Immunitätsforsch.* **29:** 1–10.

Masquelier, J., and Bailenger, J. (1949). *Compt. rend. soc. biol.* **143:** 1188–1189.

Massias, C. (1948). *Bull. mém. soc. méd. hôp. Paris* Year **1948:** 1118–1123.

Mesnil, F., Chatton, E., and Pérard, C. (1913). *Compt. rend. soc. biol.* **75:** 175–178.

Mingazzini, P. (1901). *Arch. ital. biol.* **38:** 489–490.

Moennig, H. O. (1937). *S. African J. Sci.* **33:** 845–849.

Moraes, J., (1932). *Brasil-med.* **46:** 638–639.

Morrison, D. B., and Anderson, W. A. D. (1942). *U.S. Pub. Health Service. Pub. Health Rept.* **57:** 161–174.

Parker, J. W. (1909). *Am. Vet. Rev.* **35:** 702–704.

Pawlowsky, E. N. (1927). Gifttiere und ihre Giftigkeit, Fischer, Jena.

Pfeiffer, L., (1891). Die Protozoen als Krankheitserreger. Ed. 2, Fischer, Jena.

Pomella, C. (1912). *Compt. rend. soc. biol.* **75:** 445–447.

Ransom, B. H., Harrison, W. T., and Couch, J. F. (1924). *J. Agri. Research* **28:** 577–582.

Read, H. (1931). *Aarch. Schiffs- u. Tropen-Hyg.* **35:** 227–237.

Reichenow, E. (1921). *Z. Hyg. Infektionskrankh.* **94:** 266–385.

Reinhard, E. G., and von Brand, T. (1944). *Physiol. Zoöl.* **17:** 31–41.

Rievel and Behrens (1904). *Zentr. Bakt. Parasitenk. Abt. I. Orig.* **35:** 341–352.

Rix, E., and Laas, M. E. (1936). *Arch. exptl. Zellforsch. Gewebezücht.* **18:** 467–474.

Rocha e Silva, M., and Grana, A. (1946a). *Arch. Surg.* **52:** 523–537.

Rocha e Silva, M., and Grana, A. (1946b). *Arch. Surg.* **52:** 713–728.

Rocha e Silva, M., Porto, A., and Andrade, S. O. (1946). *Arch. Surg.* **53:** 199–213.

Roskin, G. I., and Romanova, K. G. (1938). *Bull. biol. med. exptl. U.R.S.S.* **6:** 118–120.

Roubaud, E., and Pérard, C. (1924). *Bull. soc. path. exotique* **17:** 259–272.

Sabrazès, J., and Muratet, L. (1911). *Compt. rend. soc. biol.* **70:** 661–662.

Sakaguchi, T. (1928). *Arch. Schiffs- u. Tropen-Hyg.* **32:** 517–518.

Sato, S. (1926). *Japan Med. World* **6:** 62–64.

Schilling, C., and Rondoni, P. (1913). *Z. Immunitätsforsch.* **18:** 651–665.

Schilling, C., Schreck, H., Neumann, H., and Kunert, H. (1938). *Z. Immunitätsforsch.* **87:** 47–71.

Schwartz, B. (1921a). *J. Agr. Research* **22:** 379–432.

Schwartz, B. (1921b). *J. Parasitol.* **7:** 97.

Schwartz, B. (1923). *Philippine J. Sci.* **22:** 109–114.

Seyderhelm, K. R., and Seyderhelm, R. (1914). *Arch. exptl. Path. Pharmakol.* **76:** 149–201.

Seyderhelm, R. (1918). *Arch. exptl. Path. Pharmakol.* **82:** 253–326.

Shimamura, T., and Fujii, H. (1917). *J. Coll. Agr. Tokyo Imp. Univ.* **3:** 189–257.

Simonin, J. (1920). *Thèse*, Nancy (not seen).

Spain, D. M., Molomut, N., and Warshaw, L. J. (1948). *Proc. Soc. Exptl. Biol. Med.* **69:** 134–136.

Sprent, J. F. A. (1949). *J. Infectious Diseases* **84**: 221–229.
Sprent, J. F. A. (1950). *J. Infectious Diseases* **86**: 146–158.
Talice, R. V. (1949). *Trans. Roy. Soc. Trop. Med. Hyg.* **43**: 107–109.
Teichmann, E. (1910). *Arch. Protistenk.* **20**: 97–125.
Teichmann, E., and Braun, H. (1911). *Arch. Protistenk.* **22**: 351–365.
du Toit, P. J. (1920). *Monatsh. prakt. Tierheilk.* **30**: 97–118.
van Es, L., and Schalk, A. F. (1918). *Ann. inst. Pasteur* **32**: 310–362.
Vanni, V. (1938). *Compt. rend. soc. biol.* **129**: 1052–1055.
Wardle, R. A., and Green, N. K. (1941). *Trans. Roy. Soc. Canada, V*, [Ser. 3] **35**: 85–97.
Weinberg, M. (1908). *Compt. rend. soc. biol.* **65**: 75–77.
Weinman, D., and Klatchko, H. J. (1950). *Yale J. Biol. and Med.* **22**: 323–326.
Yagi, S. (1910). *Arch. exptl. Path. Pharmakol.* **62**: 156–158.
Young, M. D., and Coatney, G. R. (1941). *Pub. Am. Assoc. Advanc. Sci.* **No. 15**: 25–29.
Zibordi, D. (1920). *Clin. vet.* **43**: 470–476.

# Part II
# METABOLISM OF ENDOPARASITES

## CHAPTER 8
## WATER METABOLISM AND OSMOTIC RELATIONSHIPS

### I. PARASITIC PROTOZOA

It is a well established fact that many, if not all, fresh water protozoa show a very pronounced water exchange with the surrounding medium, as indicated by the rapid pulsation of the contractile vacuoles, especially in ciliates. In forms like *Cryptochilum nigricans* the vacuoles excrete a volume of water equal to the entire body volume in about two minutes. In others somewhat longer periods are required; in *Paramaecium caudatum*, for example, 14.7 minutes (Maupas, 1883; Herfs, 1922). It is obvious that in these cases the excreted water does not originate primarily from complete oxidation within the body, but is either water entering the body from the surface, or engulfed water taken into the food vacuoles together with formed food elements. In these cases then the contractile vacuole serves primarily to maintain the osmotic equilibrium of the organism. This view, first expressed by Hartog (1888), is strongly supported by the observation that protozoa living in a medium of higher molecular concentration than fresh water, *e.g.*, salt water or parasitic habitats, either lack contractile vacuoles or have vacuoles that pulsate only slowly. It may be mentioned as examples that the marine ciliates *Cothurnia curvula* and *Zoothamnium niveum* require about 5 to 7 hours to eliminate a volume of water corresponding to the body volume (Kitching, 1936).

Parasitic flagellates and rhizopods rarely have, and the sporozoa never have contractile vacuoles. Few data on the extent or the mechanism of the water exchange are available for these groups but it must nevertheless be assumed that such an exchange takes place. In parasitic amoebas, for example, it can easily be shown that engulfed bacteria or other motile organisms swim around for a certain time in the fluid contained in the food vacuoles. It must be assumed that at least part of this water comes from the surrounding medium and has to be excreted sooner or later. Even protozoa living on dissolved food only will have some water exchange with the medium, especially if they live, as *Giardia* for example, in surroundings where violent changes in osmotic pressure can be presumed to occur.

Pertinent data are available only for *Gregarina cuneata*. Adcock (1940) exposed them to hyper- and hypotonic solutions and found that they always reached a state of equilibrium rapidly indicating that no mechanisms exist for the regulation of the internal pressure. She was able to calculate that from 0.06 to 0.58 $\mu^3$ of water passed through 1 $\mu^2$ of surface per minute per one atmosphere difference in pressure. Further experiments showed that the gregarines were quite permeable to glucose, fructose, and glycerol, much more so than the *Arbacia* egg, for example. They resembled the latter in their permeability to lipid-soluble substances such as ethylene and propylene glycol. These mechanisms are of obvious importance for an organism lacking a special organelle for the intake of formed food.

Most parasitic protozoa must also be able to excrete relatively large amounts of water at one stage of their life cycle, the formation of resting stages. Protozoan cysts are usually markedly smaller than the trophozoites from which they are derived and this shrinkage can be accounted for only by the assumption of water excretion. In fresh-water protozoa the water content is reduced by the contractile vacuoles which are still in operation for a certain period of time after encystment has begun (von Brand, 1923). How forms lacking an organelle designed for water excretion eliminate excess water is a problem that has apparently not yet been studied. In coccidian oocysts the cyst wall is as large as the organism it encircles. During the maturation of the oocysts, however, the protoplasma body becomes definitely smaller. Hence, water excretion must have taken place also in this case (Reichenow, personal communication).

Interesting observations have been reported for *Vahlkampfia calkensis*, a parasite of the digestive tract of oysters. This amoeba does not normally possess a contractile vacuole. If the organisms are transferred to an agar medium made up with tap or distilled water, they develop from one to four contractile vacuoles (Hogue, 1923). This seems to be the only case on record where a new formation of this organelle has been observed under experimental conditions.

The parasitic ciliates, in contrast to the other parasitic protozoa, have retained their contractile vacuole with great tenacity. With the exception of the protociliates (*Opalina* and similar forms) they all have one or more contractile vacuoles. It should be pointed out that the taxonomic status of the protociliates is somewhat in doubt. The lack of a contractile vacuole may strengthen the recent view expressed by Lwoff and Valentini (1948) that they are actually flagellates.

It is difficult to adduce a definite reason for the retention of the contractile vacuoles in ciliates. The most probable explanation seems to be the one proposed by Reichenow (1929), who assumes that they do not serve exclusively for the maintenance of the osmotic equilibrium, but are also used for the excretion of metabolites. If this function is of greater importance in ciliates than in other groups, or if one assumes that only the latter could develop an alternate mechanism of excretion upon invasion of habitats with high molecular concentration, the retention becomes understandable.

It should be emphasized that the excretory function of the contractile vacuoles of parasitic ciliates has never been tested experimentally. It would seem possible to investigate the occurrence of such substances as urea, uric acid, or ammonia by microinjection of suitable reagents into the vacuoles of Ophryoscolecidae, for example. The rather disappointing results obtained with this technique in free-living ciliates (Weatherby, 1927, 1929) are not necessarily discouraging since the Ophryoscolecidae live at high temperature and under lack of oxygen, factors often responsible for a high rate of metabolism. Furthermore, their contractile vacuoles pulsate relatively slowly and thus a higher concentration of metabolites could be expected than in fresh-water protozoa. In the latter there is strong evidence that the vacuoles eliminate practically pure water (Krogh, 1939).

The available data concerning the rate of pulsation of the vacuoles in parasitic ciliates are somewhat variable. Strelkow (1931a, b) determined the interval between two systoles as 25 to 30 seconds and 30 to 45 seconds respectively in *Cycloposthium* and *Tripalmaria*, both parasitizing the cecum of the horse. Wertheim (1934a, b) found slower rates in the rumen ciliates *Entodinium*, *Isotricha*, *Ophryoscolex*, *Ostracodinium*, and others. His values vary between about 1 and 12 minutes for one pulsatory cycle, and even slower and more variable rates were found by MacLennan (1933). In *Epidinium*, for example, the cycles varied between 1 minute and more than 1 hour, in *Ophryoscolex* between 2 and 45 minutes. In no case are data available on the size of the vacuoles that would allow an approximate calculation of the amount of fluid excreted per unit time.

The source of the water expelled from the contractile vacuole of parasitic ciliates may be different in different species. MacLennan (1933) reported indications that the pellicle of Ophryoscolecidae is fairly impermeable to water and he assumes that most of the excreted water stems from fluid entering the body through the cytostome, but more experimental evidence concerning this point seems desirable. Wertheim (1934a), on the other hand, found on the whole—although he admits exceptions—that the frequency of the pulsations of the *Entodinium* vacuole is correlated with the concentration of the medium, an observation seemingly indicating a water inflow through the surface. In the above protozoa the pellicle is quite thick; in *Balantidium* and *Nyctotherus*, both studied by Eisenberg-Hamburg (1929), it is thin. This author found that the pulsations of the *Balan-*

*tidium* vacuole remained constant in media with freezing points raised from the normal −0.4 to −0.6°C, to a value of about −0.15°C. Beyond that point the pulsatory rate increased rapidly (Fig. 3). This probably indicates that the organism possesses some active defense mechanism against uncontrolled water influx through the surface, which can be maintained only over a certain range of dilutions.

Similar experiments with *Nyctotherus* and *Balantidium*, leading to essentially identical findings, had previously been done by Herfs (1922). This author reported also that *Opalina ranarum* could slowly be acclimatized

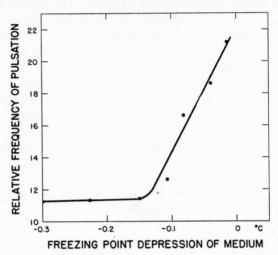

Fig. 3.   Relative speed of pulsations of contractile vacuoles of *Balantidium ento-zoon* as function of the concentration of the medium (after Eisenberg-Hamburg, 1929).

to tapwater, without this transition to a medium of very low molecular concentration leading to the appearance of a contractile vacuole. He was not able to advance definite views on how this animal can cope successfully with the water that probably enters its body under these conditions. Krogh (1939) recently pointed out that the system of branched channels and intercommunicating vacuoles described by Konsuloff (1922) as opening to the outside by means of pores, may serve to eliminate excess water without pulsations. Weatherby (1941), on the basis of Hopkins (1938) experiments with the marine amoeba *Flabellula marina*, suggests another mechanism, namely, an adjustment of the internal osmotic pressure to changing pressures of the media by losing or gaining osmotically active substances from the media, depending upon whether the surroundings are hypo- or hypertonic.

## II. Parasitic Worms

Our knowledge concerning the water metabolism of helminths is very restricted. It has been reported (Wright and Macallum, 1887; Osborn, 1905) that the excretory bladders of the ectoparasitic flukes *Sphyranura osleri* and *Cotylapsis insignis* pulsate fairly rapidly, the intervals between two pulsations varying between about 0.5 and 1.5 minutes. Similar rates, the intervals lying between 35 seconds and 3 minutes, have been observed with the cercariae of *Distomum globiporum* and *Cercaria microcotyle* (Westblad, 1922). The time required to excrete a water volume corresponding to the total body volume was 1 hour 40 minutes and 2 hours, respectively. Westblad (1922) is of the opinion that the excretory system serves probably primarily to regulate the water content of the body but there is little experimental evidence available so far to indicate whether this view is entirely correct. Herfs (1922), however, did observe that the bladder of an undetermined cercaria pulsated about twice as fast in fresh water than in Ringer's solution and that in the former medium the bladder was definitely enlarged. Pulsating excretory ampullas occur in the excretory system of larval *Ancylostoma* and *Necator*, but their possible osmoregulatory function has not yet been studied experimentally (Schuurmans-Stekhoven, 1927).

The above ectoparasites or larval worms live either their entire lives, or at least for some time, in surroundings with low molecular concentration. The molecular concentration under which adult endoparasites of vertebrates, or such larval forms as the *Trichinella* larvae, live, is generally high. It may vary rather considerably in such habitats as the alimentary canal, or in the urinary bladder; in others, for example blood or tissues, it is quite constant. Such differences should influence the water movement in various species, but hardly any precise information is available as to whether endoparasitic helminths have *in situ* a pronounced exchange of water with the surroundings. In the case of *Fasciola hepatica* a steady discharge of an aqueous fluid from the excretory pore has been reported (Stephenson, 1947b) and the well developed excretory system of cestodes is suggestive, but no definite data on its participation in the elimination of water is available.

Much more information is available in the literature on the osmotic relationships of helminths, a relatively large number of experiments having been done on weight changes of various species of helminths in response to the exposure to hyper- or hypotonic solutions. Wardle's (1937) experiments on adult *Moniezia expansa* show the enormous amount of water flowing into these tapeworms when kept in distilled water and their gradual and progressive loss of water in hypertonic solutions (Fig. 4).

The osmotic relationships of a larval tapeworm, *Cysticercus tenuicollis*, have been studied by Schopfer (1929, 1932). This larva is surrounded by two membranes, the pericystic membrane which stems from the host, and the vesicular membrane formed by the parasite. A little fluid is found between the membranes, the so called external fluid, which resembles the blood serum of the host rather closely in its chemical composition and is clearly an exudate from the latter's blood. The internal fluid, which lies inside the vesicular membrane and has a much greater volume than the external fluid, is a transudate from the host's blood and is in approximate equilibrium with the plasma of the host. It does appear then that an osmotic

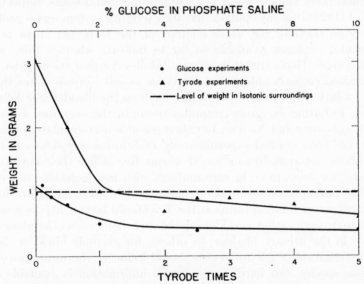

Fig. 4.   Weight per original gram of living *Moniezia expansa* after 6 hours immersion into media of various molecular concentration at 36 to 38°C. (After Wardle, 1937.)

equilibrium between the *Cysticercus* fluids and blood plasma exists *in situ*. This view is supported by Schopfer's (1932) observation that parasites placed in blood serum show but little change in weight. In sera progressively diluted with water, on the other hand, marked increases in weight occurred, ranging up to a maximum of 70% in pure water. Conversely, in sera fortified with sodium chloride, the parasites lost up to 20% in weight.

Another larval tapeworm, the plerocercoid of *Diphyllobothrium latum*, seems to be exceedingly tolerant to changes in osmotic concentrations. Birkeland (1932) reported their survival for at least 48 hours in a 10% sodium chloride solution, while the respective data for 15 and 20% salt solutions were 5 hours and 2.5 hours.

The trematodes are apparently fairly resistant to changes in environmental osmotic concentrations. Stephenson (1945, 1947a) found only small differences in the survival time of *Fasciola hepatica* in solutions containing sodium chloride varying in concentration from 58 to 230 m$M$ and Bueding (1950) observed no marked differences in metabolic activities of *Schistosoma mansoni* in media containing from 68 to 137 m$M$ sodium chloride. Stunkard and Shaw (1931) observed that cercariae derived from marine snails showed a rather marked resistance to hypotonic surroundings, remaining active in 50% sea water about as long as in undiluted sea water. Even more pronounced dilutions were tolerated for some time, although tap water was rapidly lethal.

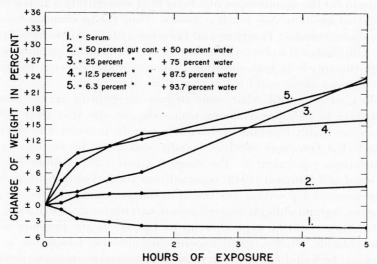

Fig. 5. Weight changes of *Parascaris equorum* specimens immersed into solutions of various molecular concentration (after Schopfer, 1926).

Experiments comparable to the *Cysticercus* experiments reviewed above have been carried out by Schopfer (1926) with *Parascaris equorum* with the difference that various dilutions of intestinal contents instead of serum were used as media. Details of his experiments are shown in Fig. 5. They indicate marked gains in weight in hypotonic solutions. Hobson, Stephenson, and Beadle studied the osmotic relationships of *Ascaris lumbricoides* in 20–40% sea water in distilled water. They found that in 30% sea water the osmotic pressure and conductivity of the body fluid were essentially unaltered, but that the latter's chloride concentration rose by about 50%. In the entire range of dilutions used there was an almost direct proportion between osmotic pressure, conductivity, and chloride concentration of medium and body fluid.

Whether these findings on *Parascaris* and *Ascaris* are characteristic for all nematodes is questionable. Panikkar and Sproston (1941) observed that the osmotic concentration of the body fluid of *Angusticaecum* sp. was equivalent to 1.3–1.6% sodium chloride after 4 days survival in tap water. This obviously indicates that this worm was able to maintain hypertonicity even in extremely dilute surroundings. On the other hand, however, the osmotic pressure of the body fluid increased when the worms were immersed in sea water. It reached a value corresponding to 3.51% sodium chloride, that is, an approximate equilibrium with the medium was established. These latter observations are to some extent similar to those mentioned above for *Ascaris*. The worms have apparently not developed a mechanism for the maintenance of a body fluid concentration hypotonic to the external medium. Not much is known about the mechanism involved in the above changes; Panikkar and Sproston (1941) did perform experiments with ligatured worms which showed that both water and ions passed through the cuticle in both directions, but which also showed that movements of water alone could not explain their results fully.

It does seem possible that some defense mechanism against osmotic disturbances is widespread among nematodes, or else that their cellular functions are highly resistant to changes in osmotic pressure. Davey (1938) observed that *Ostertagia* survived equally well in media having osmotic concentrations equivalent to the range 0.4 and 1.3% sodium chloride. Von Brand and Simpson (1942) reported that the larvae of *Eustrongylides ignotus* survived for several months in media containing, besides organic substances, sodium chloride concentrations varying between 0.5 and 1.0%, and that they could be kept alive up to 16 days in the presence of 3% sodium chloride. Stoll's (1940) experiments are also interesting in this connection; he found excellent survival of *Haemonchus contortus* larvae in balanced saline solutions ranging in concentration from 40 to 120 m$M$. The larvae of *Ascaris lumbricoides*, on the other hand, seem to have much less tolerance to osmotic changes. Their optimal survival occurred in a Tyrode solution of about 142 m$M$ (Fenwick, 1939). Ellenby (1946) demonstrated that the cyst wall of the potato eelworm (*Heterodera rostochiensis*) is permeable to water and loses water rather rapidly by evaporation, a process that becomes slower with increasing time apparently because a dried out cyst wall has lost permeability. It is not clear just how much water can be lost without interfering with the well-being of the organism.

Very little work has so far been done on the acanthocephala despite the fact that they appear to be especially suited to this type of experimentation since it is known that they rapidly imbibe fluid when placed in hypotonic solutions. Van Cleave and Ross (1944) found that *Neoechinorhynchus emydis* maintains its normally flattened form in solutions containing 0.80 to 0.85% sodium chloride, but that the worms became turgid in a few days and survived less well in 0.70 and 0.75% sodium chloride solutions. Upon being placed in tap water they became turgid in one hour, but this effect could be reversed by transfer to a 0.85% salt solution. Similar changes could be induced *in vivo* by injection of appropriate solutions into the intestine of the turtle harboring the worms. It is likely that many acanthocephala will encounter rather pronounced changes in osmotic concentration also under natural conditions. Many of these worms lack a definite excretory system and must have a way of eliminating surplus water through the cuticle.

The survival of *Neoechinorhynchus emydis* in various salt solutions had previously been studied by Gettier (1942). He found optimal survival at salt concentrations lying between 0.5 and 0.7%, but even somewhat lower and higher concentrations were tolerated fairly well. Concentrations above 2% sodium chloride, however, were rapidly lethal.

## III. Parasitic Arthropods

No experimental work on the water exchanges or osmotic relationships of endoparasitic arthropods seems to have been done as yet. This is regrettable since the differences in these respects among species of free-living arthropods lead to the suspicion that not all parasitic forms behave in an identical manner.

Krogh (1939) has pointed out that many terrestrial insects have to conserve water and achieve this by having a quite impermeable exoskeleton. A similar situation may well prevail in the adult, nonparasitic stage of *Gasterophilus* and also in many ectoparasitic arthropods. Endoparasites, on the other hand, are to be compared with aquatic rather than terrestrial animals. Krogh's (1939) review shows that the exoskeleton of several aquatic insects is also quite impermeable to water. Whether that is true also, for example, in the case of the rather heavily chitinized exoskeleton of *Gasterophilus* larvae remains to be studied. Other species of aquatic insects, especially larval forms, have developed certain appendages, *e.g.* anal gills of mosquito larvae, which are quite permeable to water and are apparently used largely for osmoregulatory purposes. It should be noted that some endoparasitic insect larvae, such as *Cryptochaetum striatum*, do possess long respiratory caudal processes (Thorpe, 1941). Whether they serve respiratory needs exclusively, or perhaps also have osmoregulatory potentialities should be an interesting problem to investigate.

Panikkar and Sproston (1941) studied the osmotic relationships of the ectoparasitic crustacean *Bopyrus squillarum*. It was taken from prawns living in sea water and its osmotic pressure was found slightly hypotonic to sea water. After removal from the host ready equilibration with sea water occurred, leading to the suggestion that the noted slight hypotonicity

may have been due to the ingestion of large amounts of the host's hypotonic blood. Panikkar and Sproston (1941) point out that some osmoregulatory mechanism may have developed in bopyrids since many species are
commonly found on hosts living in fresh or brackish water.

## LITERATURE

Adcock, E. M. (1940). *J. Exptl. Biol.* **17**: 449–463.
Birkeland, I. W. (1932). *Medicine* **11**: 1–139.
von Brand, T. (1923). *Arch. Protistenk.* **47**: 59–100.
von Brand, T., and Simpson, W. F. (1942). *Proc. Soc. Exptl. Biol. Med.* **49**: 245–248.
Bueding, E. (1950). *J. Gen. Physiol.* **33**: 475–495.
Davey, D. G. (1938). *Parasitology* **30**: 278–295.
Eisenberg-Hamburg, E. (1929). *Arch. Protistenk.* **68**: 451–470.
Ellenby, C. (1946). *Nature* **157**: 302.
Fenwick, D. W. (1939). *J. Helminthol.* **17**: 211–228.
Gettier, A. (1942). *Proc. Helminthol. Soc. Wash.* **9**: 75–78.
Hartog, M. (1888). *Brit. Assoc. Advancement Sci., Rept.* **58**: 714–716.
Herfs, A. (1922). *Arch. Protistenk.* **44**: 227–260.
Hobson, Stephenson, and Beadle, (no date). Unpublished experiment quoted by
    Hobson, A. D. (1948). *Parasitology* **38**: 183–227.
Hogue, M. J. (1923). *J. Elisha Mitchell Sci. Soc.* **39**: 49–55.
Hopkins, D. L. (1938). *Biol. Bull.* **75**: 337.
Kitching, J. A. (1936). *J. Exptl. Biol.* **13**: 11–27.
Konsuloff, S. (1922). *Arch. Protistenk.* **44**: 285–345.
Krogh, A. (1939). Osmotic Regulation in Aquatic Animals. University Press, Cam-
    bridge, England.
Lwoff, A., and Valentini, S. (1948). *Ann. inst. Pasteur* **75**: 1–7.
MacLennan, R. F. (1933). *Univ. Calif. (Berkeley) Pubs. Zool.* **39**: 205–250.
Maupas, E. (1883). *Arch. zool. exptl. et gén. Ser. 2*, **1**: 427–664.
Osborn, H. L. (1905). *Zool. Jahrb. Abt. Anat.* **21**: 201–242.
Panikkar, N. K., and Sproston, N. G. (1941). *Parasitology* **33**: 214–223.
Reichenow, E. (1929). Lehrbuch der Protozoenkunde. Fischer, Jena.
Schopfer, W. H. (1926). *Parasitology* **18**: 277–282.
Schopfer, W. H. (1929). *Rev. suisse zool.* **36**: 221–228.
Schopfer, W. H. (1932). *Rev. suisse zool.* **39**: 59–194.
Schuurmans-Stekhoven, J. H. (1927). *Proc. Koninkl. Nederland. Akad. Wetenschap.*
    **30**: 113–125.
Stephenson, W. (1945). *Nature* **155**: 240.
Stephenson, W. (1947a). *Parasitology* **38**: 116–122.
Stephenson, W. (1947b). *Parasitology* **38**: 140–144.
Stoll, N. R. (1940). *Growth* **4**: 383–406.
Strelkow, A. (1931a). *Arch. Protistenk.* **75**: 191–220.
Strelkow, A. (1931b). *Arch. Protistenk.* **75**: 221–254.
Stunkard, H. W., and Shaw, C. R. (1931). *Biol. Bull.* **61**: 242–271.
Thorpe, W. H. (1941). *Parasitology* **33**: 149–168.
Van Cleave, H. J., and Ross, E. L. (1944). *J. Parasitol.* **30**: 369–372.
Wardle, R. A. (1937). *Can. J. Research* **D15**: 117–126.
Weatherby, J. H. (1927). *Biol. Bull.* **52**: 208–218.

Weatherby, J. H. (1929). *Physiol. Zoöl.* **2**: 375–394.
Weatherby, J. H. (1941). *In* Calkins, G. N., and Summers, F. M., (1941). Protozoa in Biological Research. Columbia Univ. Press, New York, pp. 404–447.
Wertheim, P. (1934a). *Zool. Anz.* **106**: 20–24.
Wertheim, P. (1934b). *Zool. Anz.* **107**: 77–84.
Westblad, E. (1922). *Lunds Univ. Arsskr.* [N.F.] Avd. 2, **18**: 101–210.
Wright, R. R., and Macallum, A. B. (1887). *J. Morphol.* **1**: 1–48.

## CHAPTER 9

# METABOLISM OF INORGANIC SUBSTANCES

## I. INTRODUCTORY REMARKS

The metabolism of inorganic substances of parasites has so far attracted few investigators. There is some data on the saline requirements of parasites, a result of studies dealing with culture methods or attempts to keep parasites alive *in vitro*, and these will be reviewed in a later chapter.

Only phosphorus has been studied to any extent from the metabolic standpoint. This is no coincidence. Radioactive isotopes are a powerful tool in this type of experimentation and for some time one of the more easily available isotopes was radioactive phosphorus. Furthermore, since phosphorylations are of prime importance in several metabolic processes, it is not surprising that phosphorus should have been studied in preference to other inorganic substances. Some pertinent data are also known for chlorides, but practically nothing for other inorganic substances.

## II. PHOSPHORUS

A pronounced phosphorus metabolism can be presumed in those parasitic protozoa that store volutin. This has not yet been proven specifically, but it can be assumed that in this respect an analogy to free-living protozoa exists. Reichenow (1909) first demonstrated that volutin accumulates in the flagellate *Haematococcus fluvialis* only upon cultivation in phosphorus-rich media and disappears rather rapidly upon transfer of the organisms to phosphorus-free surroundings. Trypanosomes, among other parasitic protozoa, do store volutin, but the above relationship has not yet been established experimentally. Moraczewski and Kelsey (1948), however, made tracer studies on *Trypanosoma equiperdum* and found a relatively slow turnover rate of phosphorus when the flagellates were kept *in vitro;* namely, less than 4% in 90 minutes in the acid soluble fraction and, in most instances, less than 1% in the phospholipid, nucleic acid, and phosphoprotein fractions. A much higher activity of the last three fractions was observed *in vivo* and it seems obvious that the organisms were capable of synthesizing organic phosphorus compounds from the inorganic phosphate of the blood plasma.

Some data indicating a high rate of phosphorus metabolism have been reported from nematodes. Fischer (1924) observed the liberation of relatively large amounts of phosphoric acid during incubation of muscle pulp of *Parascaris*. The phosphorus probably was derived from the breakdown of organic compounds, mainly those involved in carbohydrate metabolism. Phosphorylative processes occur in nematodes, as in other organisms, quite generally (Rogers and Lazarus, 1949b). These investigators determined the various phosphorus fractions occurring in *Ascaris* muscle and compared them with those reported for other organisms. They found that the ATP phosphorus amounted to about one-third of that encountered in flies or frogs. Hexophosphate phosphorus was present in much larger amounts than in mammals or insects but this may have been an artefact since in mammals, at least, this fraction is quite labile and may increase under any kind of stimulation, which is unavoidable when parasitic worms are removed from their normal habitat. Also, it should be realized that these phosphorus fractions were determined only by hydrolysis rates and have not yet been isolated and demonstrated by other methods. Whether *Ascaris* contained phosphagen was questionable; it was present at most in traces. The values found for inorganic phosphorus were about of the same magnitude as those normally reported for frog muscle. Another indication of a pronounced need for phosphorus can be deduced from observations by Martin and Ross (1934). According to their determinations one female of *Haemonchus contortus*, a small worm, produces a daily average of about 5000 eggs containing 2.9 $\mu$g. phosphorus, which in this case is derived from the host's blood.

The first tracer studies were performed by McCoy, Downing, and Van Voorhis (1941). They fed radioactive phosphorus to rats which had been infected with *Trichinella spiralis* 8 to 10 months prior to the experiments. At specified intervals the phosphorus distribution was determined both in the muscles of the host and in the worm larvae. Details of these experiments are shown in Fig. 6. It is evident that both the uptake and loss of phosphorus were slower in the parasites' than in the host's tissues. It could not be decided, however, whether the appearance of the radioactive material in the larvae was due to a true metabolic exchange or simply to a diffusion of phosphate ions.

Rogers and Lazarus (1949a) studied the uptake of radioactive phosphorus by *Ascaris lumbricoides in vitro*, using both normal and ligatured worms. Radioautographs prepared after 1 hour's exposure and at intervals thereafter showed that in normal worms the highest concentration of radioactive phosphorus occurred in the intestinal tissues while only small amounts were found in the cuticle, the tissues surrounding the lateral lines, and, after long incubation, the reproductive organs. Ligatured worms, on the other hand, showed radioactive material only in the cuticle and the region of the lateral lines and the amounts were small. It seems then that inorganic phosphorus enters *Ascaris* predominantly, if not exclusively, through the alimentary canal.

Probably this is true also for other parasitic nematodes. Rogers and Lazarus (1949a) studied the behavior of radioactive phosphorus in *Ascaridia galli* and *Nippostrongylus muris in vivo*, not only considering the parasites but also the mucosa of the host's intestine. Details of these experiments are shown in Fig. 7. In *Ascaridia* a rapid increase and rapid loss of P$^{32}$ occurred. The worms apparently took the phosphorus up from the fluids of the intestinal lumen and much of it seems just to have passed through the alimentary tract of the worms without being absorbed. The worms

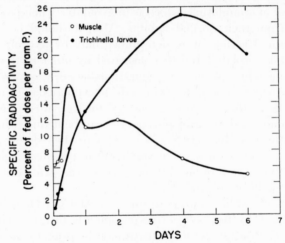

Fig. 6.  Behavior of radioactive phosphorus in rat muscle and in *Trichinella* larvae upon feeding of the compound to the host animals (after McCoy, Downing, and Van Voorhis, 1941).

did not seem to ingest host tissues, as indicated by the observation that specimens taken from chickens which had received the phosphorus intravenously rather than orally never showed any radioactivity. The maximum of radioactivity appeared much slower in *Nippostrongylus* than *Ascaridia* when P$^{32}$ was given to the hosts *per os*, and worms taken from rats that had received the radioactive material intramuscularly showed a gradual accumulation of radiophosphate in their tissues. This was interpreted as proving an active feeding of the parasites on host tissues and a higher rate of actual absorption of P$^{32}$ into the worms' tissues than occurred in the case of *Ascaridia*.

Thus while there is not much indication that phosphorus enters the body of roundworms to any large extent through the cuticle, the situation is quite different in those parasites that do not have an alimentary canal.

The only available data are Read's (1950), who showed that *Hymenolepis diminuta* readily absorbed radiophosphate from the intestinal contents of rats. If only trace amounts were administered to the hosts, a marked accumulation took place in the worms only if the phosphate was given without sugar; in the presence of glucose the radioactive level of the worms was extremely low, probably because most of the phosphorus was absorbed before reaching the level of the intestine inhabited by the worms. This follows from the observation that upon feeding of larger amounts of phosphate no such difference could be found. When phosphate was in-

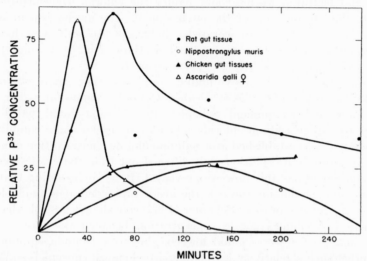

Fig. 7. Behavior of radioactive phosphorus in the gut tissues of the hosts and in parasitic worms upon feeding of the compound to rats and chicken (after Rogers and Lazarus, 1949).

jected intraperitoneally into the rats a slow but steady uptake occurred in the worms, indicating an exchange of ions between host tissues and gut contents. These latter observations are in certain contrast to those reported above for *Ascaridia* and future research will have to explain these differences.

## III. CHLORIDES

It is a curious fact that *Ascaris* is able to maintain the chloride concentration of its body fluid below that of the medium. Hobson, Stephenson, and Beadle showed that the chloride concentration of the hemocele fluid rose only from 52 to 78 mmol. upon transfer from its normal surroundings to 30% sea water with a chloride concentration of 166 mmol., and similar differences were observed also in other dilutions of sea water. Likewise, in other respects, the flow of chloride into the worms seems to depend on the medium. Rogers (1945) found a more pronounced chloride increase of the body fluid in media lacking phosphate than in those containing this salt.

Other especially interesting observations have been reported by Hobson, Stephenson, and Beadle. They first raised the chloride concentration of the hemocele fluid of *Ascaris* by exposing the worms to 30% sea water. They transferred then the worms to an isotonic salt solution in which half the chloride had been replaced by nitrate. Under these conditions both normal and ligatured worms could reduce the chloride concentration of the body fluid below that of the environment. The mechanism involved which is also operative in eviscerated cylinders of the body wall, has not yet been elucidated. Tracer studies, such as those done by Ussing (1949) on frog skin, may prove helpful in this respect.

It is not likely that the above findings apply to other classes of worms. The chloride content of *Cysticercus tenuicollis* fluid is somewhat higher than that of its normal environment. Schopfer (1932) demonstrated that during exposure to various sodium chloride solutions an approximate equilibrium in salt content was established at a sodium chloride concentration of about 0.87%. In more dilute solutions salt diffused out from the cystic fluid; in higher concentrations this flow was reversed. It is worth noting that the diffusion from the outside towards the inside proceeded at a much slower rate than the reverse process. Schopfer (1932) considers it possible that the differences in sodium chloride concentration between the host's blood plasma and the *Cysticercus* fluid may be due to a Donnan equilibrium, but whether such a relatively simple physico chemical concept is sufficient to explain a rather complex biological phenomenon remains to be seen.

In the case of some larval helminths, such as cercariae or the coracidium of *Diphyllobothrium*, the question may be raised as to the manner of their maintaining their ionic complement while living in fresh water. Since it is unlikely that they do not lose ions, a mechanism for replenishment from very dilute solutions should exist. It may well be worthwhile to look for active absorption mechanisms such as are known to occur in various free-living invertebrates as Krogh's (1939) review shows.

## IV. MISCELLANEOUS INORGANIC SUBSTANCES

Hobson, Stephenson, and Beadle observed that in sea water media the potassium content of the *Ascaris* body fluid decreased sharply, calcium decreased possibly a little, but only very small changes in magnesium content occurred. A potassium concentration increase in artificial salt media led to a potassium increase of the hemocele fluid whereas the magnesium content of the latter seemed, on the contrary, to be independent of the magnesium concentration of the medium.

Considerable differences in permeability to inorganic salts between the pericystic and vesicular membranes of *Cysticercus tenuicollis* have been reported. Schopfer (1932) demonstrated conclusively that the former rather readily allows the passage of various iron salts, but is less permeable to copper sulfate. The vesicular membrane was entirely impermeable to the salts used as long as the parasites were alive but became permeable upon death. Identical results were obtained in every case regardless of whether the salts were placed on the outside or inside of the respective membranes.

## LITERATURE

Fischer, A. (1924). *Biochem. Z.* **144:** 224–228.

Hobson, Stephenson, and Beadle, (no date). Unpublished experiment quoted in Hobson, A. D. (1948). *Parasitology* **38:** 183–227.

Krogh, A. (1939). Osmotic Regulation in Aquatic Animals. University Press, Cambridge, England.

Martin, C. J., and Ross, I. C. (1934). *J. Helminthol.* **12:** 137–142.

McCoy, O. R., Downing, V. F., and Van Voorhis, S. N. (1941). *J. Parasitol.* **27:** 53–58.

Moraczewski, S. A., and Kelsey, F. E. (1948). *J. Infectious Diseases* **82:** 45–51.

Read, C. P. (1950). *J. Parasitol.* **36:** 34–40.

Reichenow, E. (1909). *Arb. kaiserl. Gesundh.* **33:** 1–45.

Rogers, W. P. (1945). *Parasitology* **36:** 211–218.

Rogers, W. P., and Lazarus, M. (1949a). *Parasitology* **39:** 245–250.

Rogers, W. P., and Lazarus, M. (1949b). *Parasitology* **39:** 302–314.

Schopfer, W. H. (1932). *Rev. suisse zool.* **39:** 59–194.

Ussing, H. H. (1949). *Acta Physiol. Scand.* **17:** 1–37.

CHAPTER 10

# CARBOHYDRATE METABOLISM

## I. INTRODUCTORY REMARKS

Although the carbohydrate metabolism of parasites is one of the best known phases of parasite physiology, our knowledge is still far from complete both as to the mechanisms of carbohydrate utilization and the types of carbohydrate metabolism occurring in many interesting groups. Very little or nothing is known in these respects of trichomonads, acanthocephala, pentastomids, or sacculinids, to name only a few of the neglected groups.

It is no coincidence that the carbohydrate metabolism should have attracted a relatively large number of investigators. Very soon it became obvious that many endoparasites have a pronounced carbohydrate metabolism. All forms living in anaerobic or semi-anaerobic habitats (such as the intestine or the bile ducts), and having no special means of securing oxygen, utilize carbohydrate primarily because it is the best source of anaerobic energy. Anoxidative processes are primarily oxidation-reductions and Hellerman (1947) has pointed out that the intermediately oxidized carbon atoms of carbohydrates (H—C—OH) are ideally suited for such processes.

Other forms that live in oxygen-rich surroundings, for example the trypanosomes, filarias, or schistosomes, could, theoretically, derive most of their energy from the oxidation of fats or proteins, but carbohydrate metabolism predominates nevertheless. It is difficult to adduce a definite reason for this phenomenon, but it should be remembered that in free-living invertebrates metabolic specialists also occur which utilize primarily one of the great groups of food materials, or even only a very specialized substance. Examples are the honey bee for a preponderantly carbohydrate metabolism, the caterpillar of *Galleria melonella* for the utilization of wax, and so on. It is probable that the biochemical constitution, that is, essentially the enzymatic apparatus of the organisms, determines the main food groups used in these cases. Whether this explanation suffices in the case of all parasites is an interesting matter of speculation. Before coming to an arbitrary pronouncement on this point it is well to remember that some caterpillars, for example, starve to death rather than eat leaves from plants other than those which are their normal food. It is hardly likely that the metabolic enzymes are involved in such selections. Similarly, a cow cannot

92

be educated to carnivorous habits although its digestive enzymes could probably cope with animal proteins as indicated by its digesting its own rumen ciliates.

It is interesting to note that almost all hitherto studied parasites do not completely oxidize sugar to carbon dioxide and water. This, of course, is a necessary sequence of lack of oxygen when organisms live in anaerobic habitats, but it happens also even if oxygen is plentiful. In other words, most endoparasites are characterized by the prevalence of anaerobic or aerobic fermentations. The only exception found so far is *Plasmodium lophurae*, which apparently does not show aerobic fermentations (Wendel, 1946). It is quite obvious that both anaerobic and aerobic fermentations are very uneconomical since a large amount of energy contained in the carbohydrate molecule remains unutilized. From the parasites' standpoint this is no handicap, since they practically always live in surroundings that offer them a surplus of readily available food. From the host's standpoint the inefficient utilization of food may be more serious since some of the organic endproducts may well be toxic. On the other hand, however, the host may be able to utilize at least some of the endproducts of the parasites' metabolism. Harvey (1949) has pointed out that the pyruvic acid produced by pathogenic trypanosomes is probably metabolized further by the host. The most extreme examples in this direction are the termites, which have become dependent for survival upon the metabolic endproducts of their intestinal fauna (Cleveland, 1925b).

It is, at present, impossible to adduce a biological reason for the predominance of aerobic fermentation among parasites; it may be pointed out that it seems to occur among several groups of free-living invertebrates such as insects (Harnisch, 1947) or snails (von Brand, Baernstein, and Mehlman, 1950). The biochemical mechanism leading to the accumulation of partly oxidized endproducts is different in various cases. In pathogenic trypanosomes the enzymes responsible for completing the oxidations are clearly lacking (Marshall, 1948b). In *Plasmodium knowlesi* (McKee *et al.*, 1946) a differential activity of the various enzymes of the glycolytic chain is probably involved, leading to a piling up of partially oxidized endproducts. A similar situation may prevail in the nematodes *Eustrongylides* (von Brand and Simpson, 1945) and *Litomosoides* (Bueding, 1948, 1949a), organisms showing a pronounced Pasteur effect. Probably, they can utilize, interchangeably, the energy derived from fermentations and from oxidations. In schistosomes, or the nematode *Dracunculus insignis* no Pasteur effect occurs (Bueding, Peters, and Welch, 1947; Bueding, 1949c). It is possible that these parasites cannot utilize the energy derived from aerobic processes and that the persistence of fermentations even under clearly aerobic conditions is mandatory for their survival (Bueding, 1949b).

Parasites may utilize the carbohydrate present in their surroundings either directly for the production of energy, or they may transform it to reserve carbohydrate. They encounter in their natural habitats either simple sugars which are undoubtedly absorbed as such, or polysaccharides, *e.g.*, starch. Before absorption the latter are usually broken down to compounds of lower molecular weight by means of digestive enzymes, or, in some cases, such as intestinal amoebas, they are engulfed as formed particles and intracellular digestion takes place.

## II. UTILIZATION OF SIMPLE CARBOHYDRATES AND RELATED COMPOUNDS

Most parasites encounter a source of simple carbohydrates in their normal habitat, be it the intestinal contents, the blood, spinal fluid, or other body fluids and secretions. Glucose is most frequent, although other carbohydrates may predominate for some plant-parasitizing protozoa and helminths. It is not surprising, therefore, that glucose is utilized readily by most parasites studied so far (see Table 17 on parasitic protozoa). It has, however, not yet been possible to demonstrate a glucose consumption by *Trypanosoma rotatorium* (Noguchi, 1926), the bloodstream form of *Trypanosoma cruzi* (von Brand *et al.*, 1949), or the larvae of *Trichinella spiralis* (Stannard, McCoy, and Latchford, 1938).

Mannose and fructose are metabolized by some protozoa as well or nearly as well as glucose (Table 18), while galactose is rarely used to any large extent. Of the disaccharides, maltose is utilized by more parasitic protozoa than either lactose or saccharose, while pentoses are hardly available to them. Among alcohols, glycerol is metabolized more readily than any other alcohol tested and by some forms, such as *Trypanosoma hippicum* (Harvey, 1949), *Plasmodium knowlesi* (Fulton, 1939; Maier and Coggeshall, 1941), or *Plasmodium gallinaceum* (Marshall, 1948a) it is utilized at the same, or occasionally even at a higher rate, than glucose.

The amounts of glucose consumed by various parasitic species are evidently different. It is difficult to give comparable figures for protozoa since their sugar consumption is usually referred to unit numbers rather than unit weights due to the technical difficulties of obtaining reliable weight figures. Some pertinent data are given in Table 19. An approximate calculation on the basis of weight shows that at least in the case of the African pathogenic trypanosomes the rate of glucose consumption reaches extremely high values, approximating 50 to 100% of their dry weight per hour at 37°C (Christophers and Fulton, 1938). These forms are absolutely dependent on an adequate exogenous source of carbohydrate (or glycerol); in its absence they die rapidly (von Brand, 1933b).

There are differences in carbohydrate requirements among the various

TABLE 17. Qualitative tests on the utilization of various carbohydrates and related compounds by some parasitic protozoa.

| SPECIES | PENTOSES | | | HEXOSES | | | | DISACCHARIDES | | | TRISACCHARIDE | POLYSACCHARIDES | | | ALCOHOLS | | | | | GLUCOSIDE | AUTHOR |
|---|---|---|---|---|---|---|---|---|---|---|---|---|---|---|---|---|---|---|---|---|---|
| | Arabinose | Rhamnose | Xylose | Fructose | Galactose | Glucose | Mannose | Lactose | Maltose | Saccharose | Raffinose | Dextrin | Inulin | Soluble starch | Dulcite | Erythrite | Glycerol | Mannite | Sorbite | Amygdalin | |
| *Leptomonas ctenocephali* | — | — | — | —; x | — | —; x | — | — | — | — | — | — | — | — | — | — | — | — | — | — | Colas-Belcour and Lwoff (1925); Noguchi (1926) |
| *Leishmania brasiliensis* | — | — | — | x | — | x | x | — | — | —; x | x | — | — | — | — | — | — | — | — | — | Kligler (1926); Noguchi (1926) |
| *L. donovani* | —; ? | — | — | x | — | x | x | — | — | x | x | — | —; ? | — | — | — | — | — | — | — | Noguchi (1926) |
| *L. tropica* | — | — | — | x | — | x | x | — | — | x | x | — | —; ? | — | — | — | — | — | — | — | Colas-Belcour and Lwoff (1925); Kligler (1926); Noguchi (1926) |
| *Herpetomonas culicidarum* | x | — | x | x | x | x | x | — | x | x | x | — | x | — | — | — | — | — | — | x | Noguchi (1926) |
| *H. lygaeorum* | — | — | — | x | x | x | x | — | — | x | x | — | — | — | — | — | — | — | — | — | Noguchi (1926) |
| *H. media* | — | — | — | x | x | x | x | x | x | x | x | x | x | — | — | — | — | x | — | — | Noguchi (1926) |
| *H. muscidarum* | x | — | x | x | x | x | x | — | x | x | x | x | x | — | — | — | — | x | — | — | Noguchi (1926) |
| *H. oncopelti* | x | — | x | x | x | x | x | — | x | x | x | x | x | — | — | — | — | x | — | — | Noguchi (1926) |
| *H. parva* | — | — | — | x | (x) | x | x | — | x | x | x | — | — | — | — | — | — | — | — | — | Noguchi (1926) |
| *Trypanosoma brucei* | — | — | — | x | (x) | x | x | — | x | — | — | — | — | — | — | — | x | — | (x) | — | Kudicke and Evers (1924) |
| *T. equiperdum* | — | — | (x) | x | x | x | x | x | x | — | — | — | — | — | — | — | — | — | — | — | Ivanov and Jakovlev (1943) |
| *Eutrichomastix colubrorum* | —; ? | — | — | x | x | x | — | x | x | x | x | x | x | x | — | — | — | — | — | — | Cailleau (1937) |
| *Trichomonas columbae* | — | — | —; ? | x | x | x | — | x | x | x | — | x | x; — | x; — | — | — | — | — | — | — | Cailleau (1937) |
| *T. foetus* | — | — | —; ? | x | x | x | x | x; — | x; — | x; — | x; — | x | x; — | x; — | — | — | — | — | — | — | Cailleau (1937); Plastridge (1943); Cole (1950) |
| *T. vaginalis* | — | — | — | x | x | x | — | x | x | — | x | x | — | x | — | — | — | — | — | — | Trussell and Johnson (1941) |
| *Plasmodium knowlesi* | — | — | — | x | — | x | x | — | — | — | — | — | — | — | — | — | x | — | — | — | Maier and Coggeshall (1941) |

— = Compound not utilized; x = compound utilized; ? = utilization questionable; (x) = compound barely utilized.

95

TABLE 18.  Relative utilization rates of some carbohydrates by some parasitic protozoa kept in aseptic environment. The data are based either on direct determinations of the respective sugars, or on the increase in oxygen consumption induced by their presence.

| SPECIES | FORM* | GLU-COSE | MAN-NOSE | FRUC-TOSE | GALAC-TOSE | MALTOSE | AUTHOR |
|---|---|---|---|---|---|---|---|
| *Leishmania donovani*.. | C | 100 | | 80 | | 3 | Chang (1948) |
| *L. donovani*.......... | C | 100 | 69 | 77 | 31 | 5 | Fulton and Joyner (1949) |
| *L. brasiliensis*........ | C | 100 | | 93 | | 2 | Chang (1948) |
| *L. tropica*............ | C | 100 | | 88 | | 2 | Chang (1948) |
| *Trypanosoma cruzi*... | C | 100 | | 96 | | 3 | Chang (1948) |
| *T. lewisi*............. | B | 100 | 132 | 50 | 0 | 218 (?) | Mercado (1947) |
| *T. equiperdum*....... | B | 100 | 57 | 75 | 0 | 87 | Plunkett (1946) |
| *T. brucei*............. | B | 100 | 86 | 21 | 9 | 50 | von Brand (1933b) |
| *Plasmodium knowl-esi*................. | B | 100 | 125 | 100 | 0 | 24 | Maier and Coggeshall (1941) |
| *P. knowlesi*.......... | B | 100 | 46 | 85 | 0 | 12 | Fulton (1939) |

* C = culture forms; B = blood stream form.

TABLE 19.  Quantitative data on the glucose consumption of some parasitic protozoa kept under aseptic conditions at body temperature. The trypanosome data refer to the bloodstream form.

| SPECIES | GLUCOSE, MG./ 100 MILLION/ HOUR | AUTHOR |
|---|---|---|
| *Trichomonas foetus*....... | 1.6; 2.3 | Andrews and von Brand (1938); Cole (1950) |
| *Trypanosoma lewisi*...... | 0.1; 0.1 | Regendanz (1930); von Brand (1933b) |
| *T. lewisi*, young......... | 0.4 | Moulder (1948b) |
| *T. lewisi*, old............ | 0.2 | Moulder (1948b) |
| *T. congolense*............ | 0.8; 0.7 | von Brand (1933b); von Brand and Tobie (1948) |
| *T. evansi*................ | 0.9; 0.6 | Geiger, Kligler, and Comaroff (1930); von Brand and Tobie (1948) |
| *T. equinum*.............. | 0.8 | von Brand and Tobie (1948) |
| *T. equiperdum*........... | 2.0 | Chen and Geiling (1945) |
| *T. brucei*................ | 0.3; 0.8 | von Issekutz (1933); von Brand (1933b) |
| *T. gambiense*............. | 0.6; 1.0 | Yorke, Adams, and Murgatroyd (1929); von Brand and Tobie (1948) |
| *T. rhodesiense*........... | 1.0; 1.5 | von Brand and Tobie (1948) |
| *Plasmodium knowlesi*..... | 0.2; 0.2; 0.15 | Christophers and Fulton (1938) Fulton (1939); McKee et al (1946) |

stages of protozoan parasites. African trypanosomes do not require the addition of sugar to the medium in the developmental stages (Reichenow, 1937), although capable of utilizing it when present (Tobie, von Brand, and Mehlman, 1950). The culture forms of *Trypanosoma cruzi*, thrive better in the presence than in the absence of glucose (Reichenow, 1937), while the bloodstream form, as mentioned above, does not seem to utilize sugar present in the medium to any noticeable degree. Similar differences are probable also in other cases. The malarial parasites of the bloodstream are heavy sugar consumers (Wendel, 1943; Marshall, 1948a; Ball et al., 1948; Manwell and Feigelson, 1949). It may be doubted that the sporozoites developing in an oocyst or living in the salivary gland of a mosquito could satisfy analogous needs, but no data on their glucose consumption are available.

TABLE 20. Aerobic removal of glucose from the medium by some aseptically kept helminths

| SPECIES | TEMP. °C | GLUCOSE, MG/GM WET WEIGHT/ HOUR | AUTHOR |
|---|---|---|---|
| *Schistosoma mansoni*........ | 37.5 | 33.5 | Bueding, Peters, and Waite (1947) |
| *Eustrongylides ignotus*, larvae...................... | 37 | 0.03 | von Brand and Simpson (1944) |
| *E. ignotus*, larvae.......... | 20 | 0.005 | von Brand and Simpson (1944) |
| *Litomosoides carinii*........ | 37.5 | 21 | Bueding (1949a) |
| *Dracunculus insignis*........ | 37.5 | 23 | Bueding and Oliver-Gonzalez (1950) |

The older literature contains but little useful information concerning the utilization of mono- and disaccharides by parasitic worms since the worms used at that time were not kept in aseptic surroundings. Bacteria develop very rapidly in sugar-containing media at the high temperature required by parasites of warm-blooded hosts, and their activities make any conclusion rather precarious. Experiments suggestive of utilization of glucose, and in some cases also of some other hexoses, were carried out with nematodes (Weinland and Ritter, 1902), cestodes (von Brand, 1933a; Wardle, 1937; Markov, 1939), and trematodes (Stephenson, 1947).

In recent years experiments with worms kept under aseptic conditions became possible and they are of course convincing. It has been shown that glucose enhances the survival of larval *Eustrongylides in vitro*, but not fructose, mannose, or maltose (von Brand and Simpson, 1944); that glucose, fructose, and mannose, but not ribose or galactose, increase the oxygen consumption of *Litomosoides* (Bueding, 1949a) and that the same holds true for glucose and fructose in the case of *Schistosoma mansoni* (Bueding,

1949b). It is of interest that in the latter helminth the glucose consumption was independent of the glucose concentration of the medium while the extent of fructose utilization was proportional to its concentration. Bueding (personal communication) has recently found that *Schistosoma mansoni* survives in a synthetic medium equally well with glucose, fructose, or mannose, while ribose, xylose, arabinose, galactose, sucrose, maltose, and lactose were without effect.

The few quantitative data available on glucose consumption of parasitic worms are summarized in Table 20 indicating rather considerable differences between various species. The very pronounced utilization rate of schistosomes is especially noteworthy. It may reach values of about 20% of the worm's dry substance in 1 hour at body temperature (Bueding, Peters, and Waite, 1947).

### III. Utilization of Polysaccharides

#### A. Digestion of Polysaccharides

Polysaccharides apparently can be utilized by several parasitic protozoa (Table 17) even if they are not able to ingest formed particles. In these cases the utilization is probably limited to soluble polysaccharides such as soluble starch or glycogen. It is not yet known whether these organisms elaborate digestive enzymes to break down the polysaccharides to simpler compounds before absorption. No amylase has been found in *Trypanosoma brucei* or *Trypanosoma evansi* by Califano and Gritti (1930) and Krijgsman (1936a, b), respectively, but there is also no good indication that these flagellates utilize polysaccharides. It is true, however, that Mannozzi-Torini (1940) reports having demonstrated the consumption of glycogen, soluble starch, and even inulin by *Trypanosoma evansi*.

Numerous parasitic protozoa, especially amoebas and ciliates, avidly engulf starch, both in their natural habitat and in culture. There is hardly a doubt that these starch granules are utilized as food and that as a first step they are hydrolyzed by amylolytic enzymes. The disintegration of starch particles ingested by *Endamoeba histolytica* was followed by Hopkins and Warner (1946) and was also observed in the case of starch-fed rumen ciliates (Trier, 1926; Westphal, 1934). Glaessner (1908) described a potent starch-splitting enzyme from *Balantidium coli* isolated from feces; there must remain considerable doubt, however, whether his isolation technique was sufficient to exclude the action of bacterial enzymes.

Some parasitic protozoa are capable of digesting cellulose. The status of the rumen ciliates in this respect was for some time in doubt. Dogiel (1925), Margolin (1930), and Westphal (1934) assumed that they were not capable of doing so. The well known fact that many of these organisms ingest plant particles was explained by Westphal (1934) on the assumption that they utilize only the starch enclosed in the cellulose walls and excrete the cellulose as nondigestible material. Other investigators (*e.g.*, Braune, 1914; Schulze, 1924; or Weineck, 1934), on the other hand, made observations indicative of an actual digestion of cellulose. The question was settled definitely by Hungate (1942) who demonstrated in *Eudiplodinium neglectum* the occurrence of a cellulase active in the pH range of 4.0 to 6.6 and with a pH optimum of about 5.0, a significant observation in view of Weineck's (1934) demonstration that the endoplasm of these ciliates is acid. In addition to cellulase, a cellobiase was found, corroborating Weineck's (1934) postulate of cellobiose as an intermediate of cellulose digestion. In a later paper Hungate (1943a) described the presence of a cellulase from *Diplodinium maggii* also, whereas no indication of cellulose digestion was found for *Entodinium*, *Isotricha*, *Dasytricha*, or *Buetschlia*. It seems then that different genera of rumen ciliates have different digestive enzymes and that this fact explains simply enough the divergent views of the older authors.

Many termite protozoa ingest wood particles (Cleveland, 1924, 1925a; Swezy, 1923) and there can be no doubt as to their ability to digest the wood. Trager (1932) showed that the intestinal fauna of the roach *Cryptocercus punctulatus* and the termites *Reticulitermes flavipes* and *Termopsis angusticollis* contain a cellulase and a cellobiase. The enzymes could be purified partly and it was shown that the result of their action was the production of glucose. The cellulase was also found in a culture of *Trichomonas termopsidis*, an especially interesting form since it is able to use only cellulose as a carbon source (Trager, 1934). Quantitative data on cellulose utilization by termite protozoa were presented by Hungate (1943b), indicating fairly high rates.

Relatively little information is available concerning the amylolytic digestive enzymes of helminths. Kobert (1903) described starch- and inulin-splitting properties of tissue extracts from a dog ascarid and Schimmelpfennig (1903) found a starch-degrading enzyme in the body fluid of *Parascaris*. These studies merely indicate the presence of amylase-like enzymes which in nature may act primarily on the glycogen of the worms themselves, that is, they are probably tissue enzymes. The presence of true digestive amylases, enzymes preparing exogenous carbohydrates for absorption, can obviously not be inferred from such crude experiments.

More convincing is Flury's (1912) observation of the glycogen- and starch-splitting power of the extracts of the *Ascaris* intestine and Enigk's (1938) finding that *Graphidium strigosum* cannot digest raw rice starch but can digest starch heated for 30 minutes at 60°C.

The most complete study of amylolytic enzymes is due to Rogers (1940). He extracted them from the intestines of *Strongylus edentatus* and *Ascaris lumbricoides* studying both the amyloclastic action, that is, the progressive

loss of the blue color of starch due to iodine, and the saccharogenic action, the gradual appearance of reducing sugar. He found distinct differences in the pH optima between the enzymes of both species (Fig. 8) and also differences in the influence of salts upon their activity. Sodium chloride

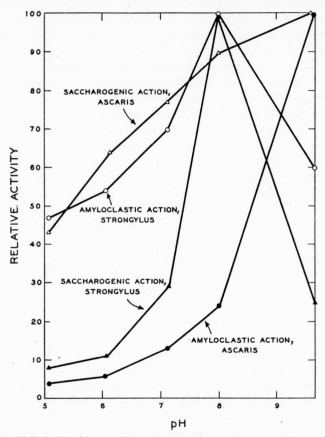

Fig. 8. pH Relationships of the amylolytic enzymes of *Ascaris* and *Strongylus* (after Rogers, 1940).

was practically ineffective as an activator of the enzymes of both species while disodium phosphate was fairly effective. Potassium iodide, on the contrary, was most potent in stimulating the amylase of *Strongylus*, but ineffective in the case of *Ascaris*. Exactly the reverse held true when sodium bicarbonate was used. Glucose was identified as endproduct of starch digestion only in the case of *Strongylus*. No definite osazone crystals could be recovered with *Ascaris* amylase.

It is rather remarkable that the properties of the carbohydrate-digesting

enzymes of these two nematodes are so different. A comparative study on a broader basis, preferably with somewhat more purified enzymes than used by Rogers (1949) should prove interesting although such a study could probably be conducted profitably only with nematodes. In flat worms, even in forms having an alimentary canal, a distinction between true digestive and tissue enzymes would hardly be possible, and in worms lacking an intestinal system an elaboration of digestive enzymes proper can hardly be expected.

Very little work has been done so far with endoparasitic arthropods. It has been shown that the salivary glands of *Gasterophilus* larvae do not contain an amylase but that such an enzyme is present in the midgut (Roy, 1937). The occurrence of a similar enzyme in the body fluid of the larvae was already known since von Kemnitz' (1914, 1916) work. This latter enzyme apparently serves to convert the glycogen derived from the tracheal cells to glucose while the former can hardly be understood on the basis of purely blood-feeding habits. Roy (1937) thinks that they derive their main food from the fluid content of the horse's stomach which surrounds them.

The larvae of *Cordylobia anthropophaga*, on the other hand, have no amylase in the body fluid. The salivary gland, however, contains an amylase and an invertase, and an amylase, invertase, and maltase was found in the midgut (Blacklock, Gordon, and Fine, 1930).

## B. Sources of Endogenous Polysaccharides

The polysaccharides stored by endoparasitic animals seem, according to our present state of knowledge, to be usually derived from exogenous carbohydrate. It has thus been shown that *Endamoeba histolytica* specimens taken from culture, that is, from a starch-containing medium, are extremely rich in glycogen (Morita, 1938), and it has been found that a parallelism exists between the starch content of the medium, the degree of starch uptake, and the glycogen deposition in rumen ciliates (Usuelli, 1930; Trier, 1926; Westphal, 1934). The paraglycogen content of *Nyctotherus ovalis* was greatly increased in specimens taken from roaches kept on a high carbohydrate diet as compared to those isolated from starving insects and hosts kept on a high protein or high fat diet (Armer, 1944). In these cases a direct connection between dietary carbohydrate and deposition of reserve carbohydrate can hardly be doubted.

Especially clear is the situation in parasitic worms. Some of the older experiments that indicate glycogen formation from hexoses present in the medium are those of Weinland and Ritter (1902) with *Ascaris* and those of Wardle (1937) and Markov (1939) with cestodes. They are not entirely convincing, however, because the worms were not kept aseptically. Such an objection cannot be raised against the experiments of Bueding (1949a) with *Litomosoides carinii*, for he kept his worms in bacteriologically sterile surroundings. He found their glycogen content to increase by about 100% upon 3 hours incubation in a medium having a 0.02 $M$ glucose content. Some light on the biochemical mechanism of glycogen formation in helminths has been shed by the experiments of Rogers and Lazarus (1949). They observed in aqueous extracts of *Ascaridia galli* a definite glycogen synthesis from glucose-1-phosphate (Cori ester) upon incubation in a medium containing 0.005 $M$ NaF, adenylic acid, and glucose-1-phosphate. Some glycogen synthesis was also found in fluoride-treated muscle brei of *Ascaris* to which no Cori ester had been added. On the whole our present knowledge, scanty as it is, seems to indicate that the chemical mechanism of glycogen synthesis in worms is similar to that described from vertebrate material.

Whether future research will reveal other materials besides carbohydrates from which helminths may be able to form glycogen, is at present only a matter of speculation. It may be of interest in this connection to note that *Schistocephalus* and *Ligula* developed and matured in a sugar-free peptone-broth medium (Smyth, 1946a, b), but no quantitative data on their glycogen reserves under these conditions are as yet available.

There is some doubt as to the origin of the glycogen deposited in large amounts in *Gasterophilus* larvae. Von Kemnitz (1916) has calculated that one larva would have to extract from the host a minimum of 40 ml of blood in 5 months in order to build up its glycogen reserve, a figure which he considers unlikely. He is inclined to assume a transformation of protein into carbohydrate, but he has not presented conclusive evidence to this effect. It is of course well known that many animals are capable of such a process and it would not be surprising if the same mechanism were realized in one or the other parasite. In so far as *Gasterophilus* is concerned, however, it must be pointed out that Roy (1937) could not find any indication for the ingestion of large amounts of blood. He believes that the larvae feed on the stomach contents of the host and his finding of an amylase in the gut of the larvae may indicate that the glycogen of the larvae is derived from ingested starch.

### C. Significance of Endogenous Carbohydrate Reserves

Endogenous carbohydrate, essentially glycogen, is most frequently an energy reserve; it may be utilized by purely fermentative processes, by oxidations, or during aerobic fermentation. These aspects will be treated in the following sections. It should be realized, however, that the production of energy is not always the sole purpose of a glycogen accumulation.

Glycogen will unquestionably be utilized by endoparasitic arthropods, just as by free-living ones, for the synthesis of the chitin of the exoskeleton. It is entirely possible that in parasites like *Peltogaster* which store but little polysaccharide (unpublished observations) this function is in the foreground. It would be interesting to study whether in this and similar instances cyclic variations in glycogen content occur directly dependent on the moulting cycle, as they do, for example, in free-living crustacea.

Similarly, part of the glycogen, though certainly only a small fraction of the total metabolized, is used for chitin synthesis in those previously mentioned nematodes and acanthocephala that produce chitinous egg membranes. It has been found that in ascarids about half the glycogen deposited in the oocytes is utilized to form the glucosamine built into the chitin of the egg membranes (Fauré-Fremiet, 1913; Szwejkowska, 1929).

It is entirely possible that in special cases the entire or part of the polysaccharide reserve is used for still other processes, although no definite information is available. In this connection the curious fact may be mentioned that in young *Endamoeba* cysts a large glycogen vacuole appears rather rapidly and that this glycogen disappears equally rapidly. A connection with the appearance of the chromatoid bodies has not been established and the significance of the glycogen deposit in this stage of the life cycle must for the present remain in doubt.

### D. Quantitative Aspects of Endogenous Polysaccharide Utilization

No quantitative data on the utilization of endogenous polysaccharide are available for parasitic protozoa. The qualitative observations of Westphal (1934) and Hungate (1943a) showed a rapid depletion of the glycogen stores of starving rumen ciliates, suggesting a high rate of utilization. The glycogen vacuole of *Iodamoeba Buetschlii*, on the other hand, disappears but gradually and very slowly (von Brand, 1932) and in gregarines starving within the intestine of mealworms no significant decrease in polysaccharide content was demonstrable by means of staining methods (von Brand, 1950). Apparently, therefore, considerable differences between species exist in this respect.

The study of the rates of glycogen consumption of helminths is generally done with worms starving *in vitro* in somewhat unphysiological conditions. The question whether values obtained in this way reflect the polysaccharide utilization as it occurs *in vivo* is difficult to answer definitely, but on the whole it seems likely that the values are fairly reliable. This is indicated by the fact that Weinland (1901) and Reid (1945), working with dog ascarids and *Ascaridia galli* respectively, found very similar rates of glycogen consumption by worms starving *in vitro* and *in vivo*. Furthermore one of the worms studied, the larva of *Eustrongylides*, survives for very long periods *in vitro* and it can be assumed that the relatively short periods of starvation used for the determinations of the polysaccharide consumption rate did not seriously interfere with its vitality.

The data of Table 21 indicate that rather considerable differences in carbohydrate consumption occur between various species of helminths and this holds true regardless of whether the aerobic or anaerobic rates are compared. *Schistosoma mansoni* and *Litomosoides carinii* thus consume from 20 to 80 times more carbohydrate per unit weight than *Fasciola hepatica* or larval *Eustrongylides*. A possibility exists that these differences are slightly exaggerated since the former worms, in contrast to the latter, had to be studied in media containing exogenous carbohydrate since their endogenous stores proved completely inadequate to maintain a high rate of metabolism. On the other hand, however, the total carbohydrate consumption of aerobically kept larval *Eustrongylides* was about equal whether an exogenous carbohydrate source was present or not. Another factor to be considered is the length of experimental period employed. In the case of *Ascaris* at least, there is a tendency for the rate of carbohydrate consumption to decline with increasing length of starvation. Weinland (1901) arrived at a rate of 0.7 gm glycogen consumed per 100 gm in 24 hours in experiments lasting up to 6 days, while von Brand (1934) found a rate of 1.4 gm in the first 24 hours.

It is nevertheless certain that the above differences between species are real and it is probable that several factors are involved in bringing them about. One factor will be the size of the worms, smaller organisms metabolizing quite generally at a higher rate than large ones. Equally important, or perhaps even of the greatest importance, may be the type of metabolism prevailing in various helminths, since it must be expected that different aerobic and anaerobic fermentations will release different amounts of energy.

The data of Table 21 emphasize also another point, namely, that in most forms studied so far there is but little difference in carbohydrate consumption whether a given species of parasite is kept aerobically or anaerobically. In most free-living invertebrates (data on a variety of species in von Brand, 1946, and Cleary, 1948) the anaerobic glycogen consumption is from several to many times greater than the aerobic rate because they oxidize carbohydrate completely in the presence of sufficient oxygen. In other words they utilize a process releasing the maximum of energy from a given amount of carbohydrate. In the absence of oxygen they must mobilize a greater amount of carbohydrate in order to gain even the minimum of energy required for the sustenance of life from the uneconomical fermentative processes. The metabolism of parasites, on the other hand, is characterized by the prevalence of aerobic fermentation, as already

mentioned, and this fermentative use of carbohydrate even in the presence
of ample oxygen drives the aerobic consumption of carbohydrate up to a
level nearly equal to that of the anaerobic rate.

TABLE 21. Carbohydrate consumption of parasitic helminths and arthropods in
gm per 100 gm wet weight at 37–41°C (essentially after von Brand, 1950)

| SPECIES | CARBOHYDRATE CONSUMPTION | | AUTHOR |
|---|---|---|---|
| | Anaerobic | Aerobic | |
| TREMATODES | | | |
| Schistosoma mansoni[a] | 79–96 | 79–96 | Bueding (personal communication) |
| Fasciola hepatica | 2.6 | | Weinland and von Brand (1926) |
| CESTODES | | | |
| Schistocephalus solidus, plerocercoids[b] | 4.1 | | Hopkins (1950) |
| Railletina cesticillus | 4.8 | | Reid (1942) |
| Moniezia expansa | 1.0 | | von Brand (1933a) |
| NEMATODES | | | |
| Eustrongylides ignotus, larvae | 0.7 | 0.2 | von Brand and Simpson (1945) |
| Ascaris lumbricoides | 1.4 | 1.2 | von Brand (1934) |
| Parascaris equorum | 1.4 | 1.6 | Toryu (1936) |
| Ascaridia galli | 3.6 | | Reid (1945) |
| Litomosoides carinii[a] | 34–41 | 42–45 | Bueding (personal communication) |
| Dracunculus insignis[a] | 58 | 55 | Bueding and Oliver-Gonzalez (1950) |
| ACANTHOCEPHALA | | | |
| Macracanthorhynchus hirudinaceus | 1.0 | 0.8 | Rudolph (vide Weinland, 1910); von Brand (1940) |
| ARTHROPODS | | | |
| Gasterophilus intestinalis, larvae | 0.7 | 1.3 | von Kemnitz (1916) |

[a] Total carbohydrate consumption in nutritive, sugar-containing media; all other
figures refer to starving parasites.

[b] Kept starving inside the pigeon intestine; conditions were presumably nearly
but not totally anaerobic.

It should be realized, however, that there is probably no fundamental
difference between parasites and free-living invertebrates in this respect.
On the one hand there are free-living invertebrates, e.g. some snail species,

that consume almost as much carbohydrate aerobically as anaerobically (von Brand, Baernstein, and Mehlman, 1950). On the other hand, the relatively low aerobic rate as compared to the anaerobic rate found in *Eustrongylides* points to the possibility that parasites exist that behave like the majority of free-living organisms in this respect. It would be of interest to study parasites having very free access to oxygen, such as monogenetic trematodes and the nematodes that parasitize the swim bladder of fishes or the trachea of birds.

It seems to be very rare that a parasite consumes less glycogen when deprived of oxygen than under aerobic conditions. The *Gasterophilus* larva is such a case. Quite obviously a very pronounced reduction in energy production must be involved, but no definite view concerning the biological significance of this reduction can be advanced at present.

## IV. ENDPRODUCTS OF AEROBIC AND ANAEROBIC FERMENTATIONS

The endproducts of parasitic aerobic and anaerobic fermentations are more varied than those occurring in vertebrate tissues where lactic acid is formed almost exclusively. They are less varied, however, than those characterizing yeasts and bacteria where a wide array of substances has been found.

Hydrogen, for example, is frequently produced by bacteria, but has been found only rarely in protozoan parasites and never in metazoan parasites. Specifically, it has been observed that during the anaerobic cellulose fermentation of termite flagellates relatively large amounts of hydrogen are produced (Cook, 1932, 1943; Cook and Smith, 1942; Hungate, 1939, 1943b). The symbiotic protozoa of *Cryptocercus punctulatus* evolve the same gas and in addition produce small amounts of an unidentified gas which gives rise to carbon dioxide upon combustion (Gilmour, 1940). *Trichomonas foetus*, finally, produces an inflammable gas (Andrews and von Brand, 1938) consisting of hydrogen with a small admixture of methane (Suzuoki and Suzuoki, 1951).

Carbon dioxide has been found universally, originating both from aerobic and anaerobic fermentations, but its sources and significance are probably different in various cases. It can be "inorganic" carbon dioxide, that is carbon dioxide set free from bicarbonates of the body or the medium by stronger acids than carbonic acid formed during the fermentation processes. Practically all the carbon dioxide evolved by aerobically maintained African trypanosomes (bloodstream form) is derived from this source (Christophers and Fulton, 1938; Harvey, 1949). This will generally be true for those fermentations in which lactic or pyruvic acids predominate as endproducts, as the following overall formulations indicate:

$$C_6H_{12}O_6 \rightarrow 2CH_3 \cdot CHOH \cdot COOH \quad \text{and}$$
$$C_6H_{12}O_6 \rightarrow 2CH_3 \cdot CO \cdot COOH + 2H_2O.$$

Other processes, however, lead to the formation of true respiratory carbon dioxide, that is carbon dioxide whose carbon is derived from the metabolized carbohydrate molecule. Examples are the dismutation of pyruvic acid to acetic acid and lactic acid, as it occurs in *Litomosoides* (Bueding, 1949a):

$$2CH_3 \cdot CO \cdot COOH + H_2O \rightarrow CH_3 \cdot COOH + CO_2 + CH_3 \cdot CHOH \cdot COOH$$

and the valeric acid fermentation of *Ascaris* which Jost (1928) formulates as follows:

$$13C_6H_{12}O_6 \rightarrow 12CH_3 \cdot CH_2 \cdot CH_2 \cdot CH_2 \cdot COOH + 18CO_2 + 18H_2O.$$

In general it can be expected that in those fermentations where fatty acids appear as endproducts true respiratory carbon dioxide will be formed.

Quantitative figures for the carbon dioxide production of anaerobically kept helminths are available for nematodes (Weinland, 1901; Schulte, 1917; von Brand, 1934), trematodes (Weinland and von Brand, 1926; Harnisch, 1932), and cestodes (von Brand, 1933a), as well as for the larval stage of the arthropod *Gasterophilus* (von Kemnitz, 1916). The earlier practice of introducing these figures into a carbon balance sheet is unsatisfactory as long as no differentiation between carbon dioxide of organic and inorganic origin has been made and as long as the question of carbon dioxide retention in the tissues and the medium has not been considered adequately (Bueding, 1949b). It is, however, probably safe to assume, in a qualitative sense, that in the above cases at least some respiratory carbon dioxide is evolved. This seems clearly indicated by the proportions of actually eliminated carbon dioxide and the organic acids produced (von Brand, 1950). A quantitative elucidation of the anaerobic carbon dioxide picture is unquestionably an urgent requirement for further progress. It is no easy problem, however, and quantitative work with large worms like *Ascaris*, or with cestodes that contain calcareous corpuscles, will be difficult. In so far as smaller worms are concerned, Stannard, McCoy, and Latchford (1938) have demonstrated unequivocally that the larvae of *Trichinella spiralis* produce true respiratory carbon dioxide in the absence of oxygen, 1 mg dried larvae evolving 1.2 mm³ respiratory carbon dioxide.

The organic endproducts of aerobic and anaerobic fermentations are different in various groups of parasites (Tables 22 and 23). Some lactic acid is produced by most parasites studied, with the exception of the bloodstream form of the pathogenic trypanosomes. These latter, contrary to the views expressed by von Fenyvessy and Reiner (1924, 1928) and Geiger, Kligler, and Comaroff (1930) definitely do not produce this acid. Termite flagellates may be another exception, although Hungate (1943b) found some lactic acid at least in one experiment. It is possible that the various species constituting the complex intestinal fauna of termites may be meta-

TABLE 22.  Organic endproducts of aerobic and anaerobic fermentations of parasitic protozoa (essentially after von Brand, 1950)

| SPECIES | CONDITION | PYRUVIC ACID | LACTIC ACID | FORMIC ACID | ACETIC ACID | OXALIC ACID | SUCCINIC ACID | ETHYL ALCOHOL | GLYCEROL | AUTHOR |
|---|---|---|---|---|---|---|---|---|---|---|
| Termite flagellates | Anaerobic | x? | x | x | x | | | | | Hungate (1939, 1943b) |
| Leishmania brasiliensis, L. donovani, L. tropica, culture forms | Aerobic | | | | | | x | | | Chang (1948); Fulton and Joyner (1949) |
| Trypanosoma lewisi, bloodstream form | Aerobic | x | | x | x | | x | x | | Reiner, Smythe, and Pedlow (1936) |
| | Anaerobic | x | | | x | | x | x | | |
| T. cruzi, culture form | Aerobic | x | | x | | | x | | | Chang (1948) |
| T. equiperdum, T. hippicum, bloodstream form | Aerobic | x | | | | x | | | | Reiner, Smythe, and Pedlow (1936); Harvey (1949) |
| | Anaerobic | x | | | | x | | | x | |
| T. brucei, bloodstream form | Aerobic | x | x | | | | | | | Glowazky (1937) |
| | Anaerobic | x | | | | | | | x | |
| T. rhodesiense, bloodstream form | Aerobic | x | x | x | x | | x | x | x | Fulton and Stevens (1945) |
| Trichomonas foetus | Anaerobic | x | x | | | | x | | | Suzuoki and Suzuoki (1951) |
| Plasmodium gallinaceum | Aerobic | x | x | | x | | x | | | Silverman, et al. (1944); Speck, Moulder, and Evans (1946) |
| | Anaerobic | x | x | | | | | | | |
| P. knowlesi | Aerobic | x | x | | | | | | | Wendel (1943); McKee et al. (1946) |

bolically different. Among the worms, *Fasciola hepatica* is not listed as having lactic acid as an endproduct. It should be realized, however, that this acid was not looked for and may well be excreted.

Quantitatively, lactic acid accounts for at least 80% of the anaerobically utilized carbohydrate in *Litomosoides carinii*, *Schistosoma mansoni*, and *Dracunculus insignis* (Bueding, 1949a, 1950; Bueding and Oliver-Gonzalez, 1950), and for practically 100% in the case of *Plasmodium gallinaceum* (Silverman *et al.*, 1944). In the above worms, and also in malarial parasites, lactic acid is nearly, but not quite, as prominent an endproduct of the aerobic fermentations.

On the contrary, in several parasitic worms lactic acid accounts only for a much smaller fraction of the metabolized carbohydrate; in *Ascaris lumbricoides* for about 2% anaerobically and 1% aerobically (von Brand, 1934); in *Moniezia expansa* for about 16% anaerobically (von Brand, 1933a). It does seem probable that in these instances the conditions under which the experiments are conducted are important. Fischer (1924) relates that living *Parascaris equorum* produced but little lactic acid while quite large amounts were formed upon using minced material.

It is of considerable interest that not all parasites produce the same type of lactic acid. It has been found that it is (D,L)-lactic acid in the case of *Schistosoma mansoni*, while in incubates of *Litomosoides carinii* L(+)-lactic acid accumulates (Bueding, 1949a, b).

Pyruvic acid is the most important endproduct of the aerobic fermentation of the bloodstream form of several African pathogenic trypanosomes, accounting for nearly the total carbohydrate consumed in such forms as *Trypanosoma equiperdum*, *T. evansi*, or *T. hippicum* (Reiner, Smythe, and Pedlow, 1936; Marshall, 1948b; Harvey, 1949) while in *Trypanosoma rhodesiense* and *Trypanosoma lewisi* succinic acid predominates (Fulton and Stevens, 1945; Reiner, Smythe, and Pedlow, 1936). In incubates of the latter species no pyruvic acid accumulates. Whether the culture form of *Leishmania donovani* produces pyruvic acid is questionable; Chang (1948) found it but Fulton and Joyner (1949) were unable to verify this finding. In this case succinic acid again seems to be the most important endproduct quantitatively. Pyruvic acid did not seem to accumulate in media in which helminths were kept either under aerobic or anaerobic conditions.

In several worms, and in the case of the larval *Gasterophilus*, fatty acids predominate. They may either be volatile fatty acids, as in *Ascaris*, or chiefly higher fatty acids, as in *Fasciola*, *Moniezia*, and *Gasterophilus*. The view that fermentative processes of animal tissues lead to the formation of fatty acids rather than lactic acid has been doubted. The chief arguments were: 1. In minced *Parascaris* material large amounts of lactic acid are formed (Fischer, 1924). 2. In saline in which ascarids had been kept and

TABLE 23.   Organic acids produced by parasitic worms and arthropods (essentially after von Brand, 1950)

| SPECIES | CONDITION | LACTIC ACID | FORMIC ACID | ACETIC ACID | PROPIONIC ACID | BUTYRIC ACID | VALERIC ACID | CAPROIC ACID | HIGHER FATTY ACIDS | SUCCINIC ACID | AUTHOR |
|---|---|---|---|---|---|---|---|---|---|---|---|
| **HELMINTHS** | | | | | | | | | | | |
| *Schistosoma mansoni* | Aerobic | x | | | | | | | | | Bueding, Peters, and Waite (1947) |
| | Anaerobic | x | | | | | | | | | |
| *Fasciola hepatica* | Anaerobic | | | | | x | | | x | | Flury and Leeb (1926); Weinland and von Brand (1926); Stephenson (1947b) |
| *Moniezia expansa* | Aerobic | x | | | | | | | x | | Alt and Tischer (1931); von Brand (1933a) |
| | Anaerobic | x | | | | | | | x | x | |
| *Echinococcus granulosus* | ? (*in situ*) | | | x | x | | x | | x | x | Flössner (1924, 1925); Coutelen (1931) |
| *Parascaris equorum* | Aerobic | x | | | x | | x | | | | Fischer (1924); Toryu (1936) |
| | Anaerobic | x | | | x | | x | | | | |
| *Ascaris lumbricoides* | Aerobic | x | x? | x | x | x | x | x | | | Weinland (1904); Flury (1912); von Brand (1934); Oesterlin (1937); Epps, Weiner, and Bueding (1950); Bueding and Yale (1951) |
| | Anaerobic | x | x? | | x | x | x | x | | | |
| *Litomosoides carinii* | Aerobic | x | | x | | | | | | | Bueding (1949a) |
| | Anaerobic | x | | x | | | | | | | |

| | | | | | | | References |
|---|---|---|---|---|---|---|---|
| *Dracunculus insignis* | Aerobic | x | | | | | Bueding(1949c); Bueding and Oliver-Gonzalez (1950) |
| | Anaerobic | x | | | | | |
| ARTHROPODS | | | | | | | |
| *Gasterophilus intestinalis*, larvae | Anaerobic | x | | | | x | von Kemnitz (1916); Blanchard and Dinulescu (1932) |

to which sugar had been added a bacterial flora developed which produced lower fatty acids (Slater, 1925). Clearly, however, the main reason for rejecting the theory of fatty acid fermentation and explaining the appearance of the acids by bacterial action was theoretical, the unwillingness to concede that in invertebrate tissues metabolic pathways may exist that are different from those prevailing in vertebrate tissues (Slater, 1928).

Beginning with Weinland (1901) the proponents of the fatty acid theory relied chiefly upon the following arguments, recently summarized by Bueding (1949b): 1. Worms of the same habitat but of different species produce different metabolic endproducts, although they presumably carry the same bacterial flora. 2. Higher fatty acids can be demonstrated by morphological methods within the excretory system of *Fasciola* and *Moniezia*, while lower fatty acids are found in the body fluid of *Ascaris*. 3. The fatty acids are demonstrable in nonnutritive media hardly conducive for bacterial development. 4. Extracts of *Ascaris* to which antiseptics had been added still produced volatile fatty acids. 5. The production rate of fatty acids does not increase with increasing length of incubation time as should be expected if a bacterial population is building up.

The controversy was recently unequivocally decided. Epps, Weiner, and Bueding (1950) succeeded in sterilizing specimens of *Ascaris lumbricoides* by means of antibiotics and found that these worms did produce lower fatty acids, the main fraction consisting of an acid or an isomeric mixture of acids containing five carbon atoms.

The chemical nature of the higher fatty acids produced has not yet been elucidated. In so far as the lower fatty acids produced by *Parascaris* and *Ascaris* are concerned, valeric acid is the most important from a quantitative standpoint, so much so in fact that the total acidity of the medium is customarily expressed as valeric acid. What isomer is produced has been a matter of some controversy. Waechter (1934) considered it as normal valeric acid, Flury (1912) as isovaleric acid, and Krueger (1936) as methyl ethyl acetic acid. Working with the excreta of sterile worms, Bueding (personal communication) found that about 50% of the five carbon acids consisted of racemic methyl ethyl acetic acid, while at most traces of isovaleric acid were present.

An interesting question that cannot yet be answered definitely in every case is whether identical or different endproducts appear during aerobic and anaerobic fermentations of a given species. In certain cases differences certainly do exist. In *Plasmodium knowlesi* no anaerobic formation of pyruvic acid takes place (Wendel and Kimball, 1942). In trypanosomes of the *brucei* group (Table 22) glycerol appears only in the absence of oxygen simply because it is further oxidized in the presence of that gas. A definite difference has also been found in *Litomosoides* where acetylmethyl carbinol has been found only among the aerobic endproducts (Bert and Bueding, according to Bueding, 1949b), if the medium contained glucose. In the presence of acetaldehyde or pyruvate, however, the compound was formed both aerobically and anaerobically (Soll and Bueding, personal communication). Whether, on the other hand, the differences implied by the figures of Table 23 in respect to ascarids are real, cannot be stated with any degree of accuracy. So far no comparative study of this problem with uniform methods has been carried out with these species.

Quantitative differences also occur, both as to the total amounts of partially oxidized endproducts and as to the proportions between various components. *Ascaris* thus produced anaerobically 0.22 gm valeric acid and 0.02 gm lactic acid per 100 gm animal in 24 hours whereas the corresponding aerobic figures were 0.16 and 0.01 gm respectively (von Brand, 1934), and *Litomosoides* produced about three times more acetic acid aerobically than anaerobically (Bueding, 1949a).

## V. INTERMEDIATE CARBOHYDRATE METABOLISM

The elucidation of the intermediate steps involved in the carbohydrate metabolism of parasites has begun to attract investigators only in very recent years. The problem will unquestionably remain a fruitful field of reasearch for many years to come.

The intimate mechanism of carbohydrate utilization can be divided into two parts, the anaerobic Embden-Meyerhof scheme and the aerobic Krebs' cycle. Both are composed of a series of reactions mediated by specific enzymes and many of the steps require the participation of one or more cofactors.

The Embden-Meyerhof sequence, the glycolytic chain of processes, operates both in aerobic and anaerobic environments. In classic cases it leads to pyruvic and lactic acids. It is illustrated in Fig. 9 showing that the initial steps are slightly different whether glycogen or glucose are being utilized. Corresponding differences will probably occur in parasites also, chiefly depending upon whether they utilize an endogenous or exogenous source of carbohydrate. A detailed theoretical discussion of the various steps of the glycolytic chain cannot be presented here; the reader is referred for further information to such books as those of Work and Work (1948) or Baldwin (1949).

Those steps of the glycolytic chain that have been found to occur in parasites are shown in Table 24. The methods employed in arriving at these results were essentially of two kinds, either (1) a study of the occurrence of intermediates of the cycle within the body of parasites or in incubates, studies sometimes helped along by the use of inhibitors leading to a piling up of certain intermediates, or (2) enzymatic studies, that is, investigations concerning the capabilities of a certain parasite to transform one intermediate into another. In evaluating the data of Table 24 it should be realized that an x sign opposite a certain enzyme only denotes that a given catalytic reaction characteristic for the specified enzyme has been found. It is not intended to imply that this catalytic activity is due to enzymes being identical in every respect in all cases. Indeed, this is not even likely. It is well known that, for example, yeast and muscle hexokinase have definitely different properties. Keeping this point in mind it can be said that at least the initial and intermediate steps of the anaerobic sugar degradation of trypanosomes and malarial parasites, as well as of helminths,

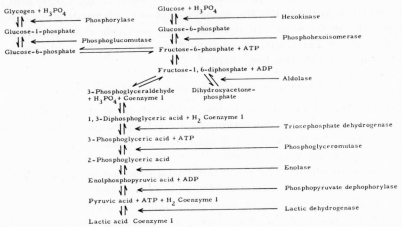

Fig. 9.   The anaerobic phase of sugar degradation (Embden-Meyerhof sequence)

follow the classical Embden-Meyerhof sequence rather closely. No information is as yet available for endoparasitic arthropods.

It should be noted especially that these recent studies have clearly demonstrated the occurrence of phosphorylations, an important point because it is a well established fact that phosphorylations are of the greatest importance in the energy transfer during cellular metabolism. Their occurrence in trypanosomes and malarial parasites had been doubted by some of the earlier workers (Reiner, Smythe, and Pedlow, 1936; Christophers and Fulton, 1938).

Certain deviations of the classical anaerobic scheme are possible, however, and some have been found in parasites. Under aerobic conditions oxygen may enter the sequence essentially at one point, the oxidation of phosphoglyceraldehyde. In that case oxygen acts as the final hydrogen acceptor instead of the latter being transferred *via* reduced coenzyme I to pyruvic acid forming lactic acid. This, according to our present knowledge, is the only place where oxygen enters the sequence in the case of those trypanosomes that break sugar down only to the pyruvate stage (Marshall, 1948b); the process may in this case well be mediated through DPN and flavo enzymes.

Another variation involves the production of glycerol. It accumulates in anaerobic incubates of *Trypanosoma equiperdum*, *T. hippicum*, and *T. brucei*, but also in aerobic incubates of *T. rhodesiense* (Table 22). Its exact mode of formation has not yet been established, but it does seem likely that it is derived from one of the triose compounds. In yeast, for example, phosphoglyceraldehyde serves as hydrogen acceptor for the reoxidation of reduced coenzyme I when the normal acceptor is blocked, the reaction yielding one molecule of phosphoglycerol for each molecule of phosphoglyceric acid formed, a phosphatase then splitting phosphoglycerol. Since the above anaerobically-kept trypanosomes do not have lactic dehydrogenase, pyruvic acid cannot act as hydrogen acceptor in the absence of oxygen, and the occurrence of this or a similar mechanism would seem logical.

The terminal steps of the glycolytic chain are more varied in parasites than in vertebrate material as the previously-discussed endproducts of aerobic and anaerobic fermentations indicate, but very little is so far known about the chemical steps involved in their formation. The only well-understood process is the anaerobic dismutation of 2 moles of pyruvic acid to 1 mole lactic acid, 1 mole acetic acid and 1 mole of carbon dioxide, a process observed by Bueding (1949a) in *Litomosoides*. The mechanism of fatty acid formation in ascarids, tapeworms, and other forms has not yet been elucidated experimentally. Jost (1928) has presented a theoretical formulation for the valeric acid production of *Ascaris* suggesting that lactic, pyruvic, propionic, and γ-hydroxyvaleric acids are intermediates. Future studies will have to show whether this mechanism is more than a theoretical construction. The appearance of a variety of fatty acids in the excreta of the worm may suggest a rather complex situation.

The second phase of sugar degradation, the so-called Krebs' or "tricarboxylic acid cycle," cannot proceed in the absence of oxygen; it is consequently of importance only in aerobic organisms. It consists essentially of a series of oxidative reactions (Fig. 10) during which much more energy is released than during the glycolytic processes of the Embden-Meyerhof sequence. The essence of the Krebs' cycle is the complete oxidation of pyruvic acid to carbon dioxide and water by a cyclic series of reactions. These reactions involve the condensation of a two-carbon derivative of pyruvic acid ("acetyl") with oxaloacetic acid to form tricarboxylic, then dicarboxylic acids and completing the cycle with the regeneration of oxaloacetic acid. The cycle can, therefore, proceed as long as pyruvic acid is

TABLE 24. Anaerobic phase of glucose utilization in parasites (essentially after von Brand, 1950)

EMBDEN-MEYERHOF SCHEME OF GLUCOSE BREAKDOWN

| Step (pathway intermediates and enzymes) | Trypanosoma evansi (1) | Trypanosoma hippicum (2) | Trypanosoma equiperdum (3) | Plasmodium gallinaceum (4, 5) | Plasmodium knowlesi (6) | Schistosoma mansoni (7) | Hymenolepis diminuta (8) |
|---|---|---|---|---|---|---|---|
| Glucose |  |  |  |  |  |  |  |
|   ↓ Hexokinase |  | X |  | X |  | X |  |
| Glucose-6-phosphate | X |  |  |  |  |  |  |
|   ↓ Phosphohexoisomerase |  |  |  |  |  |  | X |
| Fructose-6-phosphate |  | X |  | X |  |  |  |
|   ↓ Phosphohexokinase | X |  |  | X |  |  |  |
| Fructose-1,6-diphosphate | X | X | X | X |  |  |  |
|   ↓ Aldolase |  | X | X | X |  | X | X |
| Phosphoglyceraldehyde ⇌ Dihydroxyacetone phosphate |  |  |  |  |  |  |  |
|   ↓ Triosephosphate-dehydrogenase |  | X | X | X |  | X | X |
| Phosphoglyceric acid | X | X | X | X |  |  |  |
|   ↓ Enolase |  |  |  | X |  |  |  |
| Phosphopyruvic acid | X |  |  | X |  |  |  |

Pyruvic acid ⟶ Phosphopyruvate-dephosphorylase

| | | | | | | |
|---|---|---|---|---|---|---|
| x | x | | x | x | | |
| | | | | x | x | |
| | | | | x | x | x |

Lactic acid ⟶ Lactic dehydrogenase

(1) Marshall (1948b); (2) Harvey (1949); (3) Chen and Geiling (1946); (4) Speck and Evans (1945); (5) Marshall (1948a); (6) McKee *et al.* (1946); (7) Bueding (1949b); (8) Read (1949).

fed into the sequence. It is obvious, however, that the tricarboxylic acid cycle is not exclusively linked to the carbohydrate metabolism. Pyruvate

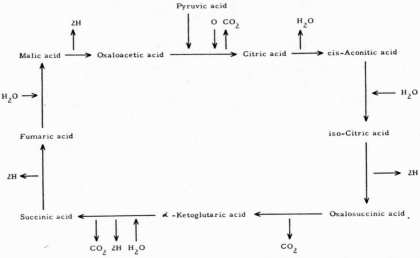

Fig. 10.  The aerobic phase of sugar degradation (Krebs' or tricarboxylic acid cycle).  See Krebs (1943) and Lorber *et al.* (1950) for details.

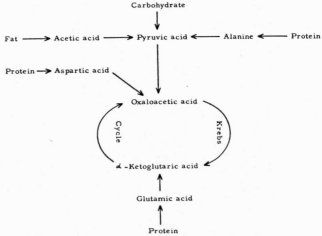

Fig. 11.  Connections between carbohydrate, protein, and fat metabolism established by the Krebs' cycle.

can originate from fatty acids *via* acetoacetate and acetate and also from alanine, that is, an amino acid. Furthermore, other intermediates of the cycle can be formed and enter the cycle at their proper places. Thus oxaloacetate can be formed by carbon dioxide fixation from pyruvic acid and by oxidative deamination or transamination of aspartate and similarly

$\alpha$-ketoglutarate by deamination or transamination from glutamate. The Krebs' cycle then represents a metabolic sequence where carbohydrate,

TABLE 25.  Utilization of intermediates of the Krebs cycle by parasites (essentially after von Brand, 1950)

| SPECIES | PYRUVATE | OXALOACETATE | CITRATE | cis-ACONITATE | α-KETOGLUTARATE | SUCCINATE | FUMARATE | MALATE | AUTHOR |
|---|---|---|---|---|---|---|---|---|---|
| **PROTOZOA** | | | | | | | | | |
| Trichomonas hepatica.... | — | | | | | — | | | Willems, Massart, and Peeters (1942) |
| T. foetus............... | (x) | — | | | | — | (x) | (x) | Suzuoki and Suzuoki (1951) |
| Trypanosoma evansi..... | (x) | | | | | — | — | | Marshall (1948b) |
| T. hippicum............ | — | — | | | | — | — | — | Harvey (1949) |
| T. lewisi............... | (x) | | | | (x) | (x) | (x) | — | Moulder (1948a) |
| Plasmodium gallinaceum. | x | x | (x) | x | x | x | x | x | Speck, Moulder, and Evans (1946) |
| P. lophurae............ | x | | | | | x | x | | Bovarnick, Lindsay, and Hellerman (1946) |
| **HELMINTHS** | | | | | | | | | |
| Fasciola hepatica........ | | | — | | | x | | x | Pennoit-DeCooman and van Grembergen (1942) |
| Moniezia benedeni....... | | | — | | | x | | x | Pennoit-DeCooman and van Grembergen (1942); van Grembergen (1944) |
| Cysticercus pisiformis... | | | | | | x | * | | Pennoit-DeCooman (1940) |
| Nematodirus spp........ | x | x | | | x | x | x | x | Massey and Rogers (1949, 1950) |
| Ascaridia galli.......... | x | x | | | x | x | x | x | Massey and Rogers (1949, 1950) |
| Neoaplectana glaseri..... | x | x | | | x | x | x | x | Massey and Rogers (1949, 1950) |

x = Compound utilized at significant rate; (x) = Compound utilized at insignificant rate; — = Compound not used.
* = Indirect proof for fumarase found.

fat, and protein metabolism meet. The more important of these connections are shown in diagrammatic form in Fig. 11.

The question whether parasites have a Krebs' cycle has been studied only recently and our knowledge is still quite fragmentary. The evidence available is summarized in Table 25. It has been gathered essentially by two methods. The first consists in studying whether intermediates of the cycle are being utilized, the criterion being whether these compounds increase the oxygen consumption. The second method is a search for the specific dehydrogenases catalyzing the various steps; the speed of decolorization of methylene blue in Thunberg experiments is used here as an index.

It is evident that the situation differs in different parasites. There is no indication that *Trichomonas hepatica*, *T. foetus*, or the bloodstream form of trypanosomes possess even an incomplete Krebs' cycle and the question is still open in so far as the large helminths are concerned. On the other hand, the malarial parasites and the small nematodes listed in Table 25 have a well developed cycle. It is not yet certain whether, or to what extent, it corresponds in its details to that occurring in vertebrates. Massey and Rogers (1949, 1950) observed that malonate inhibits the oxygen consumption of nematode mince much less than that of pigeon breast muscle and it seems that in the former succinate oxidation is less important than in the latter.

Another important question which can, however, be answered still less definitely than that concerning the Krebs' cycle, is the question of carbon dioxide fixation. The significance of this process during the intermediate metabolism of various organisms becomes increasingly obvious as the years go by. It has thus been shown, to give only one example, that during the fermentation of glycerol by propionic acid bacteria, pyruvic acid condenses with carbon dioxide to form oxaloacetic acid which in turn is reduced to succinic acid. It is not impossible that a similar process may occur in trypanosomes where, as mentioned above, succinic acid is formed in some cases but where no Krebs' cycle has been found. Direct evidence for carbon dioxide fixation is rather meager, however. Searle and Reiner (1940, 1941) reported a stimulation of the aerobic metabolism of *Trypanosoma lewisi* by carbon dioxide and an actual carbon dioxide fixation under anaerobic conditions. Moulder (1948a), on the other hand, could not verify this finding in so far as the aerobic metabolism of this flagellate is concerned. He does not deny the possibility that carbon dioxide fixation occurs. There is still less known about helminths in this respect. The only suggestive observation was made by Rogers and Lazarus (1949) who found a greater decrease in bicarbonate content of the medium than could be explained by acid formation during anaerobic incubation of *Nematodirus* and *Ascaridia*.

## VI. Energetics of Parasitic Fermentations

Any incomplete oxidation is uneconomical since part of the energy potentially available for liberation through complete oxidation remains unutilized in the endproducts. This is illustrated by the following examples taken from Porter (1946).

1. Complete aerobic oxidation:

$$C_6H_{12}O_6 + 6O_2 \rightarrow 6CO_2 + 6H_2O + 674 \text{ kg cal}$$

2. Aerobic fermentation:

$$2C_6H_{12}O_6 + 9O_2 \rightarrow 6C_2H_2O_4 + 6H_2O + 493 \text{ kg cal}$$
(Oxalic acid)

3. Anaerobic fermentations:

$$C_6H_{12}O_6 \rightarrow 2C_3H_6O_3 + 22.5 \text{ kg cal}$$
(Lactic acid)

$$C_6H_{12}O_6 \rightarrow 2C_2H_6O + 2CO_2 + 22 \text{ kg cal}$$
(Ethyl alcohol)

$$C_6H_{12}O_6 \rightarrow 3C_2H_4O_2 + 15 \text{ kg cal}$$
(Acetic acid)

Very little is known so far concerning the actual energy production of parasitic fermentations. Harvey (1949) has estimated that the overall metabolism of *Trypanosoma hippicum*, which is characterized by aerobic fermentations, liberates less than 15% of the available energy from the metabolized glucose.

Krummacher (1919) determined the heat produced by *Ascaris* but his data are difficult to evaluate since his experiments were conducted under conditions that were neither clearly aerobic or clearly anaerobic. Meier (1931), working with the same parasite, found an anaerobic heat production of 0.300 gm cal/gm worm/hour and he estimates the energy yield of the fermentation as 22%. This value is unquestionably much too high (von Brand and Jahn, 1942) since he uses for his calculations Weinland's (1901) figures on glycogen consumption, figures derived from experiments lasting much longer than his own. This must have caused a rather considerable error since the glycogen consumption of *Ascaris* decreases as the experimental periods increases in length.

## LITERATURE

Andrews, J., and von Brand, T. (1938). *Am. J. Hyg.* **28:** 138–147.
Alt, H. L., and Tischer, O. A. (1931). *Proc. Soc. Exptl. Biol. Med.* **29:** 222–224.
Armer, J. M. (1944). *J. Parasitol.* **30:** 131–142.
Baldwin, E. (1949). Dynamic Aspects of Biochemistry, University Press, Cambridge, England.
Ball, E. G., McKee, R. W., Anfinsen, C. B., Cruz, W. O., and Geiman, Q. M. (1948). *J. Biol. Chem.* **175:** 547–571.
Blacklock, D. B., Gordon, R. M., and Fine, J. (1930). *Ann. Trop. Med. Parasitol.* **24:** 5–54.
Blanchard, L., and Dinulescu, G. (1932). *Compt. rend. soc. biol.* **110:** 343–344.
Bovarnick, M. R., Lindsay, A., and Hellerman, L. (1946). *J. Biol. Chem.* **163:** 523–533.

von Brand, T. (1932). *Z. Parasitenk.* **4:** 753–775.

von Brand, T. (1933a). *Z. vergleich. Physiol.* **18:** 562–596.

von Brand, T. (1933b). *Z. vergleich. Physiol.* **19:** 587–614.

von Brand, T. (1934). *Z. vergleich. Physiol.* **21:** 220–235.

von Brand, T. (1940). *J. Parasitol.* **26:** 301–307.

von Brand, T. (1946). Anaerobiosis in Invertebrates. Biodynamica Monograph No. 4, Biodynamica, Normandy, Missouri.

von Brand, T. (1950). *J. Parasitol.* **36:** 178–192.

von Brand, T., Baernstein, H. D., and Mehlman, B. (1950). *Biol. Bull.* **98:** 266–276.

von Brand, T., and Jahn, T. (1942). *In* Christie, J. R., An Introduction to Nematology. Section 2, Part 2, pp. 356–371. Chitwood, Babylon, N. Y.

von Brand, T., and Simpson, W. F. (1944). *J. Parasitol.* **30:** 121–129.

von Brand, T., and Simpson, W. F. (1945). *Proc. Soc. Exptl. Biol. Med.* **60:** 368–371.

von Brand, T., and Tobie, E. J. (1948). *J. Cellular Comp. Physiol.* **31:** 49–68.

von Brand, T., Tobie, E. J., Kissling, R. E., and Adams, G. (1949). *J. Infectious Diseases* **85:** 5–16.

Braune, R. (1914). *Arch. Protistenk.* **32:** 111–116.

Bueding, E. (1948). *Ann. N. Y. Acad. Sci.* **50:** 115–116.

Bueding, E. (1949a). *J. Exptl. Med.* **89:** 107–130.

Bueding, E. (1949b). *Physiol. Revs.* **29:** 195–218.

Bueding, E. (1949c). *Federation Proc.* **8:** 188–189.

Bueding, E. (1950). *J. Gen. Physiol.* **33:** 475–495.

Bueding, E., and Oliver-Gonzalez, J. (1950). *British J. Pharmacol.* **5:** 62–64.

Bueding, E., Peters, L., and Waite, J. F. (1947). *Proc. Soc. Exptl. Biol. Med.* **64:** 111–113.

Bueding, E., Peters, L., and Welch, A. D. (1947). *Federation Proc.* **6:** 313.

Bueding, E., and Yale, H. W. (1951). *Federation Proc.* **10:** 168.

Cailleau, R. (1937). *Ann. inst. Pasteur* **59:** 137–172.

Califano, L., and Gritti, P. (1930). *Riv. patol. sper.* **5:** 9–15.

Chang, S. L. (1948). *J. Infectious Diseases* **82:** 109–116.

Chen, G., and Geiling, E. M. K. (1946). *Proc. Soc. Exptl. Biol. Med.* **63:** 486–487.

Chen, G., and Geiling, E. M. K. (1945). *J. Infectious Diseases* **77:** 139–143.

Christophers, S. R., and Fulton, J. D. (1938). *Ann. Trop. Med. Parasitol.* **82:** 43–75.

Cleary, M. B. (1948). Dissertation, Catholic University of America, Washington, D. C.

Cleveland, L. R. (1924). *Biol. Bull.* **46:** 177–225.

Cleveland, L. R. (1925a). *Biol. Bull.* **48:** 289–293.

Cleveland, L. R. (1925b). *Biol. Bull.* **48:** 309–326.

Colas-Belcour, J., and Lwoff, A. (1925). *Compt. rend. soc. biol.* **93:** 1421–1422.

Cole, B. A. (1950). *Proc. Helminthol. Soc. Wash.* **17:** 65–74.

Cook, S. F. (1932). *Biol. Bull.* **63:** 246–257.

Cook, S. F. (1943). *Physiol. Zoöl.* **16:** 123–128.

Cook, S. F., and Smith, R. E. (1942). *J. Cellular Comp. Physiol.* **19:** 211–219.

Coutelen, F. R. (1931). *Ann. parasitol. humaine et comparée* **9:** 97–100.

Dogiel, V. A. (1925). *Trav. soc. naturalistes Leningrad* **54:** 67–93 (not seen).

Enigk, K. (1938). *Z. Parasitenk.* **10:** 386–414.

Epps, W., Weiner, M., and Bueding, E. (1950). *J. Infectious Diseases* **87:** 149–151.

Fauré-Fremiet, E. (1913). *Arch. anat. microscop.* **15:** 435–757.

von Fenyvessy, B., and Reiner, L. (1924). *Z. Hyg. Infektionskrankh.* **102:** 109–119.

von Fenyvessy, B., and Reiner, L. (1928). *Biochem. Z.* **202:** 75–80.

Fischer, A. (1924). *Biochem. Z.* **144:** 224–228.

Flössner, O. (1924). *Z. Biol.* **80:** 255–260.

Flössner, O. (1925). *Z. Biol.* **82:** 297–301.

Flury, F. (1912). *Arch. exptl. Path. Pharmakol.* **67:** 275–392.

Flury, F., and Leeb, F. (1926). *Klin. Wochschr.* **5:** 2054–2055.

Fulton, J. D. (1939). *Ann. Trop. Med. Parasitol.* **33:** 217–227.

Fulton, J. D., and Joyner, L. P. (1949). *Trans. Roy. Soc. Trop. Med. Hyg.* **43:** 273–286.

Fulton, J. D., and Stevens, T. S. (1945). *Biochem. J.* **39:** 317–320.

Geiger, A., Kligler, I. J., and Comaroff, R. (1930). *Ann. Trop. Med. Parasitol.* **24:** 319–327.

Gilmour, D. (1940). *Biol. Bull.* **79:** 297–308.

Glaessner, K. (1908). *Zentr. Bakt. Parasitenk. Abt. I. Orig.* **47:** 351–362.

Glowazky, F. (1937). *Z. Hyg. Infektionskrankh.* **119:** 740–752.

van Grembergen, G. (1944). *Enzymologia* **11:** 268–281.

Harnisch, O. (1932). *Z. vergleich. Physiol.* **17:** 365–386.

Harnisch, O. (1947). *Biol. Zentr.* **66:** 179–185.

Harvey, S. C. (1949). *J. Biol. Chem.* **179:** 435–453.

Hellerman, L. (1947). Transactions of the 2nd Conference on Biological Antioxidants, pp. 78–92. Josiah Macy, Jr. Foundation, New York.

Hopkins, C. A. (1950). *J. Parasitol.* **36:** 384–390.

Hopkins, D. L., and Warner, K. L. (1946). *J. Parasitol.* **32:** 175–189.

Hungate, R. E. (1939). *Ecology* **20:** 230–245.

Hungate, R. E. (1942). *Biol. Bull.* **83:** 303–319.

Hungate, R. E. (1943a). *Biol. Bull.* **84:** 157–163.

Hungate, R. E. (1943b). *Ann. Entomol. Soc. Am.* **36:** 730–739.

von Issekutz, B. (1933). *Arch. exptl. Path. Pharmakol.* **173:** 479–498.

Ivanov, I. I., and Jakovlev, G. (1943). *Biokhimyia* **8:** 229–233.

Jost, H. (1928). *In* Bethe's Handbuch der normalen und pathologischen Physiologie. Vol. 5, pp. 377–466. Springer, Berlin.

von Kemnitz, G. (1914). *Verhandl. deut. zool. Ges.* **24:** 294–307.

von Kemnitz, G. (1916). *Z. Biol.* **67:** 129–244.

Kligler, I. J. (1926). *Trans. Roy. Soc. Trop. Med. Hyg.* **19:** 330–335.

Kobert, R. (1903). *Arch. ges. Physiol.* **99:** 116–186.

Krebs, H. A. (1943). *Advances in Enzymol.* **3:** 191–252.

Krijgsman, B. J. (1936a). *Natuurw. Tijdschr.* (Belg.) **18:** 237–241.

Krijgsman, B. J. (1936b). *Z. vergleich. Physiol.* **23:** 663–711.

Krueger, F. (1936). *Zool. Jahrb. Abt. allg. Zool.* **57:** 1–56.

Krummacher, O. (1919). *Z. Biol.* **69:** 293–321.

Kudicke, R., and Evers, E. (1924). *Z. Hyg. Infektionskrankh.* **101:** 317–326.

Lorber, V., Utter, M. F., Rudney, H., and Cook, M. (1950). *J. Biol. Chem.* **185:** 689–699.

Maier, J., and Coggeshall, L. T. (1941). *J. Infectious Diseases* **69:** 87–96.

Mannozzi-Torini, M. (1938). *Boll. ist. sieroterap. milan.* **17:** 830–838.

Manwell, R. D., and Feigelson, P. (1949). *Proc. Soc. Exptl. Biol. Med.* **70:** 578–582.

Margolin, S. (1930). *Biol. Bull.* **59:** 301–305.

Markov, G. S. (1939). *Compt. rend. acad. sci. U.R.S.S.* **25:** 93–96.

Marshall, P. B. (1948a). *Brit. J. Pharmacol.* **3:** 1–7.

Marshall, P. B. (1948b). *Brit. J. Pharmacol.* **3:** 8–14.

Massey, V., and Rogers, W. P. (1949). *Nature* **163:** 909.

Massey, V., and Rogers, W. P. (1950). *Australian J. Sci. Research* **B3:** 251–264.

McKee, R. W., Ormsbee, R. A., Anfinsen, C. B., Geiman, Q. M., and Ball, E. G. (1946). *J. Exptl. Med.* **84:** 569–582.

124     CHEMICAL PHYSIOLOGY OF ENDOPARASITIC ANIMALS

Meier, W. (1931). *Z. Biol.* **91:** 459–474.
Mercado, T. I. (1947). Unpublished Master's Thesis, Catholic University of America, Washington, D. C.
Morita, Y. (1938). *J. Oriental Med.* **28:** 38 (English summary).
Moulder, J. W. (1948a). *J. Infectious Diseases* **83:** 33–41.
Moulder, J. W. (1948b). *J. Infectious Diseases* **83:** 42–49.
Noguchi, H. (1926). *J. Exptl. Med.* **44:** 327–337.
Oesterlin, M. (1937). *Z. vergleich. Physiol.* **25:** 88–91.
Pennoit-DeCooman, E. (1940). *Ann. soc. roy. zool. Belg.* **71:** 76–77.
Pennoit-DeCooman, E., and van Grembergen, G. (1942). *Verhandel. Koninkl. Vlaam. Acad. Wetenschap., Belg. Klasse Wetenschap.* **4:** No. 6: 7–77.
Plastridge, W. N. (1943). *J. Bact.* **45:** 196–197.
Plunkett, A. (1946). Unpublished Master's Thesis, Catholic University of America, Washington, D. C.
Porter, J. R. (1946). Bacterial Chemistry and Physiology. Wiley, New York.
Read, C. P. (1949). *J. Parasitol.* **35** Suppl.: 26–27.
Regendanz, P. (1930). *Zentr. Bakt. Parasitenk. Abt. I. Orig.* **118:** 175–186.
Reichenow, E. (1937). *Compt. rend. 12th congr. intern. zool., Lisbonne 1935,* **3:** 1955–1968.
Reid, W. M. (1942). *J. Parasitol.* **28:** 319–340.
Reid, W. M. (1945). *J. Parasitol.* **31:** 406–410.
Reiner, L., Smythe, C. V., and Pedlow, J. T. (1936). *J. Biol. Chem.* **113:** 75–88.
Rogers, W. P. (1940). *J. Helminthol.* **18:** 143–154.
Rogers, W. P., and Lazarus, M. (1949). *Parasitology* **39:** 302–314.
Roy, D. N. (1937). *Parasitology* **29:** 150–162.
Schimmelpfennig, G. (1903). *Arch. wiss. u. prakt. Tierheilk.* **29:** 332–376.
Schulte, H. (1917). *Arch. ges. Physiol.* **166:** 1–44.
Schulze, P. (1924). *Z. Morphol. Ökol. Tiere* **2:** 643–666.
Searle, D. S., and Reiner, L. (1940). *Proc. Soc. Exptl. Biol. Med.* **43:** 80–82.
Searle, D. S., and Reiner, L. (1941). *J. Biol. Chem.,* **141:** 563–572.
Silverman, M., Ceithaml, J., Taliaferro, L. G., and Evans, E. A. (1944). *J. Infectious Diseases* **75:** 212–230.
Slater, W. K. (1925). *Biochem. J.* **19:** 604–610.
Slater, W. K. (1928). *Biol. Revs.* **3:** 303–328.
Smyth, J. D. (1946a). *J. Exptl. Biol.* **23:** 47–70.
Smyth, J. D. (1946b). *Parasitology* **38:** 173–181.
Speck, J. F., and Evans, E. A. (1945). *J. Biol. Chem.* **159:** 71–81.
Speck, J. F., Moulder, J. W., and Evans, E. A. (1946). *J. Biol. Chem.* **164:** 119–144.
Stannard, J. N., McCoy, O. R., and Latchford, W. B. (1938). *Am. J. Hyg.* **27:** 666–682.
Stephenson, W. (1947a). *Parasitology* **38:** 116–122.
Stephenson, W. (1947b). *Parasitology* **38:** 140–144.
Suzuoki, Z., and Suzuoki, T. (1952). *J. Biochem. (Japan)* **38:** 237–254.
Swezy, O. (1923). *Univ. Calif. (Berkeley) Pubs. Zool.* **20:** 391–400.
Szwejkowska, G. (1929). *Bull. intern. acad. polon. sci. Classe sci. math. nat.* **B1928:** 489–519.
Tobie, E. J., von Brand, T., and Mehlman, B. (1950). *J. Parasitol.* **36:** 48–54.
Toryu, Y. (1936). *Science Repts. Tohoku Imp. Univ. Fourth Ser.* **10:** 687–696.
Trager, W. (1932). *Biochem. J.* **26:** 1763–1771.
Trager, W. (1934). *Biol. Bull.* **66:** 182–190.
Trier, H. J. (1926). *Z. vergleich. Physiol.* **4:** 305–330.

Trussell, R. E., and Johnson, G. (1941). *Proc. Soc. Exptl. Biol. Med.* **47:** 176–178.

Usuelli, F. (1930). *Wiss. Arch. Landw.* **B3:** 4–19.

Waechter, J. (1934). *Z. Biol.* **95:** 497–501.

Wardle, R. A. (1937). *Can. J. Research* **D15:** 117–126.

Weineck, E. (1934). *Arch. Protistenk.* **7:** 71–117.

Weinland, E. (1901). *Z. Biol.* **42:** 55–90.

Weinland, E. (1904). *Z. Biol.* **45:** 113–116.

Weinland, E. (1910). *In* Oppenheimer's Handbuch Biochem. Ed. 1, Vol. 4 Sect. 2: 446–528. Fischer, Jena.

Weinland, E., and von Brand, T. (1926). *Z. vergleich. Physiol.* **4:** 212–285.

Weinland, E., and Ritter, A. (1902). *Z. Biol.* **43:** 490–502.

Wendel, W. B. (1943). *J. Biol. Chem.* **148:** 21–34.

Wendel, W. B. (1946). *Federation Proc.* **5:** 406–407.

Wendel, W. B., and Kimball, S. (1942). *J. Biol. Chem.* **145:** 343–344.

Westphal, A. (1934). *Z. Parasitenk.* **7:** 71–117.

Willems, R., Massart, L., and Peeters, G. (1942). *Naturwissenschaften* **30:** 169–170.

Work, T. S., and Work, E. (1948). The Basis of Chemotherapy. Interscience Publishers, New York.

Yorke, W., Adams, A. R. D., and Murgatroyd, F. (1929). *Ann. Trop. Med. Parasitol.* **23:** 601–618.

## CHAPTER 11

## LIPID METABOLISM

### I. Introductory Remarks

Different lipids are of quite different physiological importance. While true "fats," that is, higher fatty acids and their glycerides, represent essential energy reserves in many organisms, the importance of cholesterol, for instance, though not too well understood, lies in other directions. In the following sections, therefore, we shall review separately some of the more important groups of lipids in so far as data on their metabolism are available. The omission of other lipids does not imply that they are not of equal significance for the organisms, but merely that no data relating to their metabolism by parasites are as yet known.

### II. Metabolism of Lower Fatty Acids

There is little experimental evidence available to indicate that parasitic protozoa are capable of utilizing lower fatty acids. This is in direct contrast to a number of free-living protozoa for which acetic acid and also other volatile fatty acids are an excellent carbon source; an example is *Chilomonas paramaecium* studied by Loefer (1935). Further examples can be found in the review by Hall (1941).

A slight increase in oxygen consumption was observed when *Trypanosoma evansi* was kept in media containing the sodium salts or methyl esters of formic, acetic, propionic, or butyric acid (Mannozzi-Torini, 1940). The closely related *Trypanosoma hippicum*, on the other hand, was not able to utilize acetate (Harvey, 1949) and neither formate nor acetate increased the oxygen consumption of *Trypanosoma lewisi* (Moulder, 1948).

Almost nothing is known in this respect about parasitic worms and nothing whatever concerning endoparasitic arthropods. Bueding (1949) reported that the aerobic rate of acetate consumption by *Litomosoides carinii* was very small, the highest value found in eight experiments amounting to an acetate consumption of 0.07 mg/gm worm/hour. Szwejkowska (1929) found a diminution of volatile fatty acids from 0.46 to 0.34% during the time elapsing from fertilization to the formation of the second polar body in the case of the *Parascaris* egg.

### III. Metabolism of Higher Fatty Acids and their Glycerides

#### A. Fat as Food for Parasites

The question of whether fat serves as food for parasites can be studied essentially in two ways. Observations can be made as to whether they absorb fat from the surroundings, or it can be determined whether they secrete fat-splitting enzymes into their surroundings or into the lumens of their intestinal tracts. A positive finding represents at least circumstantial evidence for an active fat metabolism.

The evidence relating to these questions is extremely scanty for parasitic protozoa. Small amounts of fat became microscopically visible in *Endamoeba blattae* and *Nyctotherus ovalis* after their hosts were kept for 6 to 8 weeks on a high fat diet (Armer, 1944). This may indicate a small scale fat absorption. No lipase has been found in *Trypanosoma brucei* and *Trypanosoma evansi* (Califano and Gritti, 1930; Krijgsman, 1936a, b), these two species being apparently the only parasitic protozoa studied along this line.

There is known but little more about parasitic worms. Enigk (1938) could not find any indication that *Graphidium* is capable of digesting fats. The most detailed investigation is that of Rogers (1941), who compared the ability of gut extracts of *Ascaris lumbricoides* and *Strongylus edentatus* to digest olive oil and ethyl butyrate, testing in this way for the presence of lipases and esterases. He found that both types of enzymes were considerably more active in *Strongylus* than in *Ascaris*. Only the enzymes of this latter worm were stimulated by sodium glycocholate and sodium bicarbonate. It is not now possible to assess the biological significance of the fat-splitting enzymes in these worms since we do not know yet whether they actually absorb significant amounts of fatty acids from their surroundings. The lipase activity of parasitic flatworms (*Fasciola hepatica*, *Taenia taeniaeformis*, and *T. pisiformis*) was found to be quite low (Pennoit-DeCooman and van Grembergen, 1942).

The only well authenticated case of fat absorption from the environment has been reported recently by Pflugfelder (1949). He found that *Acanthocephalus ranae*, a worm lacking an intestinal tract, does not elaborate a lipase into the medium, but does absorb the degradation products of the fat digested by the lipases of the host. Pflugfelder (1949) first starved the worms for 6 weeks within the intestine of frogs after which time they were devoid of microscopically demonstrable fat droplets. He then transferred them to parasite-free new frogs which were fed with hog fat died with Scharlach R. After 12 hours stained fat droplets were visible in the neck region of the proboscis of the parasites. After 4 days large amounts of fat were deposited within the tissues of the lemnisci and in the following days even the latter's lacunae filled up with fat. The author concludes that fat absorption takes place only through the lemnisci and the adjacent parts of the body wall.

In so far as endoparasitic arthropods are concerned, an enzyme capable of splitting tributyrine has been found in the midgut of *Gasterophilus* larvae (Roy, 1937) and *Cordylobia* larvae (Blacklock, Gordon, and Fine, 1930).

Also it has been assumed that the abundant fat droplets in parasites like *Sacculina* represent essentially fat absorbed from the host's liver (Smith, 1911, 1913; Robson, 1911). This, of course, is quite possible, but has not yet been proved. Reinhard and von Brand (1944) have pointed out that the bulbous root tips of the parasites, which probably are mainly resorptive in function, are poor in fat and certainly no direct transition from the fat present in the host to that found in the parasite can be assumed.

### B. Utilization of Higher Fatty Acids

The problem of whether or not an organism metabolizes fatty acids is not always linked up with that of fat absorption. Fatty acids can readily originate from carbohydrate or from protein and one can visualize an organism building up a fat reserve and utilizing it in time of need even if it is kept on an entirely fat-free diet. It is possible that such a situation may prevail in some parasites.

As explained in the last chapter, the large worms of the intestinal tract or the bile ducts elaborate fatty acids as an endproduct of their carbohydrate metabolism. When higher fatty acids are formed, as in *Moniezia* or *Fasciola*, they are either excreted or accumulate at least partially in the body. In any event the sum of the excreted fat and the body fat is larger at the end of an experimental period than at the beginning. The question now arises whether under certain conditions this body fat can be utilized further in metabolic processes. It must be realized that the low oxygen content of the surroundings, coupled with the large size of the above worms, forces them *in situ* to a primarily anaerobic life. Fatty acids are, however, in general no useful substratum for anaerobic energy production because their carbon atoms, with the exception of the carboxyl carbon, are largely reduced. They therefore do not lend themselves readily to the internal oxidation-reductions so characteristic of anaerobic processes. Thus it can be assumed that the worms themselves cannot utilize these fatty acids further but it is possible that the fatty substances are utilized in an indirect manner, namely, by the eggs. It does seem possible that at least part of the fat present in the helminth eggs has its origin in the waste fat. The eggs of helminths, however, require access to oxygen for full development and develop only to a very limited degree in its absence. It is obvious that the above fat could be utilized in the conventional way by oxidative degradation. Chemical analysis has shown that fat disappears from the *Parascaris* egg during aerobic development (Fauré-Fremiet, 1912, 1913a, b; Szwejkowska, 1929). With the more uncertain staining methods, a decrease in fat content has also been reported from anaerobically kept eggs (Dyrdowska, 1931).

A still clearer example is *Gasterophilus*. The fat reserve of the larvae is built up either from carbohydrate or from protein, or a combination of both (von Kemnitz, 1916) and there is no indication that the larvae utilize this fat. It is extremely likely, from analogy with other insects, that the fat is utilized during the time of pupal rest and also during the adult life of the fly. It should not be too difficult to test this assumption experimentally.

A different question is whether parasites that live normally chiefly anaerobically can utilize fat when kept under aerobic conditions. Experiments concerning this point have been done with *Ascaris* only. Mueller (1929) explanted fat-containing tissues of this worm and observed a decrease in morphologically demonstrable fat droplets in 8 days. Hirsch and Bretschneider (1937) found a depletion in stainable fat droplets within the intestinal cells of ascarids kept starving *in vitro* for 6 days. These morphological observations are suggestive of chemical changes involving fat, but do not necessarily indicate that it has been oxidized. The only definite proof is chemical analysis. Quantitative determinations of the fat content of ascarids kept starving for 24 hours under aerobic conditions showed no significant fat decrease (von Brand, 1934). If the experiments were conducted for 5 days, a small decrease in body fat occurred, but it was accounted for by the fat recovered from expelled eggs (von Brand, 1941). It follows then that there is as yet no definite proof that this species can utilize fat for purposes of obtaining energy even in the presence of oxygen. One reservation has to be made, however. It must be expected that the glycogen stores of the worms were not exhausted after such limited periods of starvation and it is possible that a different result would have been obtained if longer starvation periods had proved feasible. In many free-living invertebrates the fat reserves are mobilized only after depletion of the polysaccharide stores in any event.

A final question is whether parasites that normally have access to oxygen utilize fat in their metabolism. The evidence is again scanty. Pflugfelder's (1949) feeding experiments with *Acanthocephalus ranae* have been mentioned above. After the end of the feeding period he kept the frogs starving and he reports that the fat stores of the parasites were demonstrable up to 4 months after the beginning of the starvation period. He is not explicit, however, as to what extent the fat actually disappeared. Theoretically, an oxidative fat consumption would appear possible in this case. The worms are small and the intestine of the frog is presumably not quite as poor in oxygen as that of larger animals. It is also suggestive that Bullock (1949) found a tissue lipase in the subcuticula of the trunk and in the lemnisci of several acanthocephala.

A clearly aerobic life is led by the free-living stages of parasitic nematodes. A definite decrease in morphologically demonstrable fat droplets with increasing age has been shown to occur in the larvae of *Necator americanus* and *Ancylostoma caninum* (Payne, 1923; Rogers, 1939), as well as in the filariform larvae of several roundworm species, especially when the latter were kept at 37°C (Giovannola, 1936). Quantitative chemical determinations should be possible in some of these cases, but have not as yet been done. Despite the justification of a very cautious interpretation of morphological fat findings, it does seem probable that the larvae derive energy largely from fat.

No data whatever are available as to the possible pathways of fat degradation in parasites. A theoretical discussion of this phase is therefore omitted.

## C. Utilization of Glycerol

Glycerol can, under natural conditions, become available for cellular metabolic processes in various ways. It can be set free from glycerides by the action of lipases or it can be formed during the intermediate metabolism of carbohydrates. It has been mentioned in the preceding chapter that glycerol is formed from this source by anaerobically maintained trypanosomes and it was also pointed out that several species of parasitic protozoa can utilize glycerol quite freely under aerobic conditions.

The question whether parasites are capable to metabolize glycerol in the absence of oxygen seems not yet to have been studied. From a theoretical viewpoint it would seem possible that one or the other form capable of doing so may be found. It is a well established fact that several species of bacteria are able of fermenting glycerol (for review of the literature see Stephenson, 1949).

The aerobic pathways of glycerol utilization are essentially similar to those described in the last chapter for glucose since it can readily be drawn into the glycolytic chain. Harvey (1949) has demonstrated in *Trypanosoma hippicum* the occurrence of glyceroldehydrogenase as well as of $\alpha$- and $\beta$-glycerophosphate dehydrogenase. He showed that this parasite was capable of dehydrogenating nonphosphorylated glycerol, but he also showed that a phosphorylative mechanism was present which prepared glycerol for the entry into the metabolic chain.

## IV. Synthesis of Phospholipids

A pronounced synthesis of phospholipids has been demonstrated in red blood cells parasitized by *Plasmodium knowlesi*, the phospholipid-phosphorus in these cells being from 2 to 4 times as high as in normal erythrocytes. The molar ratio between fatty acids was fairly close in nonparasitized and parasitized cells, the average values being 2.46 and 2.64, respectively. There can be no doubt that the synthesis was due to the parasites (Ball-

*et al.*, 1948). A relatively high rate of phospholipid synthesis has also been reported from *Trypanosoma equiperdum in vivo* (Moraczewski and Kelsey, 1948).

## LITERATURE

Armer, J. M. (1944). *J. Parasitol.* **30**: 131–142.

Ball, E. G., McKee, R. W., Anfinsen, C. B., Cruz, W. O., and Geiman, Q. M. (1948). *J. Biol. Chem.* **175**: 547–571.

Blacklock, D. B., Gordon, R. M., and Fine, J. (1930). *Ann. Trop. Med. Parasitol.* **24**: 5–54.

von Brand, T. (1934). *Z. vergleich. Physiol.* **21**: 220–235.

von Brand, T. (1941). *Proc. Soc. Exptl. Biol. Med.* **46**: 417–418.

Bueding, E. (1949). *J. Exptl. Med.* **89**: 107–130.

Bullock, W. L. (1949). *J. Morphol.* **84**: 185–200.

Califano, L., and Gritti, P. (1930). *Riv. patol. sper.* **5**: 9–15.

Dyrdowska, M. (1931). *Compt. rend. soc. biol.* **108**: 593–596.

Enigk, K. (1938). *Z. Parasitenk.* **10**: 386–414.

Fauré-Fremiet, E. (1912). *Bull. soc. zool. France* **37**: 233–234.

Fauré-Fremiet, E. (1913a). *Arch. anat. microscop.* **15**: 435–757.

Fauré-Fremiet, E. (1913b). *Compt. rend. soc. biol.* **75**: 90–92.

Giovannola, A. (1936). *J. Parasitol.* **22**: 207–218.

Hall, R. P. (1941). *In* Calkins, G. N., and Summers, F. M. (1941). Protozoa in Biological Research. Columbia University Press, New York, pp. 475–516.

Harvey, S. C. (1949). *J. Biol. Chem.* **179**: 435–453.

Hirsch, G. C., and Bretschneider, L. H. (1937). *Cytologia (Tokyo), Fujii Jubil. Vol.* 424–436.

von Kemnitz, G. (1916). *Z. Biol.* **67**: 129–244.

Krijgsman, B. J. (1936a). *Natuurw. Tijdschr. (Belg.)* **18**: 237–241.

Krijgsman, B. J. (1936b). *Z. vergleich. Physiol.* **23**: 663–711.

Loefer, J. B. (1935). *Arch. Protistenk.* **84**: 456–471.

Mannozzi-Torini, M. (1940). *Arch. sci. biol. (Italy)* **26**: 565–580.

Moraczewski, S. A., and Kelsey, F. E. (1948). *J. Infectious Diseases* **82**: 45–51.

Moulder, J. W. (1948). *J. Infectious Diseases* **83**: 33–41.

Mueller, J. F. (1929). *Z. Zellforsch. mikroskop. Anat.* **8**: 361–403.

Payne, F. K. (1923). *Am. J. Hyg.* **3**: 547–583.

Pennoit-DeCooman, E., and van Grembergen, G. (1942). *Verhandel. Koninkl. Vlaam. Acad. Wetenschap. Belg. Klasse Wetenschap.* **4**: No. 6, 7–77.

Pflugfelder, O. (1949). *Z. Parasitenk.* **14**: 274–280.

Reinhard, E. G., and von Brand, T. (1944). *Physiol. Zoöl.* **17**: 31–41.

Robson, G. C. (1911). *Quart. J. Microscop. Sci.* **57**: 267–278.

Rogers, W. P. (1939). *J. Helminthol.* **17**: 195–202.

Rogers, W. P. (1941). *J. Helminthol.* **19**: 35–46.

Roy, D. N. (1937). *Parasitology* **29**: 150–162.

Smith, G. (1911). *Quart. J. Microscop. Sci.* **57**: 251–265.

Smith, G. (1913). *Quart. J. Microscop. Sci.* **59**: 267–295.

Stephenson, M. (1949). Bacterial Metabolism. Third edition, Longmans, Green and Co., London.

Szwejkowska, G. (1929). *Bull. intern. acad. polon. sci. Classe sci. math. nat.* **B1928**: 489–519.

# CHAPTER 12

# PROTEIN METABOLISM

## I. Introductory Remarks

Many, though not all, animals can dispense with either carbohydrate or fat in their diets because these substances are frequently interchangeable in the production of energy. The situation is different in regard to the metabolism of nitrogenous compounds. Without exception animals must be provided with at least a minimum of nitrogenous material because the latter serves not only as fuel for the production of energy, but is indispensable for building up of new protoplasm during growth, the replacement of old protoplasm in adult life, as well as for the maintenance of the enzyme complex of the cells. The following account will show that our knowledge of the protein metabolism of parasites is extremely limited and requires much more work.

## II. Protein Synthesis

Although there is no quantitative data on the protein synthesis of parasites it follows from differences in growth patterns that its extent varies in different species and often also at different periods in the life cycle of one species.

Large scale protein synthesis takes place, for example, during the infection of small rodents with pathogenic trypanosomes. Hoppe and Chapman (1947) observed that *Trypanosoma equiperdum* increased in sugar-fed rats from about 20 million per ml blood to about 4 billion per ml within 100 hours. Other examples of pronounced protoplasm synthesis are the malarial parasites. Morrison and Jeskey (1948) estimated that about half the amino acids liberated from the breakdown of the erythrocytes are used by *Plasmodium knowlesi* for the synthesis of the parasites' body substance. Gregarines, on the other hand, only need to replace what nitrogenous compounds are being used up once the trophozoites are fully grown until they encyst and a new growth cycle sets in.

Similar differences occur also in parasitic worms. Tapeworms often grow very rapidly and they produce proglottids throughout their life span. *Hymenolepis diminuta* thus reaches an average length of 35 cm in 14 days (Addis and Chandler, 1946) and it has been reported that the small tapeworm, *Davainea proglottina*, sheds about one proglottis daily (Levine, 1938).

132

Since the whole worm has only seven segments normally and since the last proglottis is always the largest, the daily synthesis must be considerable. *Diphyllobothrium latum* specimens in dogs increased 61.5 mm in length daily from the 15th to 30th day after infection (Wardle and Green, 1941).

Rapid growth is also common in larval trematodes where 10,000 cercariae may be derived from a single miracidium of *Schistosoma japonicum* and more than 200,000 from one miracidium of *Schistosoma mansoni* (Faust and Hoffman, 1934). One *Littorina* infected by *Cryptocotyle lingua* shed 1,300,000 cercariae in 1 year (Meyerhof and Rothschild, 1940).

Trematodes, nematodes, and acanthocephala cease growing once they have reached adulthood. They must nevertheless possess marked powers of protein synthesis as evidenced by the fact that most parasitic helminths produce much greater numbers of reproductive cells than their free-living relatives. One *Haemonchus contortus* produces 5000 eggs daily on an average (Martin and Ross, 1934), one *Ancylostoma duodenale* 24,000 eggs (Augustine et al., 1928), one *Ascaris lumbricoides* 200,000 eggs (Brown and Cort, 1927), and one *Fasciolopsis buski* 25,000 eggs (Stoll, Cort, and Kwei, 1927).

Several free-living protozoa, such as *Polytoma uvella* or *Astasia* sp., can satisfy their nitrogenous requirements from inorganic compounds, especially ammonium salts and nitrates. These substances in conjunction with an organic carbon source like acetate are sufficient to enable these organisms to synthesize all their own nitrogen-containing compounds (Pringsheim, 1921; Lwoff and Dusi, 1938; Schoenborn, 1940). Similar faculties have not yet been described from parasites. It would, however, be interesting to study in this respect forms like *Euglenomorpha hegneri*, *Euglenomorpha pellucida*, or *Hegneria leptodactyli*, all apparently true parasites of amphibians (Kirby, 1941), since the above faculties are widely distributed among free-living euglenids.

As far as we know at present, all parasites, both protozoa and metazoa, require organic nitrogenous compounds for their synthetic processes. We have little precise information concerning their actual synthetic powers; that is, information concerning the question of what are the simplest compounds from which they can build their protoplasm. One of the chief difficulties is that parasites have rarely been grown so far in a chemically well-defined medium. It is evident that any conclusion drawn from observations on complex, ill-defined media must remain rather insecure. One case may exemplify this. Trypanosomidae are usually cultivated on blood agar media or extracts therefrom; media containing all the water soluble compounds extractable from the blood agar. Tobie and Rees (1948) recently have cultivated *Trypanosoma cruzi* in cellophane bags filled with Locke solution immersed in the fluid overlaying a blood agar base. This procedure eliminated all compounds with high molecular weight and indicates that this species can synthesize its protoplasm from substances passing through the cellophane membrane.

The analysis of the protein metabolism of higher animals has shown that the amino acids of the food material can be divided into essential and non-essential ones. Only the latter can be omitted from the diet because they can be synthesized by the animals themselves in quantity sufficient to meet the need; the former have to be provided in order to allow the organisms to thrive. The only study made so far in a chemically well defined medium is that by Weiss and Ball (1947) on *Trichomonas foetus*. They found the following amino acids to be essential: Arginine, glycine, histidine, isoleucine, leucine, lysine, methionine, phenylalanine, proline, serine, threonine, and valine. This list contains all the amino acids considered essential in higher animals (Baldwin, 1949); glycine, proline, and serine are nonessential.

It has also been shown that methionine is essential for the growth of *Plasmodium knowlesi* (McKee, Geiman, and Cobbey, 1947; McKee and Geiman, 1948). This demonstration was only possible because the methionine content of the red cells is low and does not suffice for the needs of the parasites. It is very probable that other amino acids are essential also. To date they have not been identified because they seem to be produced in such quantity during the breakdown of the erythrocytes' protoplasm that a selective depletion of the medium is not possible.

Nonessential amino acids presumably can be synthesized by the organisms and one mechanism involved is often that of transamination in which an amino group is transferred by means of an enzymatic reaction to a keto acid. An example is the transfer of the amino group of glutamic acid to pyruvic acid, a process resulting in the formation of $\alpha$-ketoglutaric acid and alanine. Marshall (1948) has pointed out that in experiments with *Trypanosoma evansi* frequently somewhat less pyruvic acid accumulates than should be expected from the glucose consumption and he is inclined to assume that the missing pyruvic acid has been drawn into the protein-synthesizing processes.

Most rapidly growing parasites will undoubtedly also synthesize rather large amounts of nucleic acid. A case in point is *Plasmodium knowlesi* where desoxyribose nucleic acid is formed (Deane, 1945). Ball *et al.* (1948) have calculated that $5 \times 10^{12}$ parasitized red cells corresponding to 481 gm contain 5.456 gm more nucleic acid than normal ones. From their *in vitro* studies they conclude that this parasite can synthesize its own nucleic acid from simpler compounds, but whether it can synthesize all the purines and pyrimidines built into the nucleic acid has not yet been established. A high rate of nucleic acid synthesis also has been reported from the bloodstream form of African pathogenic trypanosomes (Morac-zewski and Kelsey, 1948). No definite data on protein synthesis of hel-minths or endoparasitic arthropods are as yet available.

## III. Proteolytic Enzymes

Enzymes capable of splitting proteins can be of different biological significance. The first group comprises enzymes that assist parasites in invading the host's tissues. Some indications that *Endamoeba histolytica* contains an enzyme capable of digesting intestinal mucosa have been re-corded by Craig (1927). Whether this enzyme is identical with the enzyme digesting the gluten surrounding starch granules (Anderson and Hansen, 1947; Reardon and Bartgis, 1949) is questionable. An enzyme having diges-tive action on the skin and muscles of tadpoles has been found in an aque-ous extract of macerated cercariae of *Diplostomum flexicaudum* (Davis, 1936a). It is presumably secreted by glands present in the body of the animals and probably is involved in the penetration mechanism (Davis, 1936b).

A second group of proteolytic enzymes is represented by tissue enzymes. They play an especially significant role during the metamorphosis of insects by destroying the larval tissues and preparing them for the rebuilding of the adult body. In conformity with other insects it can be expected that such enzymes occur in *Gasterophilus*, *Cordylobia*, and other pupae of endo-parasitic arthropods, but the problem has not yet been approached experi-mentally.

Proteolytic enzymes belonging to this second group have been described from several other groups of parasites. Clearly intracellular proteolytic enzymes have been found in *Trypanosoma evansi* (Krijgsman, 1936). It is evident that all enzymes occurring in a parasite whirled constantly around in the bloodstream can only have significance if they act on substrates present within the cell. In the above case cathepsin, carboxypolypeptidase, aminopolypeptidase, and dipeptidase have been encountered.

Proteolytic enzymes have been found in several metazoan parasites lack-ing an intestinal tract. It is unlikely that these would be secreted to the outside through the 'cuticle and prepare food for absorption. It is much more likely that they are tissue enzymes used in movements of the para-sites' own proteins. Specifically, such enzymes with apparently fairly high rates of activity have been reported from *Diphyllobothrium latum*, *Taenia saginata*, and *Taenia solium* (Tallqvist, 1907; Smorodincev and Bebesin, 1936). Pennoit-DeCooman and van Grembergen (1942), on the other hand, found only a very low proteolytic activity in *Taenia saginata*, *Taenia pisiformis*, *Dipylidium caninum*, and *Moniezia benedeni*. These investigators also reported the absence of polypeptidases but the presence of a strong dipeptidase in these worms. The biological significance of the proteolytic enzymes encountered by Lemaire and Ribère (1935) in the *Echinococcus* cystic fluid requires further clarification.

Corresponding enzymes found in *Fasciola hepatica* (Abderhalden and Heise, 1909; Flury and Leeb, 1926; Pennoit-DeCooman and van Grembergen, 1942) cannot be properly assessed; for obvious reasons no distinction between tissue and truly digestive enzymes can be made. The histological studies of Müller (1923) make it likely that the epithelium of the intestine of this worm has a secretory function; it may secrete some of the above enzymes.

The third group of proteolytic enzymes can be considered as true digestive enzymes in the sense that they prepare extraneous food material for absorption. Their occurrence has been studied only in nematodes where an isolation of the intestinal tract does not offer particular difficulties. However, the above mentioned gluten-digesting enzyme reported for *Endamoeba histolytica* probably belongs into this group also.

There is good histological evidence that several species of intestinal nematodes produce lesions in the host by an extra-corporeal digestion of the latter's intestinal mucosa (von Linstow, 1907; Hoeppli, 1927; Hoeppli and Feng, 1931; Wetzel, 1927, 1931; Schuurmans-Stekhoven and Botman, 1932) and it does seem probable that at least in some cases the enzyme responsible is contained in the secretions of the esophageal glands. The only chemical evidence to that effect is Chitwood's (1938) finding of a protease in extracts from the esophagus of *Ascaris lumbricoides* which, however, is not usually considered as a tissue feeder.

The proteolytic enzymes of the intestine proper have been studied in *Toxocara* by Abderhalden and Heise (1909) who reported the presence of a polypeptide-splitting enzyme, and in *Ascaris* by Flury (1912) who found that intestinal extracts of the worms digested egg albumen readily and fibrin more slowly. The most detailed study is that of Rogers (1941). He studied intestinal extracts of *Ascaris lumbricoides* and *Strongylus edentatus* in respect to their ability to digest gelatin, blood albumin, and casein. Quantitative estimation showed that the proteolytic enzymes of *Strongylus* were considerably more active than those of *Ascaris,* the former digesting 4.9 to 8.3 times more gelatin, from 12.5 to 40.9 times more casein, and from 2.5 to 5.2 times more blood albumin. The optimum pH of the enzymes of both worms was 6.2, that is, it was on the alkaline side of the isoelectric points of the digested proteins.

The exact nature of the proteolytic enzymes of helminths has not yet been established. It has been reported sometimes that in one and the same worm several different proteolytic enzymes occur, as indicated by several maxima of activity at different hydrogen ion concentrations (*e.g.* Smorodincev and Bebesin, 1936). Attempts have been made to identify them with mammalian enzymes such as pepsin or trypsin. These attempts have but little significance because so far not one investigation has been carried out with purified preparations. The most that can be said, and that only tentatively, is that our present knowledge indicates on the whole that helminthic proteolytic activity is more of tryptic than peptic nature.

This is also true for endoparasitic arthropods where only trypsin-like enzymes have been reported from the gut of *Cordylobia* larvae (Blacklock, Gordon, and Fine, 1930) and *Gasterophilus* larvae (Roy, 1937).

## IV. DIGESTION OF BLOOD

There is virtually no useful information available on the digestion of naturally occurring proteins by parasites with the exception of that of blood. Our present knowledge concerning this topic has recently been reviewed by Geiman and McKee (1950).

The blood-consuming protozoa, that is the malarial parasites, live in the closest connection possible with the hemoglobin of the red cells. Many metazoan parasites, on the other hand, must gain access to the blood in order to ingest it, in other words, they suck blood out of blood vessels. Since blood removed from the vascular system usually clots very rapidly it is not surprising that many blood-sucking organisms secrete anticoagulants in order to assure a flow of blood through the punctured blood vessel and to prevent an obstruction of their own alimentary passages. This is well known about free-living organisms; for example, leeches and mosquitoes. But relatively little is known in this respect about helminths and endoparasitic arthropods.

Anticoagulants have been reported from the following nematodes: *Ancylostoma caninum* (Loeb and Smith, 1904; Loeb and Fleisher, 1910), various members of the family Strongylidae (Schwartz, 1921), and *Bunostomum trigonocephalum* (Hoeppli and Feng, 1933). The only data available on trematodes are those of Dent and Schuellein (1950) who observed that the prothrombin time of the blood of *Rana pipiens* and *Bufo americanus* infected with *Pneumoneces* sp. and unidentified lung flukes respectively was longer than that of uninfected specimens. The authors consider this as strong evidence for the release of anticoagulating factors by the worms. An anticoagulant also has been found in the salivary gland of *Gasterophilus* larvae (Dinulescu, 1932), apparently this being the only recorded instance for endoparasitic arthropods.

Not much is known about the further fate of ingested blood. Rogers (1941) found in *Ascaris* first a reduction of oxyhemoglobin to hemoglobin, the latter substance then being split into globin and hematin. The same process probably took place in *Strongylus*, and the hematological observations of Rogers (1940) on the gut content of other species of nematodes and of schistosomes made it probable that an identical sequence occurred also in such forms as *Syngamus trachea, Schistosoma mattheei,* and *Schistosoma mansoni.* Nothing is known, however, of the further fate of the globin which, presumably, is of the greatest nutritive value to the worms.

*Gasterophilus* larvae, though probably not constant blood suckers (Roy, 1937) seem at least intermittently to ingest blood. Dinulescu (1932) relates that the blood clots in the gut, that it is then hemolyzed and split into globin and hematin. Part of the globin is supposedly used for the synthesis of fat reserves of the larvae while the pigmented prosthetic group is decomposed to a hemochromogen-like substance and iron. During pupation the hemoglobin of the red organ and other body tissues is transformed to biliverdin, a process occasionally also observed in third stage larvae where the pigment originates from ingested blood (Beaumont, 1948).

Relatively well known is the utilization of hemoglobin by malarial parasites. Moulder and Evans (1946) observed a high rate of amino nitrogen production by red cells parasitized by *Plasmodium gallinaceum* indicating the probability that hemoglobin was used. Cell-free extracts of the parasites, however, hydrolyzed hemoglobin only very slowly; they did on the other hand rapidly utilize denatured globin. The authors assume that in intact parasites an enzyme system is present which splits hemoglobin into heme and globin, the latter then being readily available for the action retained by the lysed parasites. It has already been mentioned in the chapter dealing with parasitic pigments that hematin is one of the endproducts of hemoglobin utilization. That relatively large amounts of hemoglobin are turned over during these processes by various species of *Plasmodium* follows from the data presented by Ball *et al.* (1948) and Morrison and Jeskey (1948). The morphological studies of Black (1947) showed differences in the extent of hemoglobin consumption by various species of malarial parasites as well as of various stages in the life cycle. Especially large consumption was indicated in the case of the amoeboid stages. It is clear that the exoerythrocytic stages of these parasites must be able to satisfy their nitrogenous needs from other sources, since they have no hemoglobin at their disposition. Their nitrogen metabolism has not yet been studied, but it is known that, expectedly, they do not accumulate malarial pigment, that is, they do not form hematin (Huff and Bloom, 1935; Huff and Coulston, 1944; Mudrow and Reichenow, 1944).

## V. PROTEIN AS FUEL

It is very difficult to state at present to what extent protein is used by parasites for the production of energy. Theoretically, it can be metabolized along oxidative pathways during aerobic conditions, but it may also serve as a source of anaerobic energy. The most common processes requiring no oxygen, decarboxylation and anaerobic deamination, seem in general to release only little energy. Stephenson (1939) has pointed out, however, that protein decomposition leading to the production of hydrogen "may perhaps be regarded as an anaerobic device for obtaining energy from amino acids without the use of oxygen or a hydrogen acceptor." She formulates the process as follows:

$$5C_5H_9O_4N + 6H_2O \rightarrow 6CH_3 \cdot COOH + 2CH_3 \cdot (CH_2)_2 \cdot COOH + 5CO_2 + H_2 + 5NH_3.$$

Since, as explained in a previous chapter, metazoan parasites seem not to produce hydrogen, such a process could be looked for profitably only in protozoa. It is not yet known whether it is realized there.

Actually our knowledge about the extent, nature, and significance of anaerobic protein metabolism is extremely scanty; indeed, we cannot state yet whether it is primarily anabolic or catabolic in nature. Moulder and Evans (1946) have shown that anaerobiosis inhibits the liberation of amino nitrogen by erythrocytes parasitized by *Plasmodium gallinaceum* from 40 to 80%. They point out that such an inhibition does not usually occur during simple enzymatic protein hydrolysis and they take it as an indication that the production of amino nitrogen is in this case somehow linked to oxidative processes, In *Ascaris lumbricoides*, on the other hand, identical amounts of nitrogenous material are excreted under aerobic and anaerobic conditions (von Brand, 1934).

Fairly good indications exist that several species of parasitic protozoa can utilize proteins as energy source under aerobic conditions. Salle and Schmidt (1928) observed in cultures of *Leishmania tropica* a marked increase in ammonia nitrogen only in the absence of sugar which, when present, is utilized in preference to proteins. Similarly, a rise in pH recognized as due to ammonia production has been reported from *Trypanosoma cruzi* cultures when the sugar initially contained in the medium became exhausted or when it did not contain sugar from the beginning (von Brand et al., 1949; Tobie, von Brand, and Mehlman, 1950). In cultures of *Trypanosoma gambiense* and *Trypanosoma rhodesiense* no comparable increase in pH occurred and no significant accumulation of ammonia was observed. The flagellates nevertheless developed in practically sugar-free media essentially the same population density as that attained in sugar-containing media. They may have utilized proteins by other processes than simple deamination (Tobie, von Brand, and Mehlman, 1950).

There is little evidence that the bloodstream form of pathogenic trypanosomes uses proteins for purposes of obtaining energy. Von Brand (1933) found in incubates of *Trypanosoma brucei* only a very small accumulation of nonprotein nitrogen and it is well known that these organisms die very rapidly in the absence of sugar. It is true, however, that Mannozzi-Torini (1940) has reported increases in the oxygen consumption of *Trypanosoma evansi* ranging from 11 to 74% under the influence of various amino acids, the most potent ones being histidine, asparagine, and valine. He also reported an increase of 111% with cysteine, but he seems not to have considered the possibility of spontaneous oxidation of this compound. It would be of interest to study whether the bloodstream form of *Trypanosoma cruzi* has a more marked rate of protein metabolism than the African forms, since in contrast to the latter the former does not consume sugar to any noticeable degree.

Of nonpathogenic trypanosomes, only the bloodstream form of *Trypanosoma lewisi* has been studied. Moulder (1948) found it unable to oxidize D,L-alanine. L-aspartate and L-asparagine were oxidized very slowly while L-glutamate and L-glutamine were utilized rapidly, increasing the oxygen consumption by 97 and 121%, respectively. The pathway of this utilization has not yet been established. α-Ketoglutarate seems not to be an intermediate.

There is at present little indication that malarial parasites use much protein for the production of energy, despite their pronounced nitrogen metabolism which seems primarily synthetic in nature. They form but little ammonia (Christophers and Fulton, 1938; Moulder and Evans, 1946) and only a very small increase in oxygen consumption over the endogenous rate was observed when amino acids were used as a substratum for the respiration of *Plasmodium knowlesi* (McKee *et al.*, 1946). It must be remembered, however, that *Plasmodium lophurae* shows a rather stable rate of endogenous respiration, at least in the presence of adenylic acid or adenosine triphosphate, even in the absence of an exogenous energy source (Hellerman, Bovarnick, and Porter, 1946). Whether in this case proteins or intracellular polysaccharides are used is not known.

Only rather circumstantial evidence is available for helminths. Schulte (1917) determined the heat of combustion of fresh and starving ascarids using separately both their total body substance and their glycogen and concluding that the carbohydrate metabolism accounted for only 80% of the total loss of calories. Since this species does not consume fat it would seem possible that the remaining 20% was covered by protein utilization. There is no indication that protein is metabolized during the development of the eggs of ascarids. Szwejkowska (1929) could not observe changes in their nitrogen content during maturation and 1.78% nitrogen were found by Kosmin (1928) both in undeveloped and developed eggs. This investigator points out that this observation does not necessarily exclude a protein metabolism since the constancy in nitrogen content may be due to an impermeability of the egg membranes preventing the excretion of nitrogenous endproducts.

In so far as endoparasitic arthropods are concerned, von Kemnitz (1916) relates that protein in the medium exerts a glycogen-sparing action in the case of *Gasterophilus* larvae kept *in vitro,* an observation possibly indicating the utilization of protein.

TABLE 26.   Endproducts of protein metabolism of some parasites

| SPECIES | MATERIAL | AMMONIA | UREA | URIC ACID | AMINO ACIDS | CREATININE | BETAINE | AMINE BASES | AUTHOR |
|---|---|---|---|---|---|---|---|---|---|
| *Leishmania tropica* | Culture | x | | | | | | | Salle and Schmidt (1928) |
| *Trypanosoma cruzi* | Culture | x | | | | | | | Tobie, von Brand, and Mehlman (1950) |
| *Plasmodium knowlesi* | Incubate | — | | | | | | | Christophers and Fulton (1938) |
| *P. gallinaceum* | Incubate | x | | | x | | | | Moulder and Evans (1946) |
| *Fasciola hepatica* | Excreta; body | x | — | — | x | | | | Flury and Leeb (1926); van Grembergen and Pennoit-DeCooman (1944) |
| *Echinococcus granulosus* | Cyst fluid | | x | x | | x | x | | Mazzocco (1923); Flössner (1925); Lemaire and Ribère (1935); Codounis and Polydorides (1936) |
| *Moniezia benedeni* | Body | x | — | — | | | | | van Grembergen and Pennoit-DeCooman (1944) |
| *Cysticercus tenuicollis* | Cyst fluid | — | x | x | | (x) | | | Schopfer (1932) |
| *C. fasciolaris* | Body | x | x | x | | | | | Salisbury and Anderson (1939) |
| *Ascaris lumbricoides* | Excreta | x | x? | — | | | | x | Weinland (1901); Flury (1912); Chitwood (1938) |
| *Dioctophyme renale* | Body fluid | | x? | | | | | | Janicki (1939) |

x = Substance found; (x) = substance found at most in traces; x? = production of substance questionable; — = substance not produced.

## VI. ENDPRODUCTS OF PROTEIN METABOLISM

The endproducts of protein breakdown (Table 26) are varied both in nature and significance. It must be emphasized that the nitrogenous endproducts recovered from the medium after incubation of organisms having an intestinal tract often do not represent endproducts of actual intracellular protein utilization. They are usually a composite between such endproducts, fecal material, and regurgitated half digested food. It is thus very likely that the peptones found among the excreta of *Ascaris* by Flury (1912), or the hemoglobin, coagulated proteins, albumoses, and peptones encountered in the dejections of *Fasciola* by Flury and Leeb (1926) stem from the latter sources.

It is possible that a situation similar in principle also exists in some organisms lacking an intestinal tract but attacking proteins by extra-corporeal digestion. The liberation of amino acids during the metabolism of malarial parasites could thus probably be understood best on the assumption that only a part of the degraded hemoglobin is actually absorbed and utilized by the parasites while the rest diffuses through the erythrocyte's membrane without passing through the parasite's body. Whether the excretion of amino acids by helminths having an intestine can be explained in a similar way, remains to be seen. It should be realized in this connection that amino acids are found also in the excreta of free-living invertebrates where in the crustacean *Maia squinado*, the cephalopod *Octopus vulgaris*, or the sea-urchin *Paracentrotus lividus* they account for 20 to 30% of the total nitrogenous excreta. Baldwin (1949) states that it is not yet known "whether this is due simply to leakage of amino acids from the body fluids of these animals, or whether it indicates some sort of metabolic disability."

Quantitatively, ammonia is the most important identified nitrogenous endproduct of the culture forms of *Leishmania* spp. and *Trypanosoma cruzi*, of *Ascaris*, *Fasciola*, and *Moniezia*. The prevalence of ammonia excretion in many parasites is not surprising since an identical situation is found in numerous free-living invertebrate animals. In the latter, ammonia is the leading endproduct in certain polychaetes, hirudinea, gephyrea, crustacea, cephalopods, and echinoderms (data in Delaunay, 1927; Baldwin, 1949). They are all aquatic organisms which can readily discharge the poisonous ammonia into a constantly changing environment which prevents an accumulation of ammonia to toxic levels in the immediate vicinity of the animals. Most parasites of course resemble aquatic animals in this respect rather closely.

The exact mechanisms of ammonia formation in parasites are not yet known. It has been reported that tapeworms and flukes do not contain an amino acid oxidase (van Grembergen and Pennoit-DeCooman, 1944). This is perhaps not too surprising since this enzyme is strictly aerobic while the worms in question lead in nature a primarily anaerobic life. It may be worthwhile searching for an enzyme active in the absence of molecular oxygen.

In the case of *Plasmodium gallinaceum* Moulder and Evans (1946) observed that parasitized erythrocytes produced little if any ammonia in the presence of glucose. In the absence of sugar, however, large amounts of ammonia were formed indicating that the parasites can deaminate amino acids under aerobic conditions.

Urea and uric acid are derived from synthetic processes and are usually produced by animals which have to conserve water since their formation is essentially a means of detoxifying ammonia. It may be significant in this connection that the only parasites apparently producing urea and uric acid in any quantity are the larval tapeworms. It is possible that the water exchanges with the tissues of the host are not sufficient to carry away all the nitrogenous endproducts in the form of the toxic ammonia especially in the case of large cysts or in that of cysts attached only by a slender bridge of tissue to the host tissues. Schopfer (1932) states that traces of ammonia were found only rarely in the fluid of *Cysticercus tenuicollis*. On the other hand the possibility cannot be overlooked that at least part of the urea and uric acid found in the cysts may have come from the host's fluids. It seems obvious that only studies conducted *in vitro* will clarify the picture further.

Urea formation is not as simple a process as it was visualized during the last century when it was assumed to be derived by a reaction of ammonia with carbon dioxide and subsequent dehydration. At present it is assumed to be formed during the so called ornithine cycle in which the enzyme arginase splits arginine into urea and ornithine, while arginine is constantly rebuilt by ammonia being fed into the cycle. It is of some interest to note in this connection that a weak arginase was found in *Cysticercus pisiformis* (van Grembergen and Pennoit-DeCooman, 1944). It is curious, however, that the same authors found a stronger arginase activity in adult cestodes and in the adult liver fluke both of which apparently do not produce urea. The significance of this finding will require further study.

In so far as parasitic nematodes are concerned, the production of urea is questionable. Janicki (1939) reported a doubtful positive reaction from the body fluid of *Dioctophyme*. Chitwood (1938) demonstrated conclusively the occurrence of urea in the fluid collected from the excretory pore of *Ascaris*, but since this reaction became negative after the worms had been kept for 24 hours *in vitro*, he assumes that the compound may not have originated in the metabolism of the helminth but that it may have been derived from the host.

Many other enzymes are involved in the protein metabolism of free-living organisms, but practically nothing is known in this respect from parasites. It has been reported that urease was absent from *Fasciola hepatica*, *Moniezia benedeni*, and *Taenia pisiformis* (van Grembergen and Pennoit-DeCooman, 1944). The absence of allantoinase and allantoicase has also been mentioned in the case of *Fasciola* (Florkin and Duchateau, 1943).

### LITERATURE

Abderhalden, E., and Heise, R. (1909). *Z. physiol. Chem.* **62:** 136–138.
Addis, C. J., and Chandler, A. C. (1946). *J. Parasitol.* **32:** 581–584.
Anderson, H. H., and Hansen, E. L. (1947). Liber Jubilaris J., Rodhain, pp. 47–61. Goemaere, Brussels.

Augustine, D. L., Nazmi, M., Helmy, M., and McGavran, E. G. (1928). *J. Parasitol.* **15:** 45–51.

Baldwin, E. (1949). Dynamic Aspects of Biochemistry. University Press, Cambridge, England.

Ball, E. G., McKee, R. W., Anfinsen, C. B., Cruz, W. O., and Geiman, Q. M. (1948). *J. Biol. Chem.* **175:** 547–571.

Beaumont, A. (1948). *Compt. rend. soc. biol.* **142:** 1369–1371.

Black, R. H. (1947). *Ann. Trop. Med. Parasitol.* **41:** 215–217.

Blacklock, D. B., Gordon, R. M., and Fine, J. (1930). *Ann. Trop. Med. Parasitol.* **24:** 5–54.

von Brand, T. (1933). *Z. vergleich. Physiol.* **19:** 587–614.

von Brand, T. (1934). *Z. vergleich. Physiol.* **21:** 220–235.

von Brand, T., Tobie, E. J., Kissling, R. E., and Adams, G. (1949). *J. Infectious Diseases* **85:** 1–16.

Brown, H. W., and Cort, W. W. (1927). *J. Parasitol.* **14:** 88–90.

Chitwood, B. G. (1938). *Proc. Helminthol. Soc. Wash.* **5:** 18–19.

Christophers, S. R., and Fulton, J. D. (1938). *Ann. Trop. Med. Parasitol.* **32:** 43–75.

Codounis, A., and Polydorides, J. (1936). *Compt. rend. III. congr. intern. pathol. comp.* **2:** 195–202.

Craig, C. F. (1927). *Am. J. Trop. Med.* **7:** 225–240.

Davis, D. J. (1936a). *J. Parasitol.* **22:** 108–110.

Davis, D. J. (1936b). *J. Parasitol.* **22:** 329–337.

Deane, H. W. (1945). *J. Cellular Comp. Physiol.* **26:** 139–145.

Delaunay, H. (1927). Recherches biochimiques sur l'excrétion azotée des invertebrés. Siraudeau, Bordeaux.

Dent, J. N., and Schuellein, R. J. (1950). *Physiol. Zoöl.* **23:** 23–27.

Dinulescu, G. (1932). *Ann. sci. nat., Zool.* **15:** 1–183.

Faust, E. C., and Hoffman, W. A. (1934). *Puerto Rico J. Pub. Health Trop. Med.* **10:** 1–97.

Flössner, O. (1924). *Z. Biol.* **80:** 255–260.

Flössner, O. (1925). *Z. Biol.* **82:** 297–301.

Florkin, M., and Duchateau, G. (1943). *Arch. intern. physiol.* **53:** 267–307.

Flury, F. (1912). *Arch. exptl. Path. Pharmakol.* **67:** 275–392.

Flury, F., and Leeb, F. (1926). *Klin. Wochschr.* **5:** 2054–2055.

Geiman, Q. M., and McKee, R. W. (1950). *J. Parasitol.* **36:** 211–226.

van Grembergen, G., and Pennoit-DeCooman, E. (1944). *Natuurw. Tijdschr. (Belg.)* **26:** 91–97.

Hellerman, L., Bovarnick, M. R., and Porter, C. C. (1946). *Federation Proc.* **3:** 400–405.

Hoeppli, R. (1927). *Arch. Schiffs- u. Tropen-Hyg.* **31:** Beiheft 3: 5–88.

Hoeppli, R., and Feng, L. C. (1931). *Chinese Med. J.* **17:** 589–598.

Hoeppli, R. and Feng, L. C. (1933). *Arch. Schiffs- u. Tropen-Hyg.* **37:** 176–182.

Hoppe, J. O., and Chapman, C. W. (1947). *J. Parasitol.* **33:** 509–516.

Huff, C. G., and Bloom, W. (1935). *J. Infectious Diseases* **57:** 315–336.

Huff, C. G., and Coulston, F. (1944). *J. Infectious Diseases* **75:** 231–249.

Janicki, M. J. (1939). *Zoologica Poloniae* **3:** 189–223.

von Kemnitz, G. (1916). *Z. Biol.* **67:** 129–244.

Kirby, H. (1941). *In* Calkins, G. N., and Summers, F. M. (1941). Protozoa in Biological Research. Columbia University Press, New York, pp. 890–1008.

Kosmin, N. (1928). *Trans. Lab. Exptl. Biol., Zoo-Park Moscow* **4:** 207–218.

Krijgsman, B. J. (1936). *Z. vergleich. Physiol.* **23:** 663–711.

Lemaire, G., and Ribère, R. (1935). *Compt. rend. soc. biol.* **118:** 1578–1579.

Levine, P. P. (1938). *J. Parasitol.* **24:** 423–431.

von Linstow, O. (1907). *Proc. Roy. Soc. Edinburgh* **B26:** 464–472.

Loeb, L., and Fleisher, M. S. (1910). *J. Infectious Diseases* **7:** 625–631.

Loeb, L., and Smith, A. J. (1904). *Zentr. Bakt. Parasitenk. Abt. I. Orig.* **37:** 93–98.

Lwoff, A., and Dusi, H. (1938). *Compt. rend. soc. biol.* **127:** 53–56.

Mannozzi-Torini, M. (1940). *Arch. sci. biol. (Italy)* **26:** 565–580.

Marshall, P. B. (1948). *Brit. J. Pharmacol.* **3:** 8–14.

Martin, C. J., and Ross, I. C. (1934). *J. Helminthol.* **12:** 137–142.

Mazzocco, P. (1923). *Compt. rend. soc. biol.* **88:** 342–343.

McKee, R. W., and Geiman, Q. M. (1948). *Federation Proc.* **7:** 172.

McKee, R. W., Geiman, Q. M., and Cobbey, T. S. (1947). *Federation Proc.* **6:** 276.

McKee, R. W., Ormsbee, R. A., Anfinsen, C. B., Geiman, Q. M., and Ball, E. G. (1946). *J. Exptl. Med.* **84:** 569–582.

Meyerhof, E., and Rothschild, M. (1940). *Nature* **146:** 367.

Moraczewski, S. A., and Kelsey, F. E. (1948). *J. Infectious Diseases* **82:** 45–51.

Morrison, D. B., and Jeskey, H. A. (1948). *J. Natl. Malaria Soc.* **7:** 259–264.

Moulder, J. W. (1948). *J. Infectious Diseases* **83:** 33–41.

Moulder, J. W., and Evans, E. A. (1946). *J. Biol. Chem.* **164:** 145–157.

Mudrow, L., and Reichenow, E. (1944). *Arch. Protistenk.* **97:** 101–170.

Müller, W. (1923). *Zool. Anz.* **57:** 273–281.

Pennoit-DeCooman, E., and van Grembergen, G. (1942). *Verhandel. Konikl. Vlaam. Acad. Wetenschap. Belg. Klasse Wetenschap.* **4:** No. 6, 7–77.

Pringsheim, E. G. (1921). *Beitr. allgem. Botan.* **2:** 88–137.

Reardon, L. V., and Bartgis, I. L. (1949). *J. Parasitol.* **35:** 218–219.

Rogers, W. P. (1940). *J. Helminthol.* **18:** 53–62.

Rogers, W. P. (1941). *J. Helminthol.* **19:** 47–58.

Roy, D. N. (1937). *Parasitology* **29:** 150–162.

Salisbury, L. F., and Anderson, R. J. (1939). *J. Biol. Chem.* **12:** 505–517.

Salle, A. J., and Schmidt, C. L. A. (1928). *J. Infectious Diseases* **43:** 378–384.

Schoenborn, H. W. (1940). *Ann. N. Y. Acad. Sci.* **40:** 1–36.

Schopfer, W. H. (1932). *Rev. suisse zool.* **39:** 59–192.

Schulte, H. (1917). *Arch. ges. Physiol.* **166:** 1–44.

Schuurmans-Stekhoven, J. H., and Botman, T. P. J. (1932). *Z. Parasitenk.* **4:** 220–239.

Schwartz, B. (1921). *J. Parasitol.* **7:** 144–150.

Smorodincev, I. A., and Bebesin, K. V. (1936). *Bull. soc. chim. biol.* **18:** 1097–1105.

Stephenson, M. (1939). Bacterial Metabolism. Ed. 2. Longmans, Green and Co. New York.

Stoll, N. R., Cort, W. W., and Kwei, W. S. (1927). *J. Parasitol.* **13:** 166–172.

Szwejkowska, G. (1929). *Bull. intern. acad. polon. sci. Classe sci. math. nat.* **B1928:** 489–519.

Tallqvist, T. W. (1907). *Z. klin. Med.* **61:** 427–532.

Tobie, E. J., von Brand, T., and Mehlman, B. (1950). *J. Parasitol.* **36:** 48–54.

Tobie, E. J., and Rees, C. W. (1948). *J. Parasitol.* **34:** 162–163.

Wardle, R. A., and Green, N. K. (1941). *Can. J. Research* **D19:** 245–251.

Weinland, E. (1901). *Z. Biol.* **42:** 55–90.

Weiss, E. D., and Ball, G. H. (1947). *Proc. Soc. Exptl. Biol. Med.* **65:** 278–283.

Wetzel, R. (1927). *Deut. tierärztl. Wochschr.* **36:** 719–722.

Wetzel, R. (1931). *J. Parasitol.* **18:** 40–43.

# CHAPTER 13

# THE AEROBIC AND POST-ANAEROBIC GASEOUS EXCHANGES

## I. Introductory Remarks

The relative importance of aerobic and anaerobic processes for a given organism depends on several factors such as the availability of oxygen, possibility of using the energy produced by either aerobic or anaerobic metabolic sequences for all vital processes, mechanisms for the excretion of toxic endproducts, and so forth. Whether an organism will in nature lead a primarily aerobic life will, therefore, largely depend on the host, that is, a parasitic species unable to survive by anaerobic processes will be limited to habitats where, among other factors, sufficient oxygen is available. The reverse may be true also, but it does not need to be. Truly anaerobic parasites, forms that are injured by even low oxygen tensions, are limited to anaerobic habitats. Forms like the schistosomes that gain their energy primarily if not exclusively through fermentation, but which are not injured by oxygen, will be able to invade oxygen-containing habitats. We will return to this problem in the following chapter. The nature of anaerobic metabolism has been characterized in the preceding chapters; it will be sufficient to recall at this point that only few species produce inflammable gases while a greater number evolve carbon dioxide. It is not minimizing the importance of anaerobic processes if a special chapter is devoted to the aerobic gaseous exchanges, but simply a matter of convenience. The latter can and have been investigated frequently independently of the other metabolic processes while such a partial study is hardly profitable in the case of anaerobic fermentations.

## II. Quantitative Aspects of the Aerobic Gaseous Exchanges

All parasites studied so far under aerobic conditions consume oxygen and produce carbon dioxide regardless of whether they lead a primarily aerobic or anaerobic life in their normal habitats. Originally (Weinland, 1901) it had been assumed that intestinal worms like *Ascaris* were not capable of consuming oxygen and the possibility of aerobic processes was conceded only for processes connected with the eggs. As Wright (1950) has pointed out, Weinland's authority was so great as to have this view accepted for the next 30 years. It was then shown, however, by Daniel (1931), Alt and Tischer (1931), and Adam (1932), all working entirely independently, that the intestinal parasites *Balantidium coli*, *Moniezia expansa*, and *Ascaris lumbricoides* were capable of consuming oxygen and it became immediately clear that all the tissues of *Ascaris* and not only the eggs had this faculty (Adam, 1932; Harnisch, 1935a; Krueger, 1936). In so far as parasites living in aerobic habitats are concerned, their capability of consuming oxygen had never been doubted. The first qualitative proof was the observation by Nauss and Yorke (1911) that blood containing trypanosomes rapidly assumed a dark color.

In the last twenty years many observations on the rate of oxygen consumption of various species of parasites have been recorded; representative data have been collected in Tables 27 and 28. They show considerable variations between different species. Some of the factors possibly responsible in bringing them about will be discussed in the following sections. The respiratory quotients are also extremely variable. This is due to the interplay of aerobic and anaerobic processes so characteristic for parasites. It is obvious that contrary to many free-living organisms, the respiratory quotient of parasites is no indication of the substances being metabolized. It is true that a comparative study in sugar-containing and sugar-free media has shown in some cases a definitely higher RQ in the former, giving a fair indication that carbohydrates were used. But even here it would be unjustified to try to calculate the percentage participation of carbohydrates in the overall metabolism.

## A. Influence of Age

It has been reported repeatedly that culture forms of parasitic protozoa show a declining rate of oxygen consumption with increasing age of the cultures. Pertinent data are available for *Trichomonas foetus* (Riedmueller, 1936), *Trypanosoma cruzi* (von Brand, Johnson, and Rees, 1946), and *Leishmania donovani* (Fulton and Joyner, 1949). Figure 12 makes it obvious that this decline is quite pronounced, but it is difficult to adduce definite reasons for it. It may be remarked that Chang (1948) has described crithidias from the later stages of such trypanosome cultures which are morphologically different from those characteristic of young cultures.

Somewhat more clarified is the case of the bloodstream form of *Trypanosoma lewisi* where Moulder (1947, 1948b) found a significantly smaller oxygen consumption of flagellates taken from young infections than from old ones while the opposite relationship held true with respect to the rates of sugar consumption. It appears that a shift between synthetic and energy-producing processes occurs; the young flagellates were dividing while the older ones had ceased doing so.

Another example is the malarial parasite, many species of which are well suited for a study of this question because of the synchronicity of their development. Velick's (1942) data (Fig. 13) show the marked increase

TABLE 27.  Rates of oxygen consumption and respiratory quotients of some parasitic protozoa

| SPECIES | STAGE | TEMP. °C | OXYGEN CONSUMPTION IN THE | | | RESPIRATORY QUOTIENT IN THE | | AUTHOR |
|---|---|---|---|---|---|---|---|---|
| | | | Absence of sugar mm³ O₂/100 million/hour | Presence of sugar mm³ O₂/100 million/hour | Presence of sugar mm³ O₂/mg dry weight/hour | Absence of sugar | Presence of sugar | |
| Strigomonas oncopelti | Culture | 28 | | (41) | 62 | | 1.0 | Lwoff (1934) |
| S. fasciculata | Culture | 28 | | (37) | 55 | | 1.0 | Lwoff (1934) |
| Leptomonas ctenocephali | Culture | 28 | | (27) | 40 | | 0.88 | Lwoff (1934) |
| Leishmania tropica | Culture | 32; 37; 28 | | 31; 45; 39 | | 0.88 | 0.95 | Soule (1925); Adler and Ashbel (1934); von Brand and Johnson (1947); Chang (1948) |
| L. brasiliensis | Culture | 28; 32 | | 42; 32 | | | | von Brand and Johnson (1947); Chang (1948) |
| L. donovani | Culture | 37; 28; 32; 25 | | 44; 18; 27; 44 | | | 0.9 | Adler and Ashbel (1934); von Brand and Johnson (1947); Chang (1948); Fulton and Joyner (1949) |
| Trypanosoma lewisi | Bloodstream, old | 37 | | 50; 51; 62 | | | 0.98; 0.91 | Reiner, Smythe, and Pedlow (1936); Moulder (1947; 1948b); von Brand, Tobie, and Mehlman (1950) |
| T. lewisi | Bloodstream, young | 37 | | 71 | | | 0.74 | Moulder (1947, 1948b) |
| T. lewisi | Culture | 28 | | | | 0.88 | 0.94 | Soule (1925) |
| T. cruzi | Bloodstream | 37 | | 124 | | | | von Brand, Tobie, and Mehlman (1950) |
| T. cruzi | Culture | 28; 32 | | 25; 43 | | 0.7 | 1.0 | von Brand, Johnson, and Rees (1946); Chang (1948) |

| Organism | Material | Temp. | A | B | C | Ratio | Authors |
|---|---|---|---|---|---|---|---|
| T. conorhini | Culture | 30 | | 26 | | | von Brand, Tobie, and Mehlman (1950) |
| T. pipistrelli | Culture | 30 | | 13 | | | von Brand, Tobie, and Mehlman (1950) |
| T. congolense | Bloodstream | 37 | | 153 | | | von Brand, Tobie, and Mehlman (1950) |
| T. evansi | Bloodstream | 37 | | 166 | | | von Brand, Tobie, and Mehlman (1950) |
| T. hippicum | Bloodstream | 38 | | 200 | 240 | | von Brand, Tobie, and Mehlman (1950) |
| T. equinum | Bloodstream | 37 | | 166 | | 0 | Harvey (1949) |
| T. equiperdum | Bloodstream | 37 | | 185 | | 0.06 | von Brand, Tobie, and Mehlman (1950) |
| T. rhodesiense | Bloodstream | 37 | | 194 | 285 | 0.16 | Reiner, Smythe, and Pedlow (1936); von Brand, Tobie, and Mehlman (1950) |
| T. gambiense | Bloodstream | 37 | | 170 | | | Christophers and Fulton (1938) |
| T. gambiense | Culture | 30 | | 38 | | | von Brand, Tobie, and Mehlman (1950) |
| Trichomonas foetus | Culture | 28 | | 215 | 36 | | von Brand, Tobie, and Mehlman (1950); Riedmueller (1936) |
| T. hepatica | Culture | 38 | | 600 | | 0.87 | Willems, Massart, and Peeters (1942) |
| Plasmodium knowlesi | Isolated parasites | 37 | | | 53 | 0.86 | Christophers and Fulton (1938) |
| P. knowlesi | Rings | 38 | | 8 | | | Maier and Coggeshall (1941) |
| P. knowlesi | ¾-Grown segmenters | 38 | | 34 | | | Maier and Coggeshall (1941) |
| P. inui | Rings, amoeb. | 38 | | 9 | | | Maier and Coggeshall (1941) |
| P. cynomolgi | Segmenters | | | 47 | | | Maier and Coggeshall (1941) |
| P. cathemerium | ¼ Grown | 38 | | 10 | | | Maier and Coggeshall (1941) |
| P. cathemerium | ¾ Grown | 38 | | 25 | | | Maier and Coggeshall (1941) |
| P. lophurae | ½-¾ Grown | 38 | | 18 | | | Maier and Coggeshall (1941) |
| Eimeria tenella | Unsporul. oocysts | 30 | 1660 | | | | Smith and Herrick (1944) |
| E. tenella | Sporul. oocysts | 30 | 44 | | | | Smith and Herrick (1944) |
| Balantidium coli | Trophozoites | | | | | 0.84 | Daniel (1931) |

TABLE 28.    Rates of oxygen consumption and respiratory quotients of endoparasitic helminths and arthropods at an oxygen tension of about 160 mm Hg.

| SPECIES | STAGE | TEMP. °C | OXYGEN CONSUMPTION IN THE | | | | RESPIRATORY QUOTIENT IN THE | | AUTHOR |
| | | | Absence of sugar | | Presence of sugar | | Absence of sugar | Presence of sugar | |
| | | | mm³ O₂/gm fresh substance/ hour | mm³ O₂/mg dry substance/ hour | mm³ O₂/gm fresh substance/ hour | mm³ O₂/mg dry substance/ hour | | | |
|---|---|---|---|---|---|---|---|---|---|
| *Paramphistomum cervi* | Adults | 38 | (3) | 0.03 | | | 8 | | Lazarus (1950) |
| *Schistosoma mansoni* | Pairs | 37.5 | | 6.0 | | 8.7 | 1.03 | 1.02 | Bueding (1950) |
| *S. mansoni* | Males | 37.5 | | | | 9.1 | | | Bueding (1950) |
| *S. mansoni* | Females | 37.5 | | | | 10.7 | | | Bueding (1950) |
| *Fasciola hepatica* | Adults | 37.5 | (330) | 1.94 | (1350) | 15.0 | | | van Grembergen (1949) |
| *Diphyllobothrium latum* | Proglottids | 37 | (243) | 2.7 | | | | | Friedheim and Baer (1933) |
| *D. latum* | Plerocercoids | 22 | | 0.34 | | 0.67 | | | Friedheim and Baer (1933) |
| *Triaenophorus nodulosus* | Strobila | 22 | 418 | | | | | | Harnisch (1933) |
| *Moniezia expansa* | Head region | 37.5 | | | | 1.1 | | 1.05 | Alt and Tischer (1931) |
| *M. expansa* | Mature progl. | 37.5 | | | | 0.9 | | 1.08 | Alt and Tischer (1931) |
| *M. expansa* | Gravid progl. | 37.5 | | | | 0.6 | | 1.13 | Alt and Tischer (1931) |
| *Trichinella spiralis* | Larvae | 37.5 | | 2.35 | | 2.37 | 1.13 | | Stannard, McCoy, and Latchford (1938) |
| *Strongylus equinus* | Adults | 38 | | 3.3 | | | 3.0 | | Lazarus (1950) |
| *S. vulgaris* | Adults | 38 | | 3.6 | | | 3.3 | | Lazarus (1950) |
| *Haemonchus contortus* | Eggs (morula) | 30 | | 9.7 | | | 0.60 | | Rogers (1948) |
| *H. contortus* | Eggs (blastula) | 30 | | 10.7 | | | 0.58 | | Rogers (1948) |
| *H. contortus* | Larvae | 30 | | 12.6 | | | 0.64 | | Rogers (1948) |
| *Ostertagia circumcincta* | Adults | 38 | | 7.4 | | | 0.8 | | Lazarus (1950) |
| *Nematodirus* spp. | Adults | 37 | (1070) | 5.1 | | | 0.66 | | Rogers (1948) |
| *Nippostrongylus muris* | Larvae (1 day) | 30 | | 18.4 | | | 0.73 | | Rogers (1948) |

| Species | Stage | | | | | | | Reference |
|---|---|---|---|---|---|---|---|---|
| N. muris | Larvae (4 days) | 30 | | 13.0 | | | 0.74 | Rogers (1948) |
| N. muris | Larvae (12 days) | 30 | | 9.2 | | | 0.68 | Rogers (1948) |
| N. muris | Adults | 37 | (1430) | 6.8 | | | 0.69 | Rogers (1948) |
| Eustrongylides ignotus | Larvae | 37 | 140 | (0.56) | | | 1.04 | von Brand (1942) |
| Syphacia obvelata | Adults | 38 | | 4.4 | | | 1.1 | Lazarus (1950) |
| Neoaplectana glaseri | Adults | 30 | (2600) | 12.6 | | | 0.59 | Rogers (1948) |
| Heterakis spumosa | Adults | 38 | | 4.0 | | | 1.1 | Lazarus (1950) |
| Ascaris lumbricoides | Small | 39 | 80 | (0.42) | | | | Laser (1944) |
| A. lumbricoides | Males | 37 | 112 | (0.59) | | | | Adam (1932) |
| A. lumbricoides | Females | 37 | 61 | (0.32) | | | Approx. 4 | Adam (1932); von Brand (1934) |
| A. lumbricoides | Small | 37 | 156 | (0.82) | | | | Krueger (1936) |
| A. lumbricoides | Large | 37 | 72 | (0.33) | | | Approx. 3 | Krueger (1936) |
| Ascaridia galli | Adults | 37 | (525) | 2.5 | | | 0.96 | Rogers (1948) |
| Litomosoides carinii | Adults | 37.5 | 800 | | 1850 | 0.94 | 0.44 | Bueding (1949a) |
| Setaria equinum | Adults | 38 | 250 | | | | 1.04 | Toryu (1934) |
| Dracunculus insignis | Adults | 37.5 | | | 560 | | | Bueding and Oliver-Gonzalez (1950) |
| Gasterophilus intestinalis | Larvae | 37 | 300 | | | | 0.78 | Levenbook (1949) |

The figures in ( ) are not given by the author but have been calculated from available data on the dry matter percentage.

taking place during the 24 hour cycle of *Plasmodium cathemerium*. Comparable data for *Plasmodium knowlesi* have been presented by Maier and Coggeshall (1941).

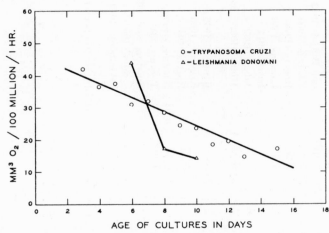

Fig. 12.   Rates of oxygen consumption of parasitic protozoa in relation to the age of the cultures. *Trypanosoma cruzi* after von Brand, Johnson, and Rees (1946), *Leishmania donovani* after Fulton and Joyner (1949).

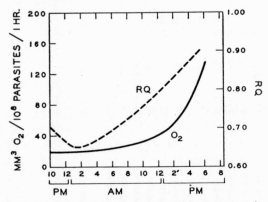

Fig. 13.   Rate of oxygen consumption and respiratory quotient of *Plasmodium cathemerium* during its developmental cycle in the bloodstream (after Velick, 1942).

There are only few relevant data at hand for parasitic worms. Alt and Tischer's (1931) data seem to indicate a decreasing rate of oxygen consumption along the strobila of *Moniezia*, but Friedheim and Baer's (1933) figures for *Diphyllobothrium* point in the opposite direction. No profitable comparison between the rates of respiration of larval and adult worms can be made because in most cases each requires a different optimal temperature. In some instances also, such as Fenwick's (1938) study of *Ascaris* larvae, the rates are referred to numbers rather than to weight, excluding a comparison with the adult form. Rogers (1948) has shown that the oxygen consumption decreased in intensity in the larvae of *Nippostrongylus* with increasing age (Table 28).

Some data are available for eggs. Huff (1936) found a gradual increase in oxygen consumption during the development of the eggs of *Ascaris*, 1000 eggs consuming at 30°C on the first day of development 0.30 mm$^3$ $O_2$ and on the tenth day 0.51 mm$^3$. A similar increase in oxygen consumption of the eggs up to the completion of the fully embryonated egg was reported by Rogers (1948) for *Haemonchus*. Brown (1928), in contrast, found a constant rate during the development of the *Ascaris* egg.

A curious and as yet not satisfactorily explained observation has been made by Huff (1936). According to him a removal of the albuminous coating of the *Ascaris* egg increased the overall consumption at least fivefold during the entire period of development. No increase with increasing age occurred, however, and his figures actually indicate rather a small decrease in the later stages.

Mature *Ascaris* eggs, just as those of many other helminths, remain viable for many months after having formed fully developed larvae. A sharp reduction in oxygen consumption at some period after reaching maturity should be expected, but no data on this point are available.

## B. *Influence of Size*

The rates of oxygen consumption of small organisms are higher generally than those of large ones, if the comparison is based on weight. This holds true also for parasites, as a comparison of the available rates based on dry weight for protozoa and worms shows (Tables 27 and 28). There is no generally accepted explanation for this phenomenon. It is somehow linked to the organization of the organisms involved. Krebs (1950) has recently shown for mammals that the tissue respiration of large forms is only little less than that of small ones, while the overall respiration of the entire organisms shows much greater differences.

It is a well established fact that this decline in respiration with increasing weight is largely eliminated if the rates of warm-blooded animals are expressed on the basis of surface area. This same pattern holds true also in several invertebrates, although certainly not strictly when invertebrates of different morphological types are compared (comprehensive review of the literature in Zeuthen, 1947). Thus, there is little value in comparing in this way the respiration of parasitic protozoa and worms, but a different question is whether fixed relationships exist between size and respiratory rate in the case of helminths. It was first raised by Krueger (1940a) who studied the rates of *Ascaris* specimens ranging in weight from 0.32 to 7.76

gm. He found that they followed the surface area fairly well and could be expressed by Meeh's formula: $O = K\sqrt[3]{W^2}$, wherein $O$ is the oxygen consumption, $W$ the weight in grams, and $K$ a constant varying from species to species. In this particular case $K$ amounted to 13.96. When different species of nematodes are studied, a comparison on the basis of relative surface area decreases the differences arising from calculations based on weight, but certainly does not eliminate them (von Brand, 1942; Rogers, 1948; Lazarus, 1950). Further work dealing both with intra- and inter-specific comparisons is required before the problem can be regarded as clarified.

## C. Influence of Motility

How much different degrees of motility contribute to the differences in metabolic rate found in parasites is difficult to say. No measure of their basal metabolism is available. Some protozoa, like the bloodstream form of the trypanosomes, are extremely active, others like the malarial parasites exhibit only slight movements. Similarly, some worms, for example, the ascarids, are quite sluggish, while many of the smaller species are much more active. The observation of Slater (1925) that electrical stimulation hastens the death of anaerobically kept *Ascaris* is an indirect sign that motility materially increases the metabolic rate of at least this species.

In very small organisms, however, motility seems to have a much smaller influence. Zeuthen (1947) found the metabolism of such micro-organisms as starfish or molluscan larvae only slightly increased during periods of activity. If the same general trend holds true for even smaller organisms, which however have not yet been studied directly in this respect, the increase in metabolism due to motility should be small indeed in protozoa. It may be mentioned in this connection that Ludwig (1928), basing his views on entirely theoretical considerations, calculated the energy required for the ciliary movement of *Paramaecium* as an extremely small fraction of the total produced. Pending direct investigations, however, a certain caution is indicated. Lwoff (1934) related that the more or less sessile gregarinoid forms of *Leptomonas ctenocephali* consumed less oxygen than the motile monadine forms, but whether the difference in motility was actually the decisive factor has not been established.

## D. Influence of Light

Light is an unphysiological stimulus for internal parasites, since they normally live in the dark. Most forms, however, are exposed to light during some period in their development. A pertinent question is whether light has an influence on their metabolic rate since it is frequently admitted more or less profusely during experimentation and since it has been observed (Davis and Slater, 1928) that the oxygen consumption of earth-worms approximately doubles in daylight as compared to darkness.

Very little is known in this respect with regard to parasites. Toryu (1936), working with very small numbers of parasites only, reported that light increased the anaerobic carbon dioxide production of *Parascaris* from 3 to 4 times, but had no noticeable effect on the aerobic metabolism. Laser and Rothschild (1949) mention an apparently as yet unpublished experiment by Levenbook according to which light seems to decrease somewhat the oxygen consumption of *Gasterophilus* larvae. It did increase markedly their carbon dioxide production, raising the respiratory quotient from 0.78 to 1.5. More work along similar lines appears indicated.

TABLE 29.   Range of hydrogen ion concentrations in which the oxygen consumption of some parasites remains unaltered

| SPECIES | MATERIAL | pH RANGE | AUTHOR |
|---|---|---|---|
| *Trypanosoma lewisi* ........ | Bloodstream form | 6.7–7.8 | Moulder (1948a) |
| *Plasmodium gallinaceum*.... | Incubates | 7.6–8.0 | Silverman *et al.* (1944) |
| *Eimeria tenella*............ | Sporulated oocysts | 4.7–8.8 | Smith and Herrick (1944) |
| *Schistosoma mansoni*....... | Adults | 6.8–8.9 | Bueding (1950) |
| *Eustrongylides ignotus*...... | Larvae | 3.4–8.3 | von Brand (1943) |
| *Litomosoides carinii*........ | Adults | 6.0–7.5 | Bueding (1949a) |

### E. Influence of Hydrogen Ion Concentration

The figures of Table 29 indicate that the pH range in which the respiration of parasites remains unaltered, is fairly narrow in blood parasites and in the body cavity parasite, *Litomosoides*, that is, in those cases in which the organisms live normally in surroundings showing but little variations in pH. The oocysts of *Eimeria tenella*, on the contrary, are often exposed to the most variable external conditions, as is the larval *Eustrongylides*, though to a lesser extent. It must be adapted to a transition from the cysts in a fish to the acid forestomach of birds. In these cases the range of tolerated pH is much wider than in the former ones. It must be realized, however, that the oocysts of coccidia are well known for their impermeability. If their respiration remains unchanged in a wide pH range, one has not necessarily to assume that their protoplasm proper is unsensitive to such changes; it is perhaps protected by the external membrane.

### F. Influence of Temperature

The temperature of the environment is one of the most important factors determining the metabolic level of invertebrates. Some parasites, such as

*Trichinella*, complete their entire life cycle at the high temperature prevailing in warm-blooded hosts. The parasites of cold-blooded animals, on the other hand, live under more variable temperature conditions. The normal upper limit lies in most cases well below that characteristic for the environment of the first mentioned group. Finally, there is a large group of parasites which alternates between warm- and cold-blooded hosts, and in many cases part of their life cycle is passed in the outside world. It is clear that the largest fluctuations in environmental temperature occur in this group. They are more pronounced than those to which aquatic free-living invertebrates are exposed, though probably not much more so than those encountered by some terrestrial invertebrates, for example, some insects.

The influence of temperature on the oxygen consumption of some parasites has been studied over a fairly wide range. As in all cold-blooded animals the rate rose to a maximum with increasing temperature and then began to fall off rapidly when a temperature injurious to the organisms was reached. If the data obtained in the range compatible with life are plotted according to Arrhenius' equation (Fig. 14) usually no single straight line but at least two bisecting lines were obtained. With the exception of *Ancylostoma caninum* larvae, the temperature increment was smaller in the higher range of tolerated temperatures than in the lower one. In the case of *Ascaris lumbricoides* indications were found that the temperature relationships are even more complicated and four bisecting lines were obtained in the range 0.5 to 45°C (Krueger, 1940b). It is true that only a straight line relationship was reported for *Diphyllobothrium latum* plerocercoids (Friedheim, Susz, and Baer, 1933), but these parasites were studied only in the range of 20 to 37°C. The significance of bisecting lines resulting from Arrhenius' equation has given rise to a good deal of speculation. Crozier (1925) assumes that in different temperature ranges different master reactions are involved, but this interpretation has not been accepted generally. For further information the reader is referred to Belehradek's (1935) monograph.

## G. Influence of Ionic Environment

The questions as to what extent the ionic concentration of the medium and the various ions occurring in it influence the metabolic activities, deserve serious consideration in selecting an optimal medium for respiratory studies. Early practice in such studies with parasitic worms was simply to use an isotonic sodium chloride solution or mammalian or frog Ringer solutions, but this was not entirely satisfactory. More recent studies indicate that the optimal conditions vary from species to species.

Moulder (1948a) has shown that a total cation concentration of 0.130

$M$ was best for the bloodstream form of *Trypanosoma lewisi*, while concentrations of 0.150 $M$ and above led in most instances to a marked decline in respiratory rate. Potassium and magnesium could be eliminated completely without deleterious effect and the phosphate concentration could be varied between 0.011 and 0.044 $M$ without changing the respiratory rate.

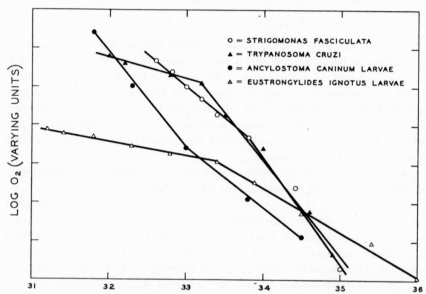

Fig. 14.   Temperature relationships of the oxygen consumption of some parasites expressed according to Arrhenius' equation. *Strigomonas fasciculata* after Lwoff (1934). Lwoff represents in his paper the temperature relationship as a straight line; a replotting of his figures showed that they fit better the two bisecting lines shown in the present figure. *Trypanosoma cruzi* after von Brand, Johnson, and Rees (1946), *Ancylostoma caninum* larvae after McCoy (1930), *Eustrongylides ignotus* after von Brand (1943).

Malarial parasites may be more sensitive. Wendel (1943) reported that the oxygen consumption of *Plasmodium knowlesi* decreased in slightly hypertonic solutions. Sodium chloride was especially damaging under these circumstances, but he found phosphate so toxic as to consider it as contraindicated for pH control. This latter finding, however, was not substantiated by the work of McKee *et al.* (1946).

Considerable differences also occur apparently among parasitic worms. Potassium markedly stimulated the metabolic activity of *Eustrongylides ignotus* and *Schistosoma mansoni* (von Brand, 1943; Bueding, 1950) while decreasing that of *Litomosoides* (Bueding, 1949a). The schistosomes were also stimulated by the magnesium ion which was practically without effect on *Eustrongylides*. *Litomosoides* was metabolically most active in solutions containing, besides a fairly high NaCl concentration, low concentrations of KCl, $CaCl_2$, and $MgCl_2$. The amount of phosphate buffer could be varied between 0.006 and 0.06 $M$ without effect on the metabolic rate. The schistosomes, on the other hand, required a high phosphate concentration for optimal respiration (Bueding, Peters, and Waite, 1947).

## H. Influence of Oxygen Tension

The question as to what influence oxygen tension has on the gaseous metabolism of parasites has given rise to numerous investigations and to a certain amount of controversy. The reason why this particular phase should have aroused so much interest is not difficult to find. The oxygen tensions under which parasites find themselves *in vivo* are quite different for various species as will be shown in greater detail in the following chapter and they have in many cases obviously a profound influence on the oxygen relationships of the organisms.

*1. General survey of the problem.* A relatively voluminous literature on this subject, reviewed in some detail by von Brand (1946) exists for free-living invertebrates. It will be sufficient for the present purpose to recapitulate it only very briefly. The invertebrates, in their relationship to oxygen tension, are customarily divided into two groups. In the first one the oxygen consumption remains constant over a wide range of tensions and begins to fall off only when very little oxygen is present, while in the second group this drop in consumption is already apparent at high tensions and the maximum oxygen consumption is frequently not reached even at oxygen tensions surpassing that of atmospheric air.

No hard and fast line can be drawn between the two groups and to what group an organism belongs can frequently, though not always, be deduced from its organization. Thus bulky animals like actinians, which lack a circulatory system, quite generally belong to the second group simply because at moderate tensions not enough oxygen can enter the body by diffusion to satisfy the maximal oxygen requirements of both the superficial and deeper layers of tissues. On the other hand such organisms as jellyfish have a respiration independent of the tension even if they are quite large because they contain very little living protoplasm and sufficient oxygen diffuses into the body through the surface to give all cells all the oxygen required even at relatively low tensions.

It must be realized, however, that cases exist which are not so simply explained. It has thus been found that the respiration of the ciliate *Spirostomum* is dependent on the tension (Specht, 1935). Although this is a large form, as far as protozoa are concerned, it is difficult to see why diffusion should be the limiting factor. Equally puzzling is the observation that some crustaceans have a respiration independent of the tension while in other species it shows a distinct dependency despite the fact that both seem to contain fairly efficient oxygen distributing mechanisms.

Parasitic protozoa and parasitic worms lack special organizational means of gathering or distributing oxygen. This is self evident for the former, but the lack of such organs as gills or a circulatory system in the latter must be emphasized. Both groups then must rely for their oxygen supply solely on diffusion either from the body surface alone or, in addition, on diffusion from their alimentary canal, if they are blood-sucking worms. Such an endoparasitic arthropod as the *Gasterophilus* larva, on the contrary, has a tracheal system usable for the distribution of oxygen to various tissues and endoparasitic insect larvae are known with special appendages that probably have a respiratory significance. All these latter forms cannot be considered further since nothing is known thus far about their reactions to various oxygen tensions.

*2. Parasitic protozoa and oxygen tension.* The respiration of only a few parasitic protozoa has so far been studied in its relation to the oxygen tension (Table 30). These forms show, in common with the great majority of free-living protozoa, an oxygen consumption independent of the tension over a wide range. This, of course, is not surprising since in such small organisms the surface/volume ratio is such as to give optimal conditions for the diffusion of oxygen into the body.

*3. Parasitic worms and oxygen tension.* The reactions of parasitic worms to variations in oxygen tension are more varied than those shown by protozoa. Some helminths (the ectoparasitic *Temnocephala*, the endoparasitic *Trichinella* larvae, and the eggs of *Diphyllobothrium*) belong to the independent group. They are all small organisms and diffusion obviously does not limit the consumption (Table 30).

To the group showing a dependency of the oxygen consumption on the tension belong the relatively large worms listed in Table 31, but also the small and delicate *Litomosoides* and *Schistosoma* (Bueding, 1949b). If diffusion were the limiting factor here, it should be expected that this dependency would disappear, or at least be drastically reduced under conditions where the distance through which the oxygen has to diffuse in order to reach all the tissues is reduced. Such conditions are realized if minced material or homogenates are used. The first fact emerging from such experiments is that initially the rate of oxygen consumption at a specified oxygen tension is appreciably higher with minced material than with total helminths (Table 32). During longer lasting experiments, however, the rate of the minced material sinks materially, often below that of the intact animal. This may or may not be a phenomenon of dying. At any rate, the

TABLE 30. Respiration of parasites having a respiration independent of the oxygen tension

| SPECIES | MATERIAL | OXYGEN CONSUMPTION AT SPECIFIED OXYGEN TENSIONS IN PERCENT OF OXYGEN CONSUMPTION AT 160 MM HG. | | | | | | AUTHOR |
|---|---|---|---|---|---|---|---|---|
| | | 760 mm | 160 mm | 38 mm | 15 mm | 8 mm | 1 mm | |
| *Trypanosoma cruzi* | Culture forms | 102 | 100 | 102 | 54 | | 9 | von Brand, Johnson, and Rees (1946) |
| *Plasmodium knowlesi* | Incubates | 90 | 100 | 114 | | | | McKee et al., (1946) |
| *Temnocephala* spp. | Adults from *Trichodactylus* | 180 | 100 | 117 | 92 | 95 | | Gonzalez (1949) |
| *Temnocephala* spp. | Adults from *Aegla* | | 100 | 114 | 95 | 97 | | Gonzalez (1949) |
| *Diphyllobothrium latum* | Eggs | 100 | 100 | | Approx. 100 | | | Friedheim and Baer (1933) |
| *Trichinella spiralis* | Larvae | 89 | 100 | 101 | 103 | 92 | | Stannard, McCoy, and Latchford (1938) |

TABLE 31.   Respiration of parasites having a respiration dependent on the oxygen tension

| SPECIES | MATERIAL | OXYGEN CONSUMPTION AT SPECIFIED OXYGEN TENSIONS IN PERCENT OF OXYGEN CONSUMPTION AT 160 MM Hg. | | | | | | | AUTHOR |
|---|---|---|---|---|---|---|---|---|---|
| | | 760 mm | 160 mm | 80 mm | 38 mm | 15 mm | 8 mm | |
| Fasciola hepatica............ | Adults | 140 | 100 | 68 | 46 | | 27 | Harnisch (1932) |
| F. hepatica................. | Adults | 140 | 100 | | 53 | | | van Grembergen (1949) |
| Diphyllobothrium latum....... | Plerocercoids | 130 | 100 | | 72 | | | Friedheim and Baer (1933) |
| D. latum................... | Anterior proglottids | 114 | 100 | | 91 | | | Friedheim and Baer (1933) |
| D. latum................... | Posterior proglottids | 180 | 100 | | 66 | | | Friedheim and Baer (1933) |
| Triaenophorus nodulosus ...... | Strobila | 133 | 100 | | | | 21 | Harnisch (1933) |
| Ascaris lumbricoides......... | Adults | 200 | 100 | 63 | 40 | 10 | | Krueger (1936) |
| A. lumbricoides............. | Adults | 300 | 100 | | 50 | | | Laser (1944) |

increased initial consumption could be taken as an indication that the
internal tissues could not get enough oxygen *in situ* by diffusion and, after
mincing, either paid off an oxygen debt or at least had an opportunity to
oxidize at their maximal capacity.

There is, however, a second point to be considered, namely, the influence
of the oxygen tension on the oxygen consumption of minced material
and this is a somewhat controversial point. Harnisch (1932, 1933) maintains that minced material of *Fasciola* and *Triaenophorus* shows essentially
the same dependency as the total animals, while on the contrary van
Grembergen (1944, 1949) reports that the oxygen consumption of minced
*Fasciola* and *Moniezia* has become independent of the tension over a wide
range. These diametrically opposed findings are impossible to reconcile
at present. Van Grembergen is inclined to accuse Harnisch of faulty techniques. Harnisch (personal communication) points to the fact that both

TABLE 32.   Comparison of the rates of oxygen consumption of entire worms and
minced worms

| SPECIES | PERIOD IN HOURS | OXYGEN CONSUMPTION IN MM³ O₂/1 GM FRESH WEIGHT/1 HOUR | | AUTHOR |
|---|---|---|---|---|
| | | Entire worms | Minced worms | |
| *Fasciola hepatica*.......... | 1 | 94 | 144 | Harnisch (1932) |
| *Fasciola hepatica*......... | 0.5 | 350 | 412 | van Grembergen (1949) |
| *Ascaris lumbricoides*...... | 1 | 80 | 260 | Laser (1944) |

used different mincing techniques and that van Grembergen studied the
oxygen consumption with succinate as substrate while Harnisch investigated the endogenous rate. In defending his technique he can further
point out that both he (Harnisch, 1933) and van Grembergen, van Damme,
and Vercruysse (1949) found a dependency of the oxygen consumption on
the tension in the case of minced *Ascaris* where both studied the endogenous rate only. In this latter case then, surely, difficulty of diffusion
alone cannot be incriminated.

There are only vague ideas on the mechanism responsible for this persistence of dependency. Harnisch (1935b, 1936, 1949, 1950) in a series of
papers has maintained that in many free-living invertebrates the normal
aerobic oxygen consumption is independent of the tension over a wide
range while their post-anaerobic oxygen consumption by which they repay
an oxygen debt, shows the same dependency as the normal oxygen consumption of parasitic helminths. He has coined for both types the terms
"primary" and "secondary" aerobiosis and he assumes that the oxygen
consumption is mediated through different enzyme systems, one of which

would be operating efficiently only at high oxygen tensions. In his view parasitic worms would possess only this latter type of enzyme.

Harnisch (1937) assumes that this enzyme is localized in the extracellular fluids. He observed that the respiration of washed, minced *Ascaris* material becomes negligible, but that it is restored materially if the pieces are subsequently suspended in the body fluid of the worms. This observation in itself is correct; the above interpretation, however, is not. Bueding (personal communication) has confirmed the increase in respiration by the use of body fluid. He obtained, however, an identical increase upon using

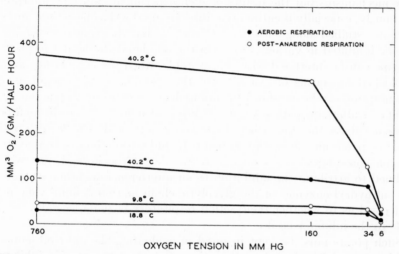

Fig. 15. Influence of temperature on the dependency of the aerobic and post-anaerobic oxygen consumption of *Eustrongylides ignotus* larvae on the oxygen tension (after von Brand, 1947).

body fluid heated for 20 minutes at 100°C while this effect was abolished completely after the body fluid had been dialyzed. This obviously indicated that an enzyme is not involved but that restoration of respiration is due to the presence of dialyzable substrates or coenzymes in the body fluid.

One more complicating factor is involved which seems to indicate that generalizations are out of place at the present time. Von Buddenbrock (1939) has pointed out that in some free-living invertebrates the oxygen consumption shows a dependency on the tension at high temperatures while this phenomenon disappears at low temperatures. The explanation seems to be that in the former case the oxygen demands of the tissues are so high that not all the tissues get enough oxygen at moderate tensions while they do, even at low oxygen tensions, when the lowering of the temperature decreases the overall demands of the organisms. In parasites, von Brand (1947) found a similar situation both in respect to the normal and the post-anaerobic oxygen consumption of larval *Eustrongylides* (Fig. 15). Obviously then a study of the entire problem with its various ramifications on a broad comparative basis will be required before we can claim to understand the situation and profitably can try explaining it.

### III. Action of Respiratory Inhibitors and Stimulants

Inhibitors and stimulants are powerful tools in elucidating the respiratory mechanisms but the results of such experiments must be interpreted cautiously, especially if entire organisms are used as has been done in most parasites studied along such lines. It is clear that the oxygen consumption can be inhibited in various ways. On the one hand the actual respiratory enzyme can be interfered with, for example, when the cytochrome system is blocked by means of cyanide. On the other hand the overall oxygen consumption can be cut down to various degrees, depending upon the availability of alternate pathways, if a compound inhibits a certain metabolic sequence above the stage where hydrogen is activated. The African pathogenic trypanosomes are a case in point. If sulfhydryl inhibitors reduce their oxygen consumption to a negligible fraction of the normal, one will be inclined to attribute the inhibition to an interference with one or more of the sulfhydryl enzymes of the glycolytic chain and no definite view point is derived as to whether their actual respiratory enzyme was also susceptible to the inhibitor used.

Such points must be kept in mind in evaluating the data presented in Tables 33 and 34 which list the action of some representative inhibitors. It was of course impossible to enumerate all the inhibitors employed by the various workers, or all the dilutions used of those compounds that have been incorporated into the tables. It is believed, however, that the presented data suffice in showing that the reactions are so diverse as to clearly indicate the occurrence of different respiratory mechanisms.

In one group of parasites (leishmanias, strigomonads, malarial parasites, *Fasciola*, *Moniezia*, *Litomosoides*) the oxygen consumption is strongly inhibited by cyanide and, where tested, by azide and carbon monoxide. This definitely indicates that a heavy metal catalysis is involved. Carbon monoxide inhibition, if reversed by light, indicates iron catalysis. Such reversal experiments have hardly been done as yet. In the case of malarial parasites no clear-cut results could be obtained with this procedure (McKee *et al.*, 1946). The malaria plasmodia are nevertheless the group for which the analysis has progressed farthest. The tentative conclusion seems justified that "oxygen transport is catalyzed by iron porphyrin proteins, flavoproteins, and pyridinoproteins similar to those demonstrated in other organisms" (Moulder, 1948c). The occurrence of flavoprotein enzymes appears very likely from the experiments of Bovarnick, Lindsay, and Hellerman (1946) who found that cresylblue restored about 40% of the cyanide blocked respiration of *Plasmodium lophurae*. Ball *et al.* (1945) reported the synthesis of flavine adenine dinucleotide by *Plasmodium knowlesi* both *in vivo* and *in vitro*. It has finally been shown that the lactic and malic dehydrogenases of *Plasmodium gallinaceum* need for maximum activity diphosphopyridine nucleotide (Speck and Evans, 1945; Speck, Moulder, and Evans, 1946).

The respiration of *Fasciola* and *Moniezia* is strongly stimulated by methylene blue and this dye is capable of reversing cyanide inhibition (van Grembergen, 1944, 1949). This author also found a stimulation by paraphenylenediamine, but this stimulation is not specific enough to indicate definitely the presence of the cytochrome system (Bueding, 1949b). As mentioned in Chapter 6, Bueding and Charms (1950) found only very little cytochrome in schistosomes and no cytochrome or cytochrome oxidase whatever in *Litomosoides* and *Ascaris*.

In other parasites the respiration is also rather strongly inhibited by cyanide, but it is insensitive to carbon monoxide. This has been observed in the culture form of *Trypanosoma cruzi*, in *Diphyllobothrium*, *Triaenophorus*, and the larvae of *Trichinella* (Tables 33 and 34). In the *Trichinella* larvae carbon monoxide even brought about a stimulation of respiration (Stannard, McCoy, and Latchford, 1938). The oxygen consumption of *Diphyllobothrium* plerocercoids was strongly stimulated by pyocyanine which also completely reversed cyanide inhibition. In the presence of $M/1000$ KCN and pyocyanine the respiratory rate was even 70% higher than the normal one (Friedheim and Baer, 1933). The respiration of *Trichinella* larvae, on the contrary, was hardly affected by methylene blue and the dye did not restore the cyanide inhibited respiration. There is some doubt, however, whether the dye did actually penetrate into the worms (Stannard, McCoy, and Latchford, 1938). Whether *Eustrongylides* belongs to this group is uncertain since its reactions to carbon monoxide have not yet been studied. Its response to methylene blue was essentially similar to that mentioned for *Trichinella* (von Brand, 1945). In both cases there was some stimulation of the oxygen consumption by paraphenylenediamine and the respiration of *Eustrongylides* was also stimulated by dinitrophenol. The nature of the respiratory systems operative in these cases is not yet known.

In a third group of parasites (bloodstream form of the African pathogenic trypanosomes, trichomonads, *Paramphistomum*, *Ascaris*) the respiration is essentially unaffected by cyanide, or even stimulated, this latter phenomenon possibly due to the carbonyl combining property of cyanide

TABLE 33.   Effect of some inhibitors on the oxygen consumption of some parasitic protozoa

| SPECIES | STAGE | Carbon monoxide 95% | Cyanide $M/1000$ | Azide $M/100$ | Iodo-acetate $M/10,000$ | Fluoro-acetate $M/1000$ | Malo-nate $M/100$ | AUTHOR |
|---|---|---|---|---|---|---|---|---|
| | | PERCENT INHIBITION UNDER THE INFLUENCE OF | | | | | | |
| Strigomonas oncopelti........ | Culture | | 90 | | | | | Lwoff (1934) |
| S. fasciculata............ | Culture | 95 | 90 | | | | | Lwoff (1934) |
| Leptomonas ctenocephali.... | Culture | | 95 | | | | | Lwoff (1934) |
| Leishmania tropica........ | Culture | | 94 | | | | | von Brand and Johnson (1947) |
| L. brasiliensis............ | Culture | | 95 | | | | | von Brand and Johnson (1947) |
| L. donovani.............. | Culture | | 100 | 34 | 64* | | | Fulton and Joyner (1949) |
| L. donovani.............. | Tissue | | 78 | 32 | 73* | | | Fulton and Joyner (1949) |
| Trypanosoma lewisi........ | Bloodstream | | 100; 95 | 48* | 8 | 34 | 15 | von Brand and Johnson (1947); Moulder (1948a); von Brand, Tobie, and Mehlman (1950) |
| T. lewisi................ | Culture | | 86 | | 26 | 42 | | von Brand and Johnson (1947); von Brand, Tobie, and Mehlman (1950) |
| T. cruzi................. | Bloodstream | | 83 | | 0 | 38 | | von Brand and Johnson (1947); von Brand, Tobie, and Mehlman (1950) |
| T. cruzi................. | Culture | 0 | 86 | 47 | 14 | 40 | | von Brand, Johnson, and Rees (1946); von Brand and Johnson (1947); von Brand, Tobie, and Mehlman (1950); Baernstein and Tobie (1951) |
| T. conorhini............. | Culture | | 68 | | 39 | 27 | | von Brand and Johnson (1947); von Brand, Tobie, and Mehlman (1950) |
| T. pipistrelli............. | Culture | | | | 17 | 0 | | von Brand, Tobie, and Mehlman (1950) |
| T. congolense............ | Bloodstream | | 59 | | 31 | 0 | | von Brand and Tobie (1948); von Brand, Tobie, and Mehlman (1950) |
| T. evansi................ | Bloodstream | | 8; 0 | | 92; 64 | 10 | | Marshall (1948); von Brand and Tobie (1948); von Brand, Tobie, and Mehlman (1950) |

| Organism | Source | | | | | | | References |
|---|---|---|---|---|---|---|---|---|
| T. hippicum................. | Bloodstream | | 0 | 38** | | | 0 | von Brand and Johnson (1947); Harvey (1949) |
| T. equinum................. | Bloodstream | | 0 | | 65 | 5 | | von Brand and Tobie (1948); von Brand, Tobie, and Mehlman (1950) |
| T. equiperdum............. | Bloodstream | | 0 | | 66 | 4 | | von Fenyvessy and Reiner (1924, 1928); von Brand, Tobie, and Mehlman (1950) |
| T. brucei.................. | Bloodstream | | 0 | | | | | von Brand and Johnson (1947) |
| T. rhodesiense............. | Bloodstream | | 0 | | 51 | 7 | | Christophers and Fulton (1938); von Brand and Tobie (1948); von Brand, Tobie, and Mehlman (1950) |
| T. gambiense.............. | Bloodstream | | 0 | | 74 | 4 | | von Brand and Tobie (1948); von Brand, Tobie, and Mehlman (1950) |
| T. gambiense.............. | Culture | | 18 | | 63 | 4 | | von Brand and Johnson (1947); von Brand, Tobie, and Mehlman (1950) |
| Trichomonas foetus......... | Culture | 0 | 0*** | 0** | 70 | | 0 | Riedmueller (1936); Suzuoki and Suzuoki (1951) |
| T. hepatica............... | Culture | | 0 | 0 | | | | Willems, Massart, and Peeters (1942) |
| Plasmodium knowlesi........ | Incubates | 73 | 91; 88 | | | | | Christophers and Fulton (1938); McKee et al. (1946) |
| P. lophurae............... | Incubates | | 92 | 74 | | | | Bovarnick, Lindsay, and Hellerman (1946) |

$* = M/1000; ** = M/10; *** = M/100.$

TABLE 34. Influence of some inhibitors on the oxygen consumption of some parasitic helminths

| SPECIES | MATERIAL | PERCENT INHIBITION UNDER THE INFLUENCE OF | | | | | AUTHOR |
|---|---|---|---|---|---|---|---|
| | | Carbon monoxide 95% | Cyanide $M/1000$ | Urethane 5% | Cyanine dyes $M/2,000,000$ | Malonate $M/100$ | |
| *Paramphistomum cervi* | Adults | | 0 | | | | Lazarus (1950) |
| *Schistosoma mansoni* | Adults | | 43 | | 85* | | Bueding (1950) |
| *Fasciola hepatica* | Mince | 53 | 100 | 74 | | 15 | van Grembergen (1949) |
| *Diphyllobothrium latum* | Eggs | 0 | 100 | 100 | | | Friedheim and Baer (1933) |
| *D. latum* | Plerocercoids | 0 | 78 | | | | Friedheim and Baer (1933) |
| *D. latum* | Scolex region | | | | | | Friedheim and Baer (1933) |
| *Triaenophorus lucii* | Strobila | 0 | 100** | | | | Friedheim and Baer (1933) |
| *Cysticercus fasciolaris* | Whole larva | | 26 | | | | Wilmoth (1945) |
| *Trichinella spiralis* | Larvae | 0 | 88 | | | | Stannard, McCoy, and Latchford (1938) |
| *Strongylus vulgaris* | Adults | | 15 | | | | Lazarus (1950) |
| *Haemonchus contortus* | Eggs | | 68 | | | | Rogers (1948) |
| *H. contortus* | Adults | | 50*** | | | | Lazarus (1950) |
| *Ostertagia circumcincta* | Adults | | 50 | | | | Lazarus (1950) |
| *Nematodirus spp.* | Adults | | 64 | | | 25 | Rogers (1948); Massey and Rogers (1949) |
| *Nippostrongylus muris* | Infective larvae | | 34 | | | | Rogers (1948) |
| *N. muris* | Adults | | 36 | | | | Rogers (1948) |
| *Eustrongylides ignotus* | Larvae | | 70 | 0 | | | von Brand (1945) |
| *Syphacia obvelata* | Adults | | 40 | | | | Lazarus (1950) |
| *Neoaplectana glaseri* | Larvae, adults | | 96 | | | 8 | Rogers (1948); Massey and Rogers (1949) |
| *Heterakis spumosa* | Adults | | 50 | | | | Lazarus (1950) |
| *Ascaris lumbricoides* | Eggs | | 89 | | | | Huff and Boell (1936) |

| | | | | | | References |
|---|---|---|---|---|---|---|
| A. lumbricoides | Pieces, mince | 20 | 0 | 33 | 50 | Harnisch (1935a); Laser (1944); van Grembergen, van Damme, and Vercruysse (1949) |
| Ascaridia galli | Adults | | 62 | | 11 | Rogers (1948); Massey and Rogers (1949) |
| Litomosoides carinii | Adults | | 98 | 79 | | Bueding (1949a) |
| Dracunculus insignis | Adults | | 98 | 83 | | Bueding and Oliver-Gonzalez (1950) |

* = $M/1,000,000$; ** = initially total inhibition, later resumption of oxygen consumption; *** = $M/50$.

(von Brand and Tobie, 1948; van Grembergen, van Damme, and Vercruysse, 1949). It is probable that in these organisms no heavy metal catalysis takes place, although the presence of a dual mechanism, the cyanide insensitive one substituting fully for the cyanide sensitive one in the case of the latter being blocked, cannot be ruled out definitely. The nature of the cyanide insensitive respiratory enzyme has not been established yet.

The situation is especially interesting in trypanosomes where the cyanide sensitivity or insensitivity follows rather closely the taxonomic groups established by Hoare (1948) on the basis of morphological and developmental grounds. It can be assumed that the appearance of the cyanide insensitive system is a secondary development since the bloodstream inhabiting species are probably derived from insect inhabiting ancestors and the respiration of the latter has so far always been found to be cyanide sensitive. It is also suggestive that the respiration of the culture form of *Trypanosoma gambiense*, corresponding to the form developing in the gut of *Glossina*, is somewhat cyanide sensitive, in contrast to that of the bloodstream form of the same species. The idea that a loss of an enzyme system is involved is in accord with the views of Krijgsman (1936) and Lwoff (1940) who postulated that the trypanosomes have lost many enzymes and many synthetic powers. Another interesting point has been brought out by Moulder (1950). He pointed out that the cyanide insensitive trypanosomes consume oxygen at a faster rate than the cyanide sensitive species, the loss of the sensitive system must therefore have been accompanied by the appearance of an enzyme whose catalytic activity is higher than that of the original heavy metal enzyme. Why such a shift should have occurred just in some groups of trypanosomes while the malarial parasites which are more specialized in many respects have retained a rather full complement of enzymes, is a complete riddle (Moulder, 1948c).

The respiration of *Trichomonas hepatica* is not stimulated but rather inhibited by methylene blue and dinitrophenol (Willems, Massart, and Peeters, 1942). The respiration of *Ascaris*, on the contrary, is strongly stimulated by methylene blue, this stimulation being especially high (up to 1000%) in the presence of succinate. It is slightly stimulated by paraphenylenediamine, but not by dinitrophenol (Laser, 1944; van Grembergen, van Damme, and Vercruysse, 1949). It is interesting to note that in contrast to the adult worms, the respiration of the *Ascaris* and *Parascaris* eggs is very strongly inhibited by cyanide (Zawadowsky, 1926; Huff and Boell, 1936), seemingly indicating different respiratory mechanisms. In *Paramphistomum* cyanide stimulates the respiration around 100% at an oxygen tension of 160 mm; when the oxygen tension was raised to 760 mm only very slight stimulation took place, or even inhibition up to 30%. No activation by cyanide was observed when brei instead of intact animals was employed in the presence of methylene blue (Lazarus, 1950).

## IV. THE CARBON DIOXIDE TRANSPORT

No investigation dealing with the mechanism of carbon dioxide transport has been carried out with parasitic protozoa or helminths and the general assumption apparently is that simple diffusion accounts for the elimination of that gas. Levenbook (1950a, b) and Levenbook and Clark (1950) have recently studied the problem with an endoparasitic arthropod, the larval stage of *Gasterophilus*. The average carbon dioxide content of its blood was 72.4 volumes % and the carbon dioxide content of the tissues was always close to that of the blood. From 30 to 50% of the gas occurred in solution and the remainder in the form of bicarbonate, while no carbamate formation could be observed. A study of the carbon dioxide dissociation curves at different temperatures revealed an adaptation to high tensions; the actual carbon dioxide tension of the blood varied between about 300 and 500 mm Hg. It was also found that the larval blood contained no carbonic anhydrase and no substance inhibiting hydration of carbon dioxide. The tracheal system of the larvae seems not to be very effective in eliminating carbon dioxide. A damaging effect on the tissues by the accumulation of that gas is however avoided by the strong buffer capacity of the blood which actually is better developed on both sides of its normal pH. *Gasterophilus* has this last feature in common with other insects, in contrast to what is found in other groups of animals, and this may be an adaptation to difficulties in carbon dioxide elimination inherent in the tracheal type of respiratory mechanisms.

## V. THE POST-ANAEROBIC RESPIRATION

Many free-living invertebrates, after having been exposed to lack of oxygen, show an increased oxygen consumption lasting for a certain period when they are brought back to oxygenated surroundings. This phenomenon is known as the repayment of an oxygen debt or the respiratory rebound. The extent to which free-living invertebrates repay an oxygen debt is very variable, ranging from a fraction of the incurred debt to a more or less pronounced overpayment (review of the literature in von Brand, 1946). The reasons for these variations are not very well understood. They seem to be correlated with different powers of excreting metabolic endproducts during the anoxic period and different types of recovery processes.

It is probable that a respiratory rebound occurs only when endproducts of the anaerobic metabolism accumulate within the tissues; they seem to serve as substrates for the increased oxygen consumption. An interesting question is why organisms revert at all to an aerobic type of metabolism upon readmission of oxygen. It has been considered recently from a theoretical physicochemical standpoint by Zimmerman (1949). She concludes that it is probably due to differences in the entropies of activation between the anaerobic and the aerobic pathways, the former placing higher energy requirements on the cells than the latter. A different question is why the post-anaerobic oxygen consumption proceeds usually at a faster rate than the pre-anaerobic one. From the biological standpoint it can be said that in this way the anaerobic endproducts which frequently are toxic, are rapidly altered to nontoxic substances, either by total oxidation or by partial resynthesis to glycogen. From the physicochemical standpoint the increased rate is due to an increased probability of enzyme and substrate molecules colliding if the concentration of the latter has increased.

In so far as parasites are concerned, it has been found by Bueding (1949a, 1950) that *Litomosoides carinii* and *Schistosoma mansoni* do not show any sign of accumulating an oxygen debt during an anoxic period. He has also shown that practically all the anaerobically consumed carbohydrate is accounted for by acids appearing in the medium, that is, by excreted acids. Hence it does appear probable that the failure to show a respiratory rebound may be due to a failure of substrate accumulation in the tissues since there is no reason to postulate that excreted substances should be reabsorbed in order to be oxidized further. It is rather remarkable that an identical situation prevails in this respect in these two worms, which are quite different in their sensitivity to lack of oxygen, the former being damaged very rapidly, while the latter is quite resistant.

*Ascaris* is a worm that repays a small amount of an incurred oxygen debt. Originally (Adam, 1932; Harnisch, 1933) no increase in post-anaerobic oxygen consumption of entire worms had been observed, although it was found in isolated anterior ends. More recently, however, Laser (1944) was able to show that entire ascarids consume oxygen at a higher than normal rate for 2 hours after having been exposed for 18 hours to strictly anaerobic conditions. This is in line with the observation by von Brand (1937) that these worms rebuild a small amount of glycogen during a post-anaerobic period. It is certain that the repayment of the oxygen debt is quite incomplete in *Ascaris* and it can again be assumed that this is connected with its well known ability to excrete anaerobic metabolic endproducts.

The larvae of *Eustrongylides ignotus* repay about 30% of their oxygen debt following 16 to 18 hours anaerobiosis (von Brand, 1942) and the respiratory quotient is exceedingly low during the initial periods of the repayment phase. This is clearly due to the retention of carbon dioxide used to rebuild the bicarbonate reserves depleted by the preceding production of acidic anaerobic endproducts. The actual increase in oxygen consumption is marked, amounting to about 300% during the first half hour (von Brand, 1947).

## LITERATURE

Adam, W. (1932). *Z. vergleich. Physiol.* **16:** 229–251.

Adler, S., and Ashbel, R. (1934). *Arch. zool. ital.* **20:** 521-527.

Alt, H. L., and Tischer, O. A. (1931). *Proc. Soc. Exptl. Biol. Med.* **29:** 222–224.

Baernstein, H. D., and Tobie, E. J. (1951). *Federation Proc.* **10:** 159.

Ball, E. G., Anfinsen, C. B., Geiman, Q. M., McKee, R. W., and Ormsbee, R. A. (1945). *Science* **101:** 542–544.

Belehradek, J. (1935). Temperature and Living Matter. Protoplasma Monographien No. 8, Berlin.

Bovarnick, M. R., Lindsay, A., and Hellerman, L. (1946). *J. Biol. Chem.* **163:** 523–533.

von Brand, T. (1934). *Z. vergleich. Physiol.* **21:** 220–235.

von Brand, T. (1937). *J. Parasitol.* **23:** 316–317.

von Brand, T. (1942). *Biol. Bull.* **82:** 1–13.

von Brand, T. (1943). *Biol. Bull.* **84:** 148–156.

von Brand, T. (1945). *J. Parasitol.* **31:** 381–393.

von Brand, T. (1946). Anaerobiosis in Invertebrates. Biodynamica Monograph No. 4. Biodynamica, Normandy, Missouri.

von Brand, T. (1947). *Biol. Bull.* **92:** 162–166.

von Brand, T., and Johnson, E. M. (1947). *J. Cellular Comp. Physiol.* **29:** 33–50.

von Brand, T., Johnson, E. M., and Rees, C. W. (1946). *J. Gen. Physiol.* **30:** 163–175.

von Brand, T., and Tobie, E. J. (1948). *J. Cellular Comp. Physiol.* **31:** 49–68.

von Brand, T., Tobie, E. J., and Mehlman, B. (1950). *J. Cellular Comp. Physiol.* **35:** 273–300.

Brown, H. W. (1938). *J. Parasitol.* **14:** 141–160.

von Buddenbrock, W. (1939). Grundriss der Vergleichenden Physiologie. 2nd edition, Vol. 2, Borntraeger, Berlin.

Bueding, E. (1949a). *J. Exptl. Med.* **89:** 107–130.

Bueding, E. (1949b). *Physiol. Revs.* **29:** 195–218.

Bueding, E. (1950). *J. Gen. Physiol.* **33:** 475–495.

Bueding, E., and Charms, B. (1950). *Nature* **167:** 149.

Bueding, E., and Oliver-Gonzalez, J. (1950). *Brit. J. Pharmacol.* **5:** 62–64.

Bueding, E., Peters, L., and Waite, J. F. (1947). *Proc. Soc. Exptl. Biol. Med.* **64:** 111–113.

Chang, S. L. (1948). *J. Infectious Diseases* **82:** 109–116.

Christophers, S. R., and Fulton, J. D. (1938). *Ann. Trop. Med. Parasitol.* **82:** 43–75.

Crozier, W. J. (1925). *J. Gen. Physiol.* **7:** 189–216.

Daniel, G. E. (1931). *Am. J. Hyg.* **14:** 411–420.

Davis, J. G., and Slater, W. K. (1928). *Biochem. J.* **22:** 338–343.

Fenwick, D. W. (1938). *Proc. Zool. Soc. London* **A108** [Part I]: 85–100.

von Fenyvessy, B., and Reiner, L. (1924). *Z. Hyg. Infektionskrankh.* **102:** 109–119.

von Fenyvessy, B., and Reiner, L. (1928). *Biochem. Z.* **202:** 75–80.

Friedheim, E. A. H., and Baer, J. G. (1933). *Biochem. Z.* **265:** 329–337.

Friedheim, E. A. H., Susz, B., and Baer, J. G. (1933). *Compt. rend. soc. phys. hist. nat. Genève* **50:** 177–182 (not seen).

Fulton, J. D., and Joyner, L. P. (1949). *Trans. Roy. Soc. Trop. Med. Hyg.* **43:** 273–286.

Gonzalez, M. D. P. (1949). *Bol. faculdade filosof. ciênc. e letras Univ. São Paulo* **99** [*Zool. No. 14*]: 277–324.

van Grembergen, G. (1944). *Enzymologia* **11:** 268–281.

van Grembergen, G. (1949). *Enzymologia* **13:** 241–257.

van Grembergen, G., van Damme, R., and Vercruysse, R. (1949). *Enzymologia* **13:** 325–342.

Harnisch, O. (1932). *Z. vergleich. Physiol.* **17:** 365–386.

Harnisch, O. (1933). *Z. vergleich. Physiol.* **19:** 310–348.

Harnisch, O. (1935a). *Z. vergleich. Physiol.* **22:** 50–66.

Harnisch, O. (1935b). *Z. vergleich. Physiol.* **22:** 450–465.

Harnisch, O. (1936). *Z. vergleich. Physiol.* **23:** 391–419.

Harnisch, O. (1937). *Z. vergleich. Physiol.* **24:** 667–686.

Harnisch, O. (1949). *Experientia* **5:** 369–370.

Harnisch, O. (1950). *Z. vergleich. Physiol.* **32:** 482–498.

Harvey, S. C. (1949). *J. Biol. Chem.* **179:** 435–453.

Hoare, C. A. (1948). *Proc. Intern. Congr. Trop. Med. Malaria. 4th. Congr. Wash. D. C.* **2:** 1110–1116.

Huff, G. C. (1936). *J. Parasitol.* **22:** 455–463.

Huff, G. C., and Boell, E. J. (1936). *Proc. Soc. Exptl. Biol. Med.* **34:** 626–628.

Krebs, H. A. (1950). *Biochem. et Biophys. Acta* **4:** 249–269.

Krijgsman, B. J. (1936). *Z. vergleich. Physiol.* **23:** 663–711.

Krueger, F. (1936). *Zool. Jahrb. Abt. allgem. Zool.* **57:** 1–56.

Krueger, F. (1940a). *Z. wiss. Zool.* **152:** 547–570.

Krueger, F. (1940b). *Zool. Jahrb. Abt. allgem. Zool.* **60:** 103–128.

Laser, H. (1944). *Biochem. J.* **38:** 333–338.

Laser, H., and Rothschild, L. (1949). *Biochem. J.* **45:** 598–612.

Lazarus, M. (1950). *Australian J. Sci. Research* **B3:** 245–250.

Levenbook, L. (1949). Unpublished experiments quoted in Laser, H., and Rothschild, L. (1949).

Levenbook, L. (1950a). *J. Exptl. Biol.* **27:** 158–174.

Levenbook, L. (1950b). *J. Exptl. Biol.* **27:** 184–191.

Levenbook, L., and Clark, A. M. (1950). *J. Exptl. Biol.* **27:** 175–183.

Ludwig, W. (1928). *Arch. Protistenk.* **62:** 12–40.

Lwoff, A. (1934). *Zentr. Bakt. Parasitenk. Abt. I. Orig.* **130:** 498–518.

Lwoff, M. (1940). Recherches sur le pouvoir de synthèse des flagellés trypanosomides. Monographie de l'Institut Pasteur, Masson et Cie. Paris.

Maier, J., and Coggeshall, L. T. (1941). *J. Infectious Diseases* **69:** 87–96.

Marshall, P. B. (1948). *Brit. J. Pharmacol.* **3:** 8–14.

Massey, V., and Rogers, W. P. (1949). *Nature* **163:** 909.

McCoy, O. R. (1930). *Am. J. Hyg.* **11:** 413–448.

McKee, R. W., Ormsbee, R. A., Anfinsen, C. B., Geiman, Q. M., and Ball, E. G. (1946). *J. Exptl. Med.* **84:** 569–582.

Moulder, J. W. (1947). *Science* **106:** 168–169.

Moulder, J. W. (1948a). *J. Infectious Diseases* **83:** 33–41.

Moulder, J. W. (1948b). *J. Infectious Diseases* **83:** 42–49.

Moulder, J. W. (1948c). *Ann. Rev. Microbiol.* **1948:** 101–120.

Moulder, J. W. (1950). *J. Parasitol.* **36:** 193–200.

Nauss, R. W., and Yorke, W. (1911). *Ann. Trop. Med. Parasitol.* **5:** 199–214.

Reiner, L., Smythe, C. V., and Pedlow, J. T. (1936). *J. Biol. Chem.* **113:** 75–88.

Riedmueller, L. (1936). *Zentr. Bakt. Parasitenk. Abt. I. Orig.* **137:** 428–433.

Rogers, W. P. (1948). *Parasitology* **39:** 105–109.

Silverman, M., Ceithaml. J., Taliaferro, L. G., and Evans, E. A. (1944). *J. Infectious Diseases* **75:** 212–230.

Slater, W. K. (1925). *Biochem. J.* **19**: 604–610.

Smith, B. F., and Herrick, C. A. (1944). *J. Parasitol.* **30**: 295–302.

Soule, M. H. (1925). *J. Infectious Diseases* **36**: 245–308.

Specht, H. (1935). *J. Cellular Comp. Physiol.* **5**: 319–333.

Speck, J. F., and Evans, E. A. (1945). *J. Biol. Chem.* **159**: 71–81.

Speck, J. F., Moulder, J. W., and Evans, E. A. (1946). *J. Biol. Chem.* **164**: 119–144.

Stannard, J. N., McCoy, O. R., and Latchford, W. B. (1938). *Am. J. Hyg.* **27**: 666–682.

Suzuoki, Z., and Suzuoki, T. (1951). *J. Biochem. (Japan)* **38**: 237–254.

Toryu, Y. (1934). *Science Repts. Tôhoku Imp. Univ. Fourth Ser.* **9**: 61–70.

Toryu, Y. (1936). *Science Repts. Tôhoku Imp. Univ. Fourth Ser.* **11**: 1–17.

Velick, S. F. (1942). *Am. J. Hyg.* **35**: 152–161.

Weinland, E. (1901). *Z. Biol.* **42**: 55–90.

Wendel, W. B. (1943). *J. Biol. Chem.* **148**: 21–34.

Willems, R., Massart, L., and Peeters, G. (1942). *Naturwissenschaften* **30**: 169–170.

Wilmoth, J. H. (1945). *Physiol. Zoöl.* **18**: 60-80.

Wright, W. H. (1950). *J. Parasitol.* **36**: 175–177.

Zawadowsky, M. (1926). *Biol. Generalis* **2**: 442–456.

Zeuthen, E. (1947). *Compt. rend. trav. lab. Carlsberg. Ser. chim.* **26** [No. 3]: 17–161.

Zimmerman, June F. (1949). *Biochim. et Biophys. Acta* **3**: 198–204.

# CHAPTER 14

# BIOLOGICAL OXYGEN RELATIONSHIPS

## I. Introductory Remarks

An analysis of the metabolic activities of parasites is necessarily based largely on experiments conducted *in vitro* since at the present state of our experimental technique *in vivo* experiments are confined to very limited aspects of the problem. In order to draw conclusions as to what type of activity endoparasites show *in vivo* it is necessary to consider both the results of *in vitro* experiments and the peculiarities of their habitat. In regard to the oxygen relationships that means an evaluation of two main points: 1. The oxygen tension in the surroundings of endoparasites, and 2. The parasites' reactions to oxygen and their resistance to the lack of that gas.

## II. Oxygen Tension of Parasitic Habitats

Parasitic habitats can be divided roughly into environments offering no, or at least only very little molecular oxygen and habitats in which a more or less plentiful supply of this gas is available. The best known of the former group are the intestine of warm-blooded animals and their bile ducts (Table 35), while the oxygen tension is moderate to high in most other parasitic habitats tested.

It must be realized, however, that the oxygen tensions listed are overall tensions that do not necessarily reflect accurately the oxygen content of the immediate surroundings of the parasites. On the one hand factors exist that in certain cases tend to lower the oxygen tension. Campbell (1931) has thus shown that inflammatory processes have a tendency to decrease the local tension. This may be important in parasitic lesions. In nonsterile habitats the local bacterial flora may well have a similar influence. It should be noted in this connection that *Trichomonas buccalis* has been described by Hinshaw (1927) as an obligate anaerobe. This becomes understandable only on the assumption that the local bacterial flora depletes the micro-atmosphere in touch with the parasites to such an extent that it becomes more or less anaerobic (von Brand, 1946), since the mouth cavity is obviously normally an aerobic habitat.

On the other hand, the oxygen tension locally may be appreciably higher than indicated by measurements of the overall tension of a given tissue or body fluid. The oxygen tension in the immediate vicinity of small blood vessels will certainly be higher than that farther away, since oxygen will diffuse through their walls and be largely consumed by the cells in their immediate vicinity. In this way an oxygen gradient will be established. Such gradients are especially important at the borders of anaerobic habitats. McIver, Redfield, and Benedict (1926) have demonstrated that oxygen diffuses from the intestinal wall into the lumen when an isolated loop is filled with an oxygen-free gas and the oxygen values of Rogers (1949a) for the small intestine of sheep are about two to three times higher than those found by von Brand and Weise (1932). The former investigated the oxygen tension of the thin layer of fluid in contact with the mucous membranes, while the latter studied the oxygen content of the bulk of the intestinal contents. It follows then that in this type of habitat much will depend upon the question of how near a parasite lives to the mucosa. It may be interpolated that this is an important point also in other directions. Read (1950) has recently pointed out that the space near the mucosa may be quite similar physiologically to the intracellular spaces of the host, in contrast to the intestinal contents.

Little definite information is available concerning the oxygen tensions to which parasites of invertebrates are subjected. It is known that varying amounts of oxygen, ranging from 2 to 18% of that found in air, occur under the chitin of some insects (Campbell, 1931). Conditions in the intestine of invertebrates probably vary from species to species. It is thus probable that largely aerobic conditions prevail in the intestine of sandflies, as can be inferred from the fact that the developmental stages of leishmanias require oxygen in culture. Conditions in the termite intestine, on the other hand, are probably fairly strictly anaerobic, since the termite fauna is quite sensitive to oxygen.

As the above review shows, we know little at present about the oxygen tension in the immediate surroundings of parasites. This, doubtless, is due in part to technical difficulties. With the older methods it would scarcely be feasible to determine the oxygen tension in such small structures as, for example, a cyst of *Trichinella spiralis*. It seems therefore appropriate to draw attention to the microelectrodes developed by Davies and Brink (1942) for measuring local oxygen tensions in animal tissues which seem admirably suited for such determinations. They have so far been used only by Rogers (1949a) for parasitological purposes.

### III. REACTIONS TO OXYGEN AND TO LACK OF OXYGEN

Truly anaerobic animals can maintain all their vital functions in the absence of oxygen and are injured by oxygen even at low tensions. Our present knowledge indicates that only two groups of parasites belong into this category: The rumen ciliates and the termite flagellates. The former

TABLE 35. Oxygen tensions in some parasitic habitats

| HABITAT | HOST SPECIES | OXYGEN TENSION MM HG. | AUTHOR |
|---|---|---|---|
| Skin | Man | 50–100 | Montgomery and Horwitz (1948) |
| Subcutaneous tissues | Fowl, rabbit, rat, guinea pig, cat, monkey, man, hedge hog | 20–43 | Campbell (1931); Meyer (1935); Seevers (1936) |
| Subcutaneous tissues | Frog, toad | 48–100 | Campbell (1931) |
| Subcutaneous tissues | Snake, tortoise | 20–24 | Campbell (1931) |
| Arterial blood | Dog, rabbit, man, fish | 70–100 | Fredericq (1893); Firket (1910); Dill, Edwards, and Florkin (1932); Barcroft et al. (1923) |
| Venous blood (heart) | Duck, horse, man | 37–40 | von Buddenbrock (1939) |
| Venous blood (heart) | Fish | 2–14 | Root (1931); Dill, Edwards, and Florkin (1932) |
| Venous blood (portal vein) | Dog, cat | 49–66 | Blalock and Mason (1936); Engel, Harrison, and Long (1944) |
| Peritoneal cavity | Rabbit, rat, guinea pig, cat, monkey | 28–40 | Campbell (1931) |
| Pleural cavity | Monkey, man, dog | 12–39 | Webb, et al. (1914); Tachau and Thilenius (1916); Grass (1921); Grass and Meiners (1922); Dautrebande and Spehl (1922); Campbell (1931) |
| Urine | Man | 14–60 | Krogh (1916); Campbell (1928) Buckmaster and Hickman (1928); Sarre (1937) |
| Bile | Cattle, sheep, dog | 0–30 | Buckmaster and Hickman (1926); von Brand and Weise (1932) |
| Abomasum (near mucosa) | Sheep | 4–13 | Rogers (1949a) |
| Rumen (gases) | Cattle, sheep, goat | 0–2 | Tappeiner (1883) |
| Stomach (gases) | Horse, rabbit, dog | 0–6 | Planer (1860); Tappeiner (1883) |
| Stomach (gases) | Man | 70 | Ewald and Rubstein (vide Bardier, 1931) |

| | | | |
|---|---|---|---|
| Small intestine (near mucosa) | Sheep | 4-13 | Rogers (1949a) |
| Small intestine (near mucosa) | Rat | 8-30 | Rogers (1949a) |
| Small intestine (gases) | Horse, cattle, dog | 0-6 | Tappeiner (1883); Planer (1860) |
| Small intestine (gases) | Pig | 8-65 | Long and Fenger (1917); von Brand and Weise (1932) |
| Large intestine (gases) | Horse, cattle, goat, sheep, rabbit, dog | 0-5 | Planer (1860); Tappeiner (1883) |

can be cultivated only under fairly strictly anaerobic conditions and die quickly in the presence of oxygen (Knoth, 1928; Westphal, 1934; Hungate, 1941, 1942) and the same appears true for the latter (Trager, 1934; Hungate, 1939). Cleveland (1925a) had already previously demonstrated that termites can readily be defaunated by oxygenation. It is curious that Gilmour (1940) found the number of flagellates decreasing within the intestine of termites when the hosts were deprived of oxygen; he explains this by assuming an injurious action of accumulating metabolic end-products.

Most other endoparasites are facultative anaerobes, that is, they can withstand lack of oxygen for longer or shorter periods of time, or sometimes even indefinitely, but they do utilize oxygen when available and are not injured by moderate oxygen tensions. It is evident that a whole series of gradations exists between parasites surviving equally well in the absence of oxygen and in the presence of at least some oxygen to forms that tolerate anaerobic conditions for relatively short periods only. Some groups of parasites will now be surveyed briefly along these lines.

## A. Parasitic Protozoa

*Endamoeba histolytica* is best cultivated under anaerobic or at least near-anaerobic conditions. It seems to be injured by oxygen tensions well below that of atmospheric air, but can apparently grow in the presence of small concentrations of oxygen (Dobell and Laidlaw, 1926; Snyder and Meleney, 1941, 1942, 1943; Chang, 1946, 1948; Jacobs, 1941). Intestinal trichomonads (Andrews, 1926; Cleveland, 1928a, b; Jirovec and Rodova, 1940), *Trichomonas foetus* (Witte, 1933), *T. vaginalis* (Johnson, 1942), and *T. buccalis* (Hinshaw, 1927) have been cultivated anaerobically and appear to thrive better under complete lack of oxygen than in the presence of oxygen at high tensions, but they are in most cases not injured by moderate tensions. *Trichomastix* (Chatton, 1918a, b) seems to require some oxygen, but is injured by higher tensions. *Balantidium* (Barret and Yarbrough, 1921; Scott, 1927; Pritze, 1928; Schumaker, 1931; Tanabe and Komada, 1932; Nagahana, 1932; Levitanskaja, 1938) can tolerate anoxic conditions rather well, but certainly is not injured readily even by fairly high oxygen tensions. The frog parasites *Nyctotherus* and species of opalinids have also been cultivated in the absence of oxygen and at least the latter may be fairly sensitive to this gas (Pütter, 1905; Konsuloff, 1922; Lwoff and Valentini, 1948).

The culture forms of trypanosomidae are more exacting in their oxygen requirements. They withstand lack of oxygen on the whole fairly well, but the majority of investigators states that anaerobiosis prevents multiplication (Rogers, 1905; Soule, 1925; Adler and Theodor, 1931; Ray, 1932) while, it is true, Senekjie (1941) reported multiplication of *Leishmania* in anoxic cultures. The bloodstream form of pathogenic trypanosomes, on the contrary, seems to survive only a few hours in complete absence of oxygen (von Brand, 1933b).

Relatively little is known so far about sporozoa. Anfinsen *et al.* (1946) found 95% oxygen unsuitable for the cultivation of *Plasmodium knowlesi*; it grew equally well in the presence of 20 and 0.37% oxygen. The formation of micro- and macrogametes of *Haemoproteus columbae* does not require oxygen (Marchoux and Chorine, 1932) but the oocysts of coccidia, while quite resistant to lack of oxygen, need it for maturation (Balbiani, 1884; Pfeiffer, 1892; Metzner, 1903; Moroff and Fiebiger, 1905; Fiebiger, 1913; Reichenow, 1929). Gregarines have not yet been cultivated *in vitro*, but it has been observed that mealworm gregarines withstand anaerobiosis within the intestine of their hosts at least as long as the mealworms themselves (von Brand, 1943).

## B. *Parasitic Worms*

The parasitic worms studied so far can all be classified as facultative anaerobes, all showing a rather marked tolerance to lack of oxygen, but all being able to consume it when kept in its presence. Again a series of gradations exists as the data of Table 36 indicate. Table 36 gives also a comparative view of the aerobic and anaerobic survival of helminths *in vitro*, but only such data have been incorporated which have been reported from one author since a comparison of anaerobic and aerobic life spans in different media is not profitable. A survey of these data shows that trematodes and several nematodes are highly resistant to lack of oxygen, but no clear connection with the oxygen supply of the normal habitat exists in all cases. The free-living hookworm larvae, for example, tolerate anoxic conditions rather well, while the small nematodes of the intestinal tract succumb rapidly. Hobson (1948) has pointed out justifiedly that all data on the aerobic survival are derived from experiments carried out at the oxygen tension of atmospheric air, while unquestionably the endoparasitic forms usually encounter much lower tensions in nature. The problem of how such tensions would influence the survival of the worms has not yet been approached. It is, however, interesting to note in this connection that the first parasitic ecdysis of *Haemonchus contortus* proceeds best in cultures with a limited supply of oxygen (Stoll, 1940).

The eggs of many helminths are quite resistant to lack of oxygen. This is not only of theoretical but also of practical interest since many forms can survive the anaerobic digestion practiced in many sewage disposal installations. The eggs of most helminths require oxygen, however, for full development, or for hatching, if eggs with developed juvenile stages are

TABLE 36.   Survival of some parasitic worms *in vitro* under anaerobic conditions and comparison of anaerobic and aerobic survival (essentially after von Brand, 1946)

| SPECIES | MEDIUM | TEMP. °C | SURVIVAL TIME IN DAYS | | AUTHOR |
|---|---|---|---|---|---|
| | | | Anaerobic | Aerobic | |
| **TREMATODES** | | | | | |
| Sphaerostoma bramae | NaCl, 1% | Room temp. | 5 | 4 | Hausmann (1897) |
| Cryptocotyle lingua, metacercariae | Modified Ringer's + glucose | Room temp. | >4 | 12 | Stunkard (1930) |
| Fasciola hepatica | Blood | 38–39 | 1.5 | 1.5 | Weinland and von Brand (1926) |
| F. hepatica | Borax-saline + glucose | 38 | 1.5 | 2 | Stephenson (1947) |
| Opisthorchis felineus | Ringer's | 37 | 18 | 18 | Erhardt (1939) |
| Schistosoma mansoni | Serum ultrafiltrate | 37 | 5 | 12 | Ross and Bueding (1950) |
| **CESTODES** | | | | | |
| Bothriocephalus bipunctatus | NaCl, 1% | Room temp. | >1 | Several | Harnisch (1937) |
| Moniezia expansa | Ringer's | 38–39 | 0.5 | | von Brand (1933a) |
| **NEMATODES** | | | | | |
| Trichinella spiralis, larvae | Tyrode | 37 | 7 or more | | Stannard, McCoy, and Latchford (1938) |
| Ancylostoma caninum, larvae | Tapwater | 17 | 21 | | Boycott (1904) |
| A. caninum, larvae | Tapwater | Room temp. | >4, <12 | | McCoy (1930) |
| Trichostrongylus colubriformis | Ringer's | 37 | <1 | 4–12 | Davey (1938) |
| T. vitrinus | Ringer's | 37 | <1 | 4–12 | Davey (1938) |
| Ostertagia circumcincta | Ringer's | 37 | <1 | 4–12 | Davey (1938) |
| Cooperia oncophora | Ringer's | 37 | <2 | 4–12 | Davey (1938) |
| C. curticei | Ringer's | 37 | <1 | 4–12 | Davey (1938) |
| Nematodirus filicollis | Ringer's | 37 | <2 | 4–12 | Davey (1938) |

| | | | | | |
|---|---|---|---|---|---|
| *Eustrongylides ignotus*, larvae | NaCl, 1% | 37 | 3 | 19 | von Brand (1938a) |
| *E. ignotus*, larvae | NaCl, 0.85% | 20 | 21 | Several months | von Brand and Simpson (1945) |
| *Ascaris lumbricoides* | NaCl, 1% | 35–38 | 7 | | Bunge (1889) |
| *A. lumbricoides* | NaCl, 1% | 37 | 9 | 6 | Weinland (1901) |
| "*Ascaris mystax*" | NaCl, 1% + $Na_2CO_3$, 0.1% | 38 | 6 | 15 | Bunge (1883) |
| *Parascaris equorum* | Ringer's | 35–38 | 2 | | Bunge (1889) |
| *P. equorum* | Ringer's | 38 | 5 | 2 | Toryu (1935) |
| *Raphidascaris acus* | NaCl, 1% | Room temp. | 6 | | Bunge (1889) |
| *Litomosoides carinii* | Ox serum | 37 | <1 | 7 | Ross and Bueding (1950) |

shed. For details on the limits of the anoxic periods tolerated by the eggs of nematodes, cestodes, and trematodes, which frequently are many weeks, the following papers should be consulted: Bataillon (1910); Looss (1911); Fauré-Fremiet (1913); Zawadowsky (1916); Zawadowsky and Orlow (1927); Zviaginzev (1934); Dinnik and Dinnik (1937); Lucker (1935); Cram (1943); Cram and Hicks (1944); Shorb (1944); Jones et al. (1947); and Newton, Bennet, and Figgat (1949).

There are some variations in oxygen requirements. The egg of *Parascaris* ceases developing under anaerobic conditions after fertilization or, possibly, the first cleavage stages (Fauré-Fremiet, 1913; Szwejkowska, 1929; Dyrdowska, 1931), the egg of *Oxyuris equi* after reaching the gastrula stage (Schalimov, 1931), and the egg of *Enterobius vermicularis* only after attaining the tadpole stage (Zawadowsky and Schalimov, 1929; Wendt, 1936). The minimal oxygen tension required to insure full development also varies in different species. In hookworm larvae it lies around 10 mm Hg (McCoy, 1930), while in *Ascaris* development is retarded about 50% at 30 mm Hg (Brown, 1928). The eggs of *Parascaris* do not show any sign of development at 5 mm, they develop only slowly between 10 and 80 mm and only at oxygen tensions above 80 mm Hg is normal development possible (Kosmin, 1928). Such observations are of obvious importance in exploring the possibility of autoinvasion in helminthic diseases. Nishigori (1928) thought to have demonstrated the anaerobic transformation of the rhabditiform larvae of *Strongyloides* into infective filariform larvae, but his findings were not confirmed by Lee (1930). Autoinvasion is certainly possible in this species and it must be assumed that full development can take place at quite low oxygen tensions, but no definite data are available.

### C. Endoparasitic Arthropods

Only the larvae of *Gasterophilus* and *Cordylobia* have been studied to some extent as to their ability to resist lack of oxygen. Both can be classified with justification among the facultative anaerobes. There is unanimity of opinion that *Gasterophilus* larvae can endure anaerobiosis for periods of several days up to several weeks (Schwab, 1858; von Kemnitz, 1916; Dinulescu, 1932; Blanchard and Dinulescu, 1932) and it has been reported that the third instar larva of *Cordylobia* withstands lack of oxygen for 27 hours, remaining motile for the first 22 hours (Blacklock, Gordon, and Fine, 1930).

### IV. Toxicity of Oxygen

It has been mentioned above that rumen ciliates and termite flagellates are readily killed by oxygen even at apparently low tensions. The question, however, whether very low tensions would be injurious has not been solved yet. One cannot even deny positively at present that small traces of that gas may not be required. It is worth noting in this connection that Krogh (1941) has reached the general tentative conclusion that in all animals minute amounts of oxygen are essential for resistance against asphyxiation, a phenomenon he compares with the necessity of metabolizing small amounts of carbohydrate together with fats.

The above protozoa are doubtless the parasites most easily injured by oxygen. It is nevertheless very probable that any organism can be killed with oxygen if the tension is raised high enough. This is true both for free-living and parasitic forms. In so far as the latter are concerned, Cleveland (1925a, b) has shown that parasitic protozoa inhabiting termites, cockroaches, earthworms, frogs, goldfish, and salamanders could be killed without injury to the host by oxygenation of the latter. The oxygen pressure required varied somewhat. The parasites of *Leucotermes*, for example, were eliminated by oxygen of 1 atmosphere pressure within 24 hours, while those of *Reticulitermes* or *Cryptotermes* were still alive after 10 days. All termite protozoa, however, were killed within 30 minutes at 3.5 atmospheres. They proved to be 67.5 times more susceptible than their hosts. The protozoa of the other cold-blooded hosts mentioned were also killed by oxygen of 3.5 atmospheres pressure faster than their hosts. The periods required were quite variable with different species. Of the cockroach parasites tested, for example, *Lophomonas* and *Polymastix* both succumbed within 40 minutes while *Nyctotherus* and *Balantidium* required an exposure period of 3 hours 30 minutes. Rat parasites, on the other hand, could not be eliminated by oxygenation, because the hosts died more rapidly than the parasites at high oxygen pressures. It was shown, however, that cultured trichomonads of rat and of man were killed by 3.5 atmospheres oxygen within 10 and 11 hours respectively.

It is to be noted that metabolic studies have shown a damaging effect even at lower tensions. Willems, Massart, and Peeters (1942) have observed an optimal respiration of *Trichomonas hepatica* in an atmosphere containing 5 to 10% oxygen, while the oxygen consumption was inhibited 40% in air and 75% in 100% oxygen. It has also been found that the oxygen consumption of malarial parasites (Silverman *et al.*, 1944; McKee *et al.*, 1946) and of trypanosomes (Moulder, 1948) was suboptimal at high oxygen tensions and that these inhibited also the growth of malarial parasites (Trager, 1941; Anfinsen *et al.*, 1946).

Much less is known of parasitic worms in this respect. The only definite information is Laser's (1944) observation that *Ascaris lumbricoides* died in an atmosphere of pure oxygen within about 1 hour.

The mechanisms by which oxygen exerts its toxic effects are not well understood and seem to be different in various cases. Laser (1944) has shown that *Ascaris* is killed in pure oxygen by the accumulation of hydrogen peroxide. This compound accumulates in this case because the ascarids contain but very little catalase, as was already known since Lesser's (1906) investigation. It is of interest to note that the catalase content of other parasitic worms, *Fasciola hepatica*, *Taenia pisiformis*, and *Cysticercus pisiformis*, is also quite low (Pennoit-DeCooman and van Grembergen, 1942) but whether hydrogen peroxide accumulates in the presence of high oxygen tensions has not been established.

This mechanism can, however, not hold true in blood parasites, especially not in the case of the intracellular malarial parasites, since it must be assumed that the catalase of the blood would rapidly destroy all the peroxides formed. This has been pointed out recently by Moulder (1950) and it is implied that either the catalase of the host can enter the parasites, or that the peroxides possibly formed diffuse readily out of the parasites' bodies. Whether these assumptions are fully justified has not been tested experimentally as yet. It is of interest to note here that the bloodstream form of the African pathogenic trypanosomes shows only very weak catalase activity (Strangeways, 1937; Harvey, 1949) while it seems to be somewhat more pronounced in *Trypanosoma lewisi*, bird- and frog-trypanosomes (Tasaka, 1935).

## V. DEDUCTIONS CONCERNING OXYGEN RELATIONSHIPS IN VIVO

The question of whether a parasite leads *in vivo* a predominantly aerobic or anaerobic life can be answered only in a few cases with anything approaching precision, and speculations based on indirect evidence are obviously fraught with possibilities of serious errors. This should be clearly realized and the following paragraphs intend only to give suggestions along the lines of interest at this point. It is entirely possible that future research will in one case or the other necessitate a revision of the views expressed.

### A. Parasites of Invertebrates

It is probable that the majority of parasites inhabiting invertebrates will be able to get significant amounts of oxygen. An indirect indication to this effect is the observation by Vogel and von Brand (1933) that the developmental stages of *Fasciola hepatica* do not excrete higher fatty acids, but do so immediately upon entering the oxygen-poor surroundings in the final host. Another similar indirect sign, the need for oxygen for the multiplication of the developmental stages of trypanosomidae, has already been mentioned in the preceding section. Exceptions do occur, however. It has been pointed out that the termite flagellates give definite evidence of living in a predominantly anaerobic habitat and it is entirely possible that in such habitats as the intestinal tract of large snails, squids, or other large invertebrates, parasites can secure only very little oxygen. The same should also hold true for such parasites that live in the deeper tissues of hosts showing a dependency of their oxygen consumption on the tension.

## B. Parasites of Vertebrates

In so far as intestinal helminths are concerned, an attempt to correlate the oxygen consumption of small nematodes with the oxygen tension prevailing in their immediate vicinity has been made by Rogers (1949b). As

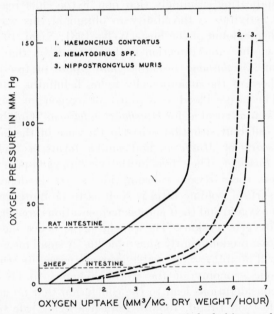

Fig. 16. Relation between the oxygen tension of the habitat and the rate of oxygen consumption of some parasitic nematodes (after Rogers, 1949b).

Fig. 16 indicates, the oxygen consumption of *Nippostrongylus muris* and *Nematodirus* spp. may reach 80 and 40% respectively of the *in vitro* rate when measured at the maximum oxygen tension occurring in their habitats. In *Haemonchus contortus*, however, the rate was much lower. Rogers (1949b) pointed out that the worms in his experiments were quite active *in vitro*, in contrast to their behavior *in vivo* and, in his view, motility may increase the *in vitro* rate ten to twentyfold. If this is true "conditions *in vivo*, especially for *Nippostrongylus* and *Nematodirus* spp., may allow oxygen consumption rates to approach the maximum *in vivo* rate." It must be pointed out, however, that the influence of motility may be much less pronounced than assumed by Rogers (see Chapter 13). It does seem fairly obvious nevertheless that in the above forms the aerobic phase of metabolism will be of great importance within their normal surroundings. This is in accord with Davey's (1937, 1938) report that small nematodes of the intestinal tract die rapidly in the complete absence of oxygen.

A similar assumption is probably justified in the case of *Ancylostoma* and *Necator*. Their rate of oxygen consumption has not been established so far with precision; Harwood and Brown (1934) state that hookworms consume per unit weight more than 10 times the oxygen used by *Ascaris*. It is furthermore known that they suck blood far in excess of their nutritional needs, indicating seemingly that one of the chief reasons for their blood sucking activities is the ability to obtain in this way the oxygen bound to the hemoglobin of the host (Wells, 1931; Nishi, 1933). A further hint pointing in the same direction is the observation that the glycogen relationships of *Ancylostoma* resemble more those of free-living aerobic worms than those of the anaerobically living helminths (von Brand and Otto, 1938). The host's blood as a source of oxygen for the parasite has recently also been advocated for *Opisthorchis felineus* (Golubeva, 1945).

An entirely different situation exists in the case of the large intestinal worms like *Ascaris* or *Moniezia*, and similar forms, as well as the bile duct parasite *Fasciola*. They live in the very oxygen-poor intestinal or bile duct lumen, their oxygen consumption is strictly dependent on the tension, their surface/volume ratio is such as to be quite unfavorable for the diffusion of oxygen, and their aerobic fermentations are very pronounced even at high oxygen tensions. The conclusion is hence inescapable that they lead *in vivo* a predominantly anaerobic life. A small measure of oxygen consumption will doubtless be possible in many cases; its true significance in the metabolic economy of the worms remains to be established.

The above considerations lead to the conclusion that no generalizations should be made (von Brand, 1938b). Parasites living side by side in the same oxygen-poor habitat can be quite different in their oxygen relationships. The old controversy whether intestinal worms lead an anaerobic or aerobic life appears pointless.

In so far as tissue helminths of vertebrates are concerned, it is convenient to make a distinction between parasites living in cysts and those inhabiting the body fluids or cavities. The oxygen tensions under which the former live are unknown as yet. Indications exist that at least one worm belonging to the former group leads a predominantly aerobic life *in situ*. Von Brand (1942) has shown that larval *Eustrongylides ignotus* accumulate an oxygen debt *in vitro* when exposed to anoxic conditions. They show, however, very little signs of having done so *in vivo*, a result compatible only with the assumption that they could get sufficient oxygen while within their cysts. It must emphasized that this reasoning can be applied only in cases where the experimental evidence proves the ability of accumulating an oxygen debt. Similar experiments with organisms like the schistosomes which do not show a respiratory rebound would obviously prove nothing either way.

Stannard, McCoy, and Latchford (1938) have found indications that the anaerobic metabolism is sufficient to keep the larvae of *Trichinella spiralis* alive, but that only the persistence of oxidative metabolism insures motility. Since the larvae are quiescent inside their cysts, the above observations do not permit deductions concerning the mode of life *in vivo*. It does seem possible, or even perhaps probable, that encysted massive parasites, like large *Cysticercus fasciolaris*, would encounter difficulties in securing the maximum of oxygen they could utilize and a predominantly anaerobic life may prevail in such cases. This is also quite probable for brood capsules of *Echinococcus* when suspended in the fluid of large cysts and, therefore, fairly far away from a source of diffusing oxygen.

Nonencysted helminths inhabiting such body fluids as urine or blood, and the different body cavities will generally live under moderate to high oxygen tensions and should be able to get, in most cases, significant amounts of oxygen. Very large parasites, such as *Ligula*, may represent exceptions, but have not yet been studied in this respect. It is suggestive that Smyth (1950) found that *Schistocephalus* kept *in vitro* under aerobic conditions becomes brown, although it is white in its normal habitat and stays white *in vitro* when kept under anaerobic or semi-anaerobic conditions.

It has been well established that *Litomosoides carinii* depends for its survival upon an adequate supply of oxygen. It has been shown that cyanine dyes (Table 34) inhibit its oxygen consumption very markedly (Welch *et al.*, 1947; Bueding, 1949a; Peters *et al.*, 1949) and that the worms die when the inhibition is induced *in vivo* by injecting appropriate amounts of the dyes into the hosts (Bueding, 1949a). This is a clear proof that the oxidative metabolism cannot be dispensed with in this worm at least.

But generalizations are again not possible. The oxygen consumption of the blood-inhabiting schistosomes also is strongly inhibited by cyanines both *in vitro* and *in vivo*, but the worms are not killed even after long exposures (Bueding and Oliver-Gonzalez, 1948; Bueding, Peters, and Welch, 1947; Bueding, 1950a, b). They can apparently gain all the energy required for their vital functions from anaerobic processes, but it is of course possible that the small residual oxygen consumption evident under the influence of the cyanines may also be required. Under normal conditions, the schistosomes consume rather large amounts of oxygen (Table 28). Bueding (1949b) has remarked that this "may be merely a rudimentary function carried over from a previous stage of the parasite, or from a different, but phylogenetically related species." Bueding (personal communication) has observed more recently that cyanine dyes inhibit the functional development of the reproductive system of the schistosomes, but only when administered to the host four weeks after exposure to cercariae, *i.e.*, before the worms are fully developed. The dyes were without this effect if given six weeks after infection. This seemingly indicates that respiration is required for the development of the reproductive system at a stage in the life cycle immediately preceding adulthood.

We have so far not mentioned the parasitic protozoa of vertebrates. It is in many cases difficult to arrive at definite views concerning their oxygen relationships *in vivo*. Due to their small size they offer no problems for a maximal oxygen supply by diffusion even at low tensions and it can be assumed that the blood and tissue forms usually can satisfy their maximal needs. This, of course, does not imply that they have a completely oxidative metabolism; on the contrary, as shown in previous chapters, the great majority of the forms studied are aerobic fermenters.

The oxygen relationships of intestinal protozoa are more difficult to evaluate. *Giardia* with its habit of affixing itself to the mucosal cells may well find an adequate source of oxygen (von Brand, 1934). The lumen parasites, on the other hand, live in competition with the bacterial flora and it can be expected that the micro-atmosphere will often be more or less completely depleted of oxygen, forcing them to an anaerobic type of metabolism (von Brand, 1946). Conditions in parasitic lesions, such as amoebic ulcers, are too obscure to allow a judgement at the present time since, as pointed out in a previous section, pathological processes sometimes have a profound influence on the local oxygen tension.

## VI. Phylogenetic Considerations

The most striking adaptation to parasitic life, from a metabolic standpoint, is the development of an anaerobic type of life in many parasites living in the intestinal tract. There can be no doubt that the helminths belonging to this group have descended ultimately from free-living organisms which required oxygen. This is indicated by the fact that practically all hitherto studied parasitic species need oxygen at one time or another during their life cycle.

It must be postulated that the worms acquired resistance to lack of oxygen before being able to establish themselves in their present oxygenpoor or oxygen-free habitats. This was first recognized by Bunge (1889). He assumed that the helminths with well developed anaerobic faculties were descended from free-living worms occurring in oxygen-poor mud which he considers as predisposing habitat ("Vorschule") for intestinal parasitism. This view has been challenged by Alsterberg (1922) who considers the phylogenetic comparisons of Bunge (1889) much too broad and points out that from a nutritional standpoint mud is entirely different from the intestine, the former being very poor, the latter very rich in nutritive material. These objections are rather well founded and further ones can be raised. It is thus hard to see how mud would predispose worms to develop a resistance against the digestive enzymes of the host (von Brand, 1946). A gradual adaptation through successive invasion of hosts showing increasing severity of oxygen deficiency may have occurred during the geological ages. Such an assumption, though not from our particular standpoint, has been made by Stunkard (1937) in regard to the development of parasitism in flatworms. It is obviously impossible to advance definite views and it is certainly remarkable that the schistosomes, although living under fairly high oxygen tensions, depend primarily, if not exclusively, on their anaerobic metabolism (Bueding, 1949b).

A mud ancestry has also been claimed as a possibility in the case of the rumen and termite protozoa. Lauterborn (1916) pointed to similarities in morphological features between these groups and the free-living sapropelic ciliates which also are anaerobic organisms, and to similarities in their respective habitats. It must be admitted that some of these features are rather striking, much more so that in the case of helminths. A direct hereditary connection between the three groups can nevertheless hardly be assumed, since all of them are actually highly specialized types showing considerable differences among themselves despite similarities in some respects. But the possibility of a remote common ancestry cannot be denied.

## LITERATURE

Adler, S., and Theodor, O. (1931). *Proc. Roy. Soc. London* **B108:** 453–463.

Alsterberg, G. (1922). *Lunds Univ. Årsskr.* [N. F.] **18:** 1–176.

Andrews, J. (1926). *J. Parasitol.* **12:** 148–157.

Anfinsen, C. B., Geiman, Q. M., McKee, R. W., Ormsbee, R. A., and Ball, E. G. (1946). *J. Exptl. Med.* **84:** 607–621.

Balbiani, E. G. (1884). Leçons sur les sporozoaires. Doin, Paris.

Barcroft, J., Binger, C. A., Bock, A. V., Doggart, J. H., Forbes, H. S., Harrop, G., Meakins, J. C., and Redfield, A. C. (1923). *Trans. Roy. Soc. London* **B211:** 351–480.

Bardier, E. (1931). *In* Traité de physiologie normale et pathologique. Vol. 2, pp. 125–201. Masson et Cie. Paris.

Barret, H. P., and Yarbrough, N. (1921). *Am. J. Trop. Med.* **1:** 161–164.

Bataillon, E. (1910). *Arch. Entwicklungsmech. Organ.* **30:** 24–44.

Blacklock, D. B., Gordon, R. M., and Fine. J. (1930). *Ann. Trop. Med. Parasitol.* **24:** 5–67.

Blalock, A., and Mason, M. F. (1936). *Am. J. Physiol.* **117:** 328–334.

Blanchard, L., and Dinulescu, G. (1932). *Compt. rend. soc. biol.* **110:** 343–344.

Boycott, A. E. (1904). *Trans. Epidemiol. Soc. London* **24:** 113–142.

von Brand, T. (1933a). *Z. vergleich. Physiol.* **18:** 562–596.

von Brand, T. (1933b). *Z. vergleich. Physiol.* **19:** 587–614.

von Brand, T. (1934). *Ergeb. Biol.* **10:** 37–100.

von Brand, T. (1938a). *J. Parasitol.* **24:** 445–451.

von Brand, T. (1938b). *Biodynamica* **2:** No. 41, 1–13.

von Brand, T. (1942). *Biol. Bull.* **82:** 1–13.

von Brand, T. (1943). *Biodynamica* **4:** 163–165.

von Brand, T. (1946). Anaerobiosis in Invertebrates. Biodynamica Monographs No. 4, Biodynamica, Normandy, Missouri.

von Brand, T., and Otto, G. (1938). *Am. J. Hyg.* **27:** 683–689.

von Brand, T., and Simpson, W. F. (1945). *Proc. Soc. Exptl. Biol. Med.* **60:** 368–371.

von Brand, T., and Weise, W. (1932). *Z. vergleich. Physiol.* **18:** 339–346.

Brown, H. W. (1928). *J. Parasitol.* **14:** 141–160.

Buckmaster, G. A., and Hickman, H. R. B. (1926). *J. Physiol.* **61:** XVII–XVIII.

Buckmaster, G. A., and Hickman, H. R. B. (1928). *J. Physiol.* **65:** XV–XVI.

von Buddenbrock, W. (1939). Grundriss der vergleichenden Physiologie. 2nd edition, Vol. 2, Borntraeger, Berlin.

Bueding, E. (1949a). *J. Exptl. Med.* **89:** 107–130.

Bueding, E. (1949b). *Physiol. Revs.* **29:** 195–218.

Bueding, E. (1950a). *J. Gen. Physiol.* **33:** 475–495.

Bueding, E. (1950b). *J. Parasitol.* **36:** 201–210.

Bueding, E., and Oliver-Gonzalez, J. (1948). *Proc. Intern. Congr. Trop. Med. Malaria. 4th. Congr., Wash., D. C.* **2:** 1025–1033.

Bueding, E., Peters, L., and Welch, A. D. (1947). *Federation Proc.* **6:** 313.

Bunge, G. (1883). *Z. physiol. Chem.* **8:** 48–59.

Bunge, G. (1889). *Z. physiol. Chem.* **14:** 318–324.

Campbell, J. A. (1928). *J. Physiol.* **65:** XVIII–XX.

Campbell, J. A. (1931). *Physiol. Revs.* **11:** 1–40.

Chang, S. L. (1946). *Parasitology* **37:** 101–112.

Chang, S. L. (1948). *Proc. Intern. Congr. Trop. Med. Malaria. 4th. Congr., Wash. D. C.* **2:** 1065–1073.

Chatton, E. (1918a). *Compt. rend. soc. biol.* **81:** 346–349.

Chatton, E. (1918b). *Compt. rend. soc. biol.* **81:** 714–717.

Cleveland, L. R. (1925a). *Biol. Bull.* **48:** 309–326.

Cleveland, L. R. (1925b), *Biol. Bull.* **48:** 455–468.

Cleveland, L. R. (1928a). *Am. J. Hyg.* **8:** 256–278.

Cleveland, L. R. (1928b). *Am. J. Hyg.* **8:** 990–1013.

Cram, E. B. (1943). *Sewage Works J.* **15:** 1119–1138.

Cram, E. B., and Hicks, D. O. (1944). *Proc. Helminthol. Soc. Wash. D. C.* **11:** 1–9.

Dautrebande, L., and Spehl, P. (1922). *Compt. rend. soc. biol.* **86:** 973–976.

Davey, D. G. (1937). *Nature* **140:** 645.

Davey, D. G. (1938). *J. Exptl. Biol.* **15:** 217–224.

Davies, P. W., and Brink, F. (1942). *Rev. Sci. Instruments* **13:** 524–533.

Dill, D. B., Edwards, H. T., and Florkin, M. (1932) *Biol. Bull.* **62:** 23–36.

Dinnik, J. A., and Dinnik, N. N. (1937). *Med. Parasitol. Parasitic Diseases (U.R.S.S.)* **5:** 603–618.

Dinulescu, G. (1932). *Ann. sci. nat., Zool.* **15:** 1–184.

Dobell, C., and Laidlaw, P. P. (1926). *Parasitology* **18:** 283–318.

Dyrdowska, M. (1931). *Compt. rend. soc. biol.* **108:** 593–596.

Engel, F. L., Harrison, H. C., and Long, C. N. H. (1944). *J. Exptl. Med.* **79:** 9–22.

Erhardt, A. (1939). *Arch. Schiffs-u. Tropen-Hyg.* **43:** 15–19.

Fauré-Fremiet, E. (1913). *Arch. anat. microscop.* **15:** 435–757.

Fiebiger, J. (1913). *Arch. Protistenk.* **31:** 95–137.

Firket, P. (1910). *Arch. intern. physiol.* **9:** 288–291.

Fredericq, L. (1893). *Zentr. Physiol.* **7:** 33–38.

Gilmour, D. (1940). *J. Cellular Comp. Physiol.* **15:** 331–342.

Golubeva, N. A. (1945). *Med. Parasitol. Parasitic Diseases (U.R.S.S.).* **14:** 45–48.

Grass, H. (1921). *Beitr. Klin. Tuberk.* **46:** 46–54.

Grass, H., and Meiners, H. H. (1922). *Beitr. Klin. Tuberk.* **51:** 134–145.

Harnisch, O. (1937). *Z. vergleich. Physiol.* **24:** 667–686.

Harvey, S. C. (1949). *J. Biol. Chem.* **179:** 435–453.

Harwood, P. D., and Brown, H. W. (1934). *J. Parasitol.* **20:** 128.

Hausmann, L. (1897). *Rev. suisse zool.* **5:** 1–42.

Hinshaw, H. C. (1927). *Univ. Calif. (Berkeley) Pubs. Zool.* **31:** 31–51.

Hobson, A. D. (1948). *Parasitology* **38:** 183–227.

Hungate, R. E. (1939). *Ecology* **20:** 230–245.

Hungate, R. E. (1941). *Anat. Record* **81:** Suppl.: 69.

Hungate, R. E. (1942). *Biol. Bull.* **83:** 303–319.

Jacobs, L. (1941). *J. Parasitol.* **27** Suppl.: 31.

Jirovec, O., and Rodova, H. (1940). *Zentr. Bakt. Parasitenk, Abt. I. Orig.* **145:** 351–360.

Johnson, G. (1942). *J. Parasitol.* **28:** 369–379.

Jones, M. F., Newton, W. L., Weibel, S. R., Warren, H. B., Steinle, M. L., and Figgat, W. B. (1947). *Natl. Inst. Health Bull.* No. **189:** 137–172.

von Kemnitz, G. (1916). *Z. Biol.* **67:** 129–244.

Knoth, M. (1928). *Z. Parasitenk.* **1:** 262–282.

Konsuloff, S. (1922). *Arch. Protistenk.* **44:** 285–345.

Kosmin, N. P. (1928). *Z. vergleich. Physiol.* **8:** 625–634.

Krogh, A. (1916). The Respiratory Exchange of Animals and Man. Longmans, Green and Co. London.

Krogh, A. (1941). The Comparative Physiology of Respiratory Mechanisms. University of Pennsylvania Press, Philadelphia.

Laser, H. (1944). *Biochem. J.* **38:** 333–338.

Lauterborn, R. (1916). *Verhandl. naturhist. med. Ver. Heidelberg* [N.F.] **13:** 395–481.

Lee, C. U. (1930). *Arch. Schiffs-u. Tropen-Hyg.* **34:** 262–274.

Lesser, E. J. (1906). *Z. Biol.* **48:** 1–18.

Levitanskaja, P. B. (1938). *Med. Parasitol. Parasitic Diseases (U.R.S.S.)* **7:** 436–449.

Long, J. H., and Fenger, F. (1917). *J. Am. Chem. Soc.* **39:** 1278–1286.

Looss, A. (1911). *Records Egypt. Govt. School Med.* **4:** 163–613.

Lucker, J. T. (1935). *Proc. Helminthol. Soc. Wash. D. C.* **2:** 54–55.

Lwoff, A., and Valentini, S. (1948). *Ann. inst. Pasteur* **75:** 1–7.

Marchoux, E., and Chorine, V. (1932). *Ann. inst. Pasteur* **49:** 75–102.

McCoy, O. R. (1930). *Am. J. Hyg.* **11:** 413–448.

McIver, M. A., Redfield, A. C., and Benedict, E. B. (1926). *Am. J. Physiol.* **76:** 92–111.

McKee, R. W., Ormsbee, R. A., Anfinsen, C. B., Geiman, Q. M., and Ball, E. G. (1946). *J. Exptl. Med.* **84:** 569–582.

Metzner, R. (1903). *Arch. Protistenk.* **2:** 13–72.

Meyer, F. (1935). *Arch. exptl. Path. Pharmakol.* **177:** 693–713.

Montgomery, H., and Horwitz, O. (1948). *J. Clin. Invest.* **27:** 550.

Moroff, T., and Fiebiger, J. (1905). *Arch. Protistenk.* **6:** 166–174.

Moulder, J. W. (1948). *J. Infectious Diseases* **83:** 33–41.

Moulder, J. W. (1950). *J. Parasitol.* **36:** 193–200.

Nagahana, M. (1932). *J. Med. Coll. Keijo* **3:** 492–500.

Newton, W. L., Bennet, H. J., and Figgat, W. B. (1949). *Am. J. Hyg.* **49:** 166–175.

Nishi, M. (1933). *J. Formosan Med. Assoc.* **32** Suppl.: 61–62.

Nishigori, M. (1928). *J. Formosan Med. Assoc.* **1928:** No. 276 (not seen).

Pennoit-DeCooman, E., and van Grembergen. G. (1942). *Verhandel. Koninkl. Vlaam. Acad. Wetenschap. Belg. Klasse Wetenschap.* **4;** No. 6: 7–77.

Peters, L., Bueding, E., Valk, A., Higashi. A., and Welch, A. D. (1949). *J. Pharmacol. Exptl. Therap.* **95:** 212–239.

Pfeiffer, R. (1892). Beitraege zur Protozoenforschung II. Hirshwald, Berlin.

Planer (1860). *Sitzber. Akad. Wiss. Wien. Math.-naturw. Klasse* **42:** 307–354.

Pritze, F. (1928). *Z. Parasitenk.* **1:** 345–415.

Pütter, A. (1905). *Z. allgem. Physiol.* **5:** 566–612.

Ray, I. C. (1932). *Indian J. Med. Research* **20:** 355–367.

Read, C. P. (1950). *Rice Inst. Pamphlet* **37;** No. 2: 1–94.

Reichenow, E. (1929). Lehrbuch der Protozoenkunde. 5th edition, Fischer, Jena.

Rogers, L. (1905). *Lancet* **83** (1): 1484–1487.

Rogers, W. P. (1949a). *Australian J. Sci. Research* **B2:** 157–165.

Rogers, W. P. (1949b). *Australian J. Sci. Research* **B2:** 166–174.

Root, R. W. (1931). *Biol. Bull.* **61:** 427–456.

Ross, O. A., and Bueding, E. (1950). *Proc. Soc. Exptl. Biol. Med.* **73:** 179–182.

Sarre, H. (1937). *Arch. ges. Physiol.* **239:** 377–399.

Schalimov, L. G. (1931). *Trans. Dynamics Development (U.R.S.S.)* **6:** 181–196.

Schumaker, E. (1931). *Am. J. Hyg.* **13:** 281–295.

Schwab, K. L. (1858). Die Oestraciden, Bremsen der Pferde, Rinder und Schafe. Muenchen (not seen).

Scott, M. J. (1927). *J. Morphol.* **44:** 417–465.

Seevers, M. H. (1936). *Am. J. Physiol.* **115:** 38–42.

Senekjie, H. A. (1941). *Am. J. Hyg.* **34:** Sect. C: 67–70.

Shorb, D. A. (1944). *J. Agr. Research* **69:** 279–287.

Silverman, M., Ceithaml, J., Taliaferro, L. G., and Evans, E. A. (1944). *J. Infectious Diseases* **75:** 212–230.

Smyth, J. D. (1950). *J. Parasitol.* **36:** 371–383.

Snyder, T. L., and Meleney, H. E. (1941). *Am. J. Trop. Med.* **21:** 63–73.

Snyder, T. L., and Meleney, H. E. (1942). *J. Parasitol.* **28;** Suppl.: 11.

Snyder, T. L., and Meleney, H. E. (1943). *J. Parasitol.* **29:** 278–284.

Soule, M. H. (1925). *J. Infectious Diseases* **36:** 245–308.

Stannard, J. N., McCoy, O. R., and Latchford, W. B. (1938). *Am. J. Hyg.* **27:** 666–682.

Stephenson, W. (1947). *Parasitology* **38:** 116–122.

Stoll, N. R. (1940). *Growth* **4:** 383–406.

Strangeways, W. I. (1937). *Ann. Trop. Med. Parasitol.* **31:** 387–404.

Stunkard, H. W. (1930). *J. Morphol.* **50:** 143–183.

Stunkard, H. W. (1937). *Am. Museum Novitates* **No. 908:** 1–27.

Szwejkowska, G. (1929). *Bull. intern. acad. polon. sci. Classe sci. math. nat.* **B1928:** 489–519.

Tachau, H., and Thilenius, R. (1916). *Z. klin. Med.* **82:** 209–222.

Tanabe, M., and Komada, K. (1932). *Keijo J. Med.* **3:** 385–392.

Tappeiner (1883). *Z. Biol.* **19:** 228–279.

Tasaka, M. (1935). *Fukuoka Acta Med.* **28** (not seen).

Toryu, Y. (1935). *Science Repts. Tôhoku Imp. Univ. Fourth Ser.* **10:** 361–375.

Trager, W. (1934). *Biol. Bull.* **66:** 182–190.

Trager, W. (1941). *J. Exptl. Med.* **74:** 441–461.

Vogel, H., and von Brand, T. (1933). *Z. Parasitenk.* **5:** 425–431.

Webb, G. B., Gilbert, G. B., James, T. L., and Havens, L. C. (1914). *Arch. Internal Med.* **14:** 883–896.

Weinland, E. (1901). *Z. Biol.* **42:** 55–90.

Weinland, E., and von Brand, T. (1926). *Z. vergleich. Physiol.* **4:** 212–285.

Welch, A. D., Peters, L., Bueding, E., Valk, A., and Higashi, A. (1947) *Science* **105:** 486–488.

Wells, H. S. (1931). *J. Parasitol.* **17:** 167–182.

Wendt, H. (1936). *Z. Kinderheilk.* **58:** 375–387.

Westphal, A. (1934). *Z. Parasitenk.* **7:** 71–117.

Willems, R., Massart, L., and Peeters, G. (1942). *Naturwissenschaften* **30:** 169–170.

Witte, J. (1933). *Zentr. Bakt. Parasitenk. Abt. I. Orig.* **128:** 188–195.

Zawadowsky, M. (1916). *Compt. rend. soc. biol.* **68:** 595–598.

Zawadowsky, M., and Orlow, A. P. (1927). *Trans. Lab. Exptl. Biol. Zoo-Park Moscow* **3:** 99–116.

Zawadowsky, M., and Schalimov, L. G. (1929). *Trans. Lab. Exptl. Biol. Zoo-Park Moscow* **5:** 1-42.

Zviaginzev, S. N. (1934). *Trans. Dynamics Development (U.R.S.S.)* **8:** 186–202.

# CHAPTER 15

# THE GROWTH REQUIREMENTS OF PARASITES

## I. Introductory Remarks

The growth requirements of parasites can be determined with certainty only by experimentation *in vitro* for *in vivo* experiments are difficult to interpret. If a parasite shows a faster or slower rate of growth or development when certain compounds are added or withheld, respectively, from the host's diet, it is seldom possible to exclude an indirect action *via* a change in the physiology of the host. Another matter of experience has been that, with rare exceptions, only bacteriologically sterile environments have allowed the elucidation of growth requirements and it seems therefore appropriate to summarize briefly the procedures used in securing parasites free from microorganisms.

## II. Methods of Securing Bacteria-Free Parasites

No difficulty is experienced in obtaining small organisms such as trypanosomes, malarial parasites, or microfilariae that live in the bloodstream bacteria-free, by simple sterile withdrawal of blood. The isolation of larger parasites, for example schistosomes, necessitates aseptic surgical procedures (Ross and Bueding, 1950). Equally easy is the procurement of larger helminths living in other sterile habitats, such as the body cavities or cysts. Examples are the plerocercoids of *Schistocephalus* and *Ligula* (Smyth, 1946, 1947b) for the former, larval *Eustrongylides* (von Brand and Simpson, 1942) for the latter habitat. Somewhat more tedious is the gathering of small tissue helminths. Usually it is impossible to isolate them directly in large numbers without contamination. Ferguson (1940) freed metacercariae of *Posthodiplostomum* from their cysts by digesting infected livers and kidneys with pepsin, isolating the worms from debris by pipetting, and finally sterilizing them by repeated settling through columns of sterile Ringer's solution. Weller (1943) obtained sterile *Trichinella* larvae by digesting infected meat in a modified Baermann apparatus with pepsin and subsequent repeated washings of the larvae with sterile saline.

Parasites that normally inhabit contaminated surroundings occasionally invade sterile habitats and then can be gathered pure without difficulty. Sterile specimens have thus been obtained of *Endamoeba histolytica* from liver abscesses (Cleveland and Sanders, 1930) and of *Eutrichomastix colubrorum* from the blood (Chatton, 1918). In other cases the habitat is sometimes contaminated with bacteria and sometimes not. It is then a matter of luck to find the former as did Witte (1934) in the case of *Trichomonas foetus* or Bos (1933) and Cauthen and Harris (1935) in that of *Trichomonas hepatica*.

In many instances, however, the parasites occur only in surroundings teeming with microorganisms. They must then be purified and various procedures have been employed. It is sometimes possible to select protozoan cysts as starting material for culture attempts and to sterilize them. This has been done with *Endamoeba histolytica* cysts by centrifugation, flotation, and treatment with mercuric chloride (Meleney *et al.*, 1940; Snyder and Meleney, 1941). Sterile cysts of the same organism have been obtained also by micro-isolation and washings in sterile medium (Rees *et al.*, 1941, 1947). The micro-isolation technique also can be applied profitably to trophozoites of some parasitic protozoa and has been used successfully by Rees (1937) with *Trichomonas foetus*. Another possibility is the application of antibiotics. Jacobs (1947) freed unibacterial cultures of *Endamoeba histolytica* from *Clostridium perfringens* by means of penicillin, an antibiotic proven useful also for sterilizing contaminated cultures of *Trichomonas vaginalis* (Rees and Reardon, 1944; Johnson, Trussell, and Jahn, 1945).

Special procedures can be applied to selected cases. Glaser and Coria (1935) used V tubes filled with semi-solid medium through which *Trichomonas foetus* migrated faster than bacteria; the flagellates could then be obtained pure from one of the arms. *Trichomonas hominis* was freed successfully from bacteria by migration through the loops of a capillary fixed to a larger tube (Stone and Reynolds, 1939) and Adler (1942) described a method including sand filtration for the sterilization of the same organism. In an exceptional case the bacteria even disappeared spontaneously from a culture of *Trichomonas vaginalis* (Trussell and Plass, 1940).

It has proven possible to free the eggs of various species of nematodes from bacteria by first concentrating them by means of flotation procedures, purifying them further by repeated washings and centrifugations in sterile water, followed by the application of some disinfectant (McCoy, 1929a, b, 1930; Lapage, 1933; Glaser and Stoll, 1938b; Lawrence, 1948). These eggs could be used either for sterile culture attempts or for cultures with known species of bacteria. Another approach has been to develop large number of larvae first in nonsterile conventional cultures and then to sterilize these larvae. This goal has been achieved in various ways. Chung (1936) sterilized filariform larvae of *Strongyloides* by letting them enter the skin of a living guinea pig, excising the piece of skin, and letting the larvae migrate out into sterile saline. Using a similar biological sterilization method, Ferguson (1943) injected cercariae of *Diplostomum flexicaudum* which had developed in snails, into the tissues surrounding the eyes of fish, subsequently recovering them from the lens. Chemical sterilization by means of the hypochlorite containing Milton or Labarraque solutions, which induce exsheathing, combined with washings in sterile solutions gave excellent results with larval stages of various nematode species (Lapage, 1933, 1935a, b; Glaser and Stoll, 1938a, 1940; Glaser, 1940a; Stoll, 1940). Sterilization methods for adult *Ascaris lumbricoides* involving the utilization of various antibiotics have been developed recently and lead in a relatively large percentage of specimens to complete elimination of all microorganisms (Epps, Weiner, and Bueding, 1950; Fairbairn and Reesal, 1950; Fairbairn, 1950).

## III. Growth Requirements of Parasitic Rhizopods

*Endamoeba histolytica* grows best under anaerobic or semi-anaerobic conditions. In mixed cultures with actively growing microorganisms no special precautions are necessary probably because the associates establish an oxygen gradient. In cultures where the growth of the microorganisms is arrested (Shaffer and Frye, 1948; Shaffer, Ryden, and Frye, 1949) a reducing agent (thioglycollate) is required and a vaseline plug proved useful. The only other definitely known growth requirement is cholesterol (Snyder and Meleney, 1943; Rees *et al.*, 1944).

The reason that little definite information has become available despite an immense amount of work, is not difficult to find. Hitherto it has not been possible to grow *Endamoeba histolytica* free from other microorganisms. Jacobs' (1947) cultures were sterile, it is true, but the amoebic growth was too poor to allow analysis of the growth factors. It is clear that in cultures with a mixed bacterial population conditions are so complex as to make it, in almost all cases, impossible to distinguish between contributions of the medium proper and those of bacteria. Somewhat more favorable are unibacterial cultures such as those employed by Cleveland and Sanders (1930), Rees *et al.* (1944), and Dobell (1947). But even here it was not possible to distinguish between the action of bacteria and amoebas even in respect to such relatively simple processes as gas production and sugar consumption (von Brand *et al.*, 1943).

The question why *Endamoeba histolytica* has so far resisted all attempts of aseptic cultivation is extremely puzzling. It has been shown that not all bacteria are equally suitable for culture of the amoebas (Cleveland and Sanders, 1930; Chinn *et al.*, 1942; Jacobs, 1950). On the other hand, streptobacillus grown for 24 hours in amoeba-free medium and then arrested by antibiotics will support luxuriant cultures (Shaffer and Frye, 1948; Shaffer, Walton, and Frye, 1948; Shaffer, Ryden, and Frye, 1949) and *Trypanosoma cruzi* can be substituted for bacteria (Phillips, 1950; Phillips and Rees, 1950). The growth factor or growth factors contributed by the associates must hence be fairly widely distributed in the bodies of other organisms or be produced by a variety of forms, but they must be very unstable. It has not been possible to substitute dead bacteria or bacterial extracts for live associates, but a certain measure of success has been achieved with *Trypanosoma cruzi* treated for 10 minutes at 48° C (Phillips and Rees, 1950). The idea has been expressed that the amoebas may have lost the power of synthesizing essential respiratory enzymes or co-factors. However, the addition of di- and triphosphopyridine nucleotide, adenosinedi- and -triphosphate, adenosine-5-phosphate, cocarboxylase, and pyridoxal phosphate was ineffective (Rees, Reardon, and Baernstein, 1948; Rees, 1950). The development of microcultures (Rees *et al.*, 1947) was an important tool in allowing the performance of the above type of experimentation.

It is, of course, undeniable that the medium itself also contributes essential factors. It is generally recognized that starch, especially rice starch, enhances amoebic growth, but in cultures where either *Trypanosoma cruzi* or but few bacteria are present, glucose can replace starch. It has also been found that B vitamins have to be added to the overlay when egg white is substituted for whole egg in diphasic media (Rees *et al.*, 1944). The fact that *Endamoeba histolytica* can be grown in cellophane bags suspended in the overlay of whole egg slants (Rees *et al.*, 1945) indicates that nitrogenous compounds of low molecular weight suffice for the complex amoebas plus bacteria. This view is substantiated by the observation that amino acids can be used as nitrogen source in monophasic cultures (Anderson and Hansen, 1947). But it must be emphasized that we do not know whether these substances have a direct beneficial action on the amoebas or only an indirect one *via* the associates.

It should be realized that the factors governing excystation are different from those allowing development and growth. Excystation can, in suitable media, be readily induced in the absence of bacteria (Meleney *et al.*, 1940; Rees, Reardon, and Bartgis, 1950). Anaerobiosis produced by a reducing agent such as cysteine or glutathione proved essential. Best results were obtained in a complex fluid medium containing, among other constituents, vitamins B and C, purines, pyrimidines, cholesterol, and inorganic salts, the latter corresponding to a solution developed by Anfinsen *et al.* (1946) for malarial parasites. It is not yet known which of the above constituents of the medium are essential for excystation.

There is no information available concerning the growth requirements of other parasitic rhizopods, despite the fact that all human intestinal amoebas and several species parasitizing animals have been cultivated. The report of Lamy (1948) that *Endamoeba invadens* could be cultivated in the presence of small pieces of organs, but in the complete absence of bacteria or bacterial extracts, requires confirmation.

IV. GROWTH REQUIREMENTS OF PARASITIC FLAGELLATES

Several trichomonads and trypanosomidae have been studied in bacteria-free cultures. The former, as mentioned in the last chapter, seem to grow best when no or only little oxygen is present, while the latter definitely need oxygen for development.

The trichomonads, investigated first in some detail by Cailleau (1935, 1936a, b, 1937, 1938a, b, 1939a, b, c) were grown in most cases in fairly complex media; media containing bouillon and serum. It was found that *Eutrichomastix colubrorum* grew best with horse serum, *Trichomonas foetus* with human serum, and *Trichomonas columbae* with pigeon serum. These three species required for growth the addition of cholesterol and ascorbic acid to the medium and the necessity for cholesterol was also demonstrated, in contaminated cultures, for *Trichomonas batrachorum* (Cailleau, 1939b). Actually, neither cholesterol nor ascorbic acid are entirely specific. Cailleau (1936b, 1937) studied 66 sterols and sterol derivatives and found that 18, amongst them dehydrocholesterol, sitosterol, ergostanol, and cinchol, supported the growth of *Trichomonas columbae* satisfactorily. Ascorbic acid could be replaced successfully by $D$-isoascorbic acid, $D$-glucoascorbic acid, $D$-glucoheptoascorbic acid, reductinic acid, and reducton (Cailleau, 1939c). There is some question whether ascorbic acid can be regarded as a growth requirement in the strict sense of the word. Guthrie (1946), in any event, was able to replace ascorbic acid by thioglycollate in cultures of *Trichomonas foetus*, an observation seemingly indicating that the beneficial action of ascorbic acid may have been due only to its reducing properties. *Trichomonas gallinarum* resembles the above species in its need for ascorbic acid, but requires, in addition, an unidentified growth factor which disappears spontaneously from culture media prepared long in advance of being used (Cailleau, 1940).

Whether *Trichomonas vaginalis* also needs cholesterol has not yet been established. It has been found that it requires pantothenic acid and that it has a definite need for phosphate (Kupferberg, Johnson, and Sprince, 1948). The nitrogenous requirements of trichomonads have been studied most intensively with *Trichomonas foetus*. As already mentioned in Chapter 12, the amino acids recognized as essential for growth corresponded rather closely to those required by higher animals. They were arginine, glycine, tryptophane, histidine, isoleucine, leucine, lysine, threonine, methionine, phenylalanine, proline, serine, and valine. Weiss and Ball (1947) who carried out this study found a relatively low rate of growth when only complete proteins were employed as substrates. The growth rate improved when partially digested proteins were used until the soluble nitrogen amounted to 50%, but it began to decline when the digestion was carried farther. The authors point out that this may indicate a need for strepogenin.

The insect-inhabiting trypanosomidae, the leishmanias, and the trypanosomes of the *lewisi* group are readily cultivated bacteria-free on a wide variety of media (complete review of the older literature in Noeller, 1928, and Lwoff, 1940; newer media are described by Little and Subbarow, 1945; Lourie, 1946; Chang, 1947; Johnson, 1947; De Freitas and De Castro, 1948; Tobie and Rees, 1948; Sampath and Little, 1949; and others). The African pathogenic trypanosomes, on the other hand, are much more difficult to cultivate, but fluid, semi-solid, and diphasic blood-containing media have been employed successfully by von Razgha (1929), Reichenow (1932, 1934), Brutsaert and Henrard (1938), Weinman (1944, 1946), and Tobie, von Brand, and Mehlman (1950). A characteristic of the cultures of all two-host trypanosomes is that the parasites develop only to the stage attained in the gut of the intermediate host. Hence, the cultures of those forms that complete their life cycle in nature in the gut, are usually infective for the final hosts, while those undergoing only partial development in the gut and final development in the salivary gland or the proboscis of the invertebrate hosts, are commonly uninfective. So far it has not been possible to cultivate any trypanosome in the form they assume in the bloodstream.

Virtually nothing is known about the growth requirements of the African pathogenic trypanosomes, with the exception of the fact that blood is an indispensable ingredient of the media. Both human and animal blood can be used for the cultivation of *Trypanosoma gambiense* and *Trypanosoma rhodesiense*, but the blood of some humans does, for unknown reasons, not support their growth (Ponselle, 1924; Reichenow, 1937a, b; van Hoof, 1947; Tobie, von Brand, and Mehlman, 1950). It has been found that strains of these parasites, maintained for some time by syringe passage in laboratory animals, lose their ability to develop in culture. In this respect a close parallelism exists to their inability of developing in glossinas (Reichenow, 1927a, b, 1939). Some older strains, however, have been found which could be established in cultures prepared from the blood of certain donors (Lwoff and Ceccaldi, 1939).

Somewhat more is known concerning the readily cultivated groups of trypanosomidae. One of the most intensively studied group is comprised by the strigomonads (A. Lwoff, 1934; M. Lwoff, 1933a, b, 1935, 1936, 1937, 1938a, 1940). It was found that some forms require hematin (*Leptomonas ctenocephali, Strigomonas fasciculata, Strigomonas culicidarum anophelis, Strigomonas muscidarum*), while others do not (*Strigomonas oncopelti, Strigomonas culicidarum culicis, Strigomonas parva, Strigomonas media*). Hematin could be replaced successfully by other iron-porphyrin compounds having protohemin as a prosthetic group; for example, by veal liver catalase in cultures of *Leptomonas pyrrhocoris* (Zotta, 1923), or peroxidases of plant origin in those of *Strigomonas fasciculata* (M. Lwoff, 1933a). A. Lwoff (1934) studied a series of porphyrin compounds as to their ability to support growth and stimulate respiration of *Strigomonas fasciculata*. He reports that only blood, hematin, protohemin, and protoporphyrin will do so. This last finding is of special interest because protoporphyrin is iron-free. If Lwoff's (1934) assumption is correct that the above compounds serve primarily to build the flagellate's iron-catalyzed respiratory enzyme system, it follows that it must be able to incorporate iron into the protoporphyrin molecule.

A need for thiamine has been shown for *Strigomonas oncepelti, Strigomonas culicidarum anophelis, Strigomonas culicidarum culicis,* and *Strigomonas fasciculata,* while the other species mentioned above have not been tested in this respect. The strigomonads are apparently not able to synthesize thiamine from pyrimidine and thiazole, but certain changes in the thiamine molecule can be made without interfering with its activity. For example, the methyl group in the 2 position of the pyrimidine fragment could be exchanged with an ethyl group and the compound was still as active as before (M. Lwoff, 1940).

The growth factors required by leishmanias and *Trypanosoma cruzi* appear to be essentially the same. M. Lwoff (1933a, 1938b, 1939, 1940) found them to require, besides unidentified factors present in blood serum, ascorbic acid and hematin. This has been proven definitely for *Leishmania tropica, Leishmania donovani,* and *Trypanosoma cruzi,* while *Leishmania agamae* and *Leishmania ceramodactyli* may be able to grow without ascorbic acid.

The nitrogenous requirements of trypanosomidae are not well understood. *Leptomonas ctenocephali, Strigomonas fasciculata,* and *Strigomonas oncopelti* develop best in peptone solutions, such as peptic digests of muscle, or in silk peptone provided that the latter is enriched with thiamine. If, however, the digestion is more complete and the milieu becomes abiuretic, a continuous culture becomes impossible (M. Lwoff, 1933a), an observation resembling findings reviewed above for trichomonads. Whether this actually, as assumed by Lwoff (1933a), necessarily indicates that amino acids do not suffice as nitrogenous food has hardly been established beyond reasonable doubt. Prolonged digestion could have destroyed some as yet unidentified growth factor.

## V. GROWTH REQUIREMENTS OF SPOROZOA

Definite data on the growth requirements of malarial parasites have become known in recent years only, since only the newer culture methods allowed experiments along these lines. The older method of Bass and Johns (1912) for the culture of human plasmodia was never very satisfactory and has contributed nothing to the question under consideration. This latter is also true for tissue culture experiments which have been carried out quite successfully allowing growth, multiplication, and survival of the exoerythrocytic stages of *Plasmodium gallinaceum* for periods up to 89 days (Hawking, 1944, 1945).

The new rocker-dilution and rocker-perfusion techniques developed by Geiman *et al.* (1946), on the contrary, have increased our knowledge of the growth requirements of the erythrocytic stages of *Plasmodium knowlesi* to a considerable degree, since the parasites remained normal and underwent development for several successive generations. The techniques consist fundamentally in keeping the erythrocytes normal and, at the same time, in providing the necessary nutriments for the parasites and removing accumulating endproducts. It could be demonstrated that the parasites definitely needed glucose and *p*-aminobenzoic acid (Anfinsen *et al.*, 1946) as well as methionine (McKee, Geiman, and Cobbey, 1947; McKee and Geiman, 1948). The nutritive solution contained in addition to the two above substances, inorganic salts in proportions corresponding to monkey plasma, various amino acids, water soluble vitamins, purines, and pyrimidines. Attempts were made to elucidate the nutritional requirements further by withholding blocks of these substances, but the presence of plasma prevented further analysis. Geiman (1948) states that it was possible to substitute 1% purified bovine albumin for the plasma thus opening apparently a new approach, but the detailed results of these experiments have not yet been published.

There is still less known about the growth requirements of other primate plasmodia. It has been established that *Plasmodium vivax* developed better when the amino acid concentration was raised above the level originally designed for the *Plasmodium knowlesi* cultures (Geiman, 1948).

The growth requirements of avian plasmodia have been studied primarily by Trager (1941, 1943, 1947) who succeeded in keeping *Plasmodium lophurae* alive for periods up to 10 to 16 days at 40 to 41° C. This long survival was achieved by the addition of fresh red cells every other day, in addition to the provision of a complicated medium and proper aeration, indicating again that the normalcy of red cells is of the utmost importance in experiments of this type. Of all the ingredients of the medium only two, glucose and calcium pantothenate, were considered with great probability as favoring the parasites directly. All the other constituents may have exerted their favorable action indirectly *via* the red cells, although of course, a direct action could not be excluded.

A first step towards the ultimate goal, cultivation of *Plasmodium lophurae* free of red cells, was taken recently by Trager (1950). He was able to maintain the parasites alive, freed from the erythrocytes by hemolysis, for 2 to 3 days, during which time some growth and development occurred. An essential ingredient of the medium was a concentrated extract of duck erythrocytes made up in a special fluid containing a variety of both inorganic and organic compounds. The relatively high potassium content of the medium is especially noteworthy. It could be ascertained that the survival of the parasites was favored by gelatin, this compound probably conferring to the medium a suitable physical consistency, by yeast adenylic acid, cozymase, and especially adenosine triphosphate and sodium pyruvate. It appears that the parasites are incapable of synthesizing ATP and this deficiency may prove an important link in explaining their normal intracellular location.

## VI. Growth Requirements of Parasitic Worms

### A. Introductory Remarks

Many data are available in the literature on the survival time of parasitic worms *in vitro*. These experiments were, in many cases, done in order to test the resistance of the parasites to extraneous conditions rather than to elucidate their growth requirements. Hence it does not seem necessary to give a complete list of the animals employed, but some representative examples drawn from helminths which survive rather well under artificial conditions, have been assembled in Table 37. They may prove amenable to work along strictly nutritional lines. More references will be found in the papers by Wardle (1937), Hoeppli, Feng, and Chu (1938), Smyth (1947a), and Hobson (1948). In the following sections only those experiments will be reviewed in which either a definite development of parasitic worms was achieved *in vitro*, or through which data on the nutritional requirements became known.

### B. Growth Requirements of Cestodes

Some success has been achieved with larval tapeworms. In Coutelen's (1927a, b) experiments scolices of *Echinococcus granulosus* kept in hydatid fluid with added ascitic serum, showed a certain measure of growth and of abnormal bladder formation. Analogous results were obtained with *Coenurus serialis* (Coutelen, 1929b). Stunkard (1932) observed a rather marked growth and segmentation of larval *Crepidobothrium lönnbergi* kept in dextrose-saline fortified with broth. The proglottids formed were, however, abnormal and sterile.

By far the best results were obtained with larval fish tapeworms that are already considerably developed in their normal habitat and attain sexual maturity rapidly upon transfer to a suitable definitive host. Joyeux and Baer (1942) brought *Ligula* to sexual maturity and oviposition, though not to sperm production, in saline plus ascitic fluid, saline plus horse

TABLE 37. Maximal survival of some helminths *in vitro*

| SPECIES | MATERIAL | TEMP. °C | MEDIUM | SURVIVAL TIME | AUTHOR |
|---|---|---|---|---|---|
| **TREMATODES** | | | | | |
| Aspidogaster conchicola | Adults | 2-9 | Mussel blood | 75 days | Van Cleave and Williams (1943) |
| Schistosoma japonicum | Adults | 37 | Serum | 5 months | Hoeppli, Feng, and Chu (1938) |
| Clonorchis sinensis | Adults | 37 | Serum plus Tyrode | 5 months | Hoeppli and Chu (1937) |
| Opisthorchis felineus | Adults | 37 | Ringer plus K-indigotri-sulfonate | 40 days | Kollath and Ehrhardt (1936) |
| O. felineus | Metacercariae | 9 | 0.9% NaCl solution | 2 months | Vogel (1934) |
| **CESTODES** | | | | | |
| Diphyllobothrium latum | Plerocercoids | 8-15 | Fish broth | 63 days | Markov (1938) |
| Triaenophorus tricuspidatus | Adults | 10 | NaCl solution plus pepsin-peptone | 3 to 4 weeks | Lönnberg (1892) |
| Crepidobothrium lönnbergi | Larvae | Room temp. | Dextrose saline plus broth | 32 days | Stunkard (1932) |
| Hymenolepis nana | Adults | 37.5 | Baker's medium A | 20 days | Green and Wardle (1941) |
| Cysticercus fasciolaris | Larvae | 37.5 | Balanced salt solution plus chick embryo extract plus horse serum | 35 days | Mendelsohn (1935) |
| **NEMATODES** | | | | | |
| Ascaris lumbricoides | Adults | 27-30 | Kronecker's solution | 26 days | Hall (1917) |
| Spirocerca sanguinolenta | Larvae | 37 | Ringer solution | 6 weeks | Hoeppli, Feng, and Chu (1938) |
| Camallanus americanus | Adults | 25 | Witte peptone plus turtle blood agar | 2 months | Magath (1919) |
| Dirofilaria immitis | Microfilariae | 37 | Defibrinated blood plus glucose | 15 days | Johns and Querens (1914) |
| Wuchereria bancrofti | Microfilariae | 22-27 | Saline plus hemoglobin | 32 days | Coutelen (1929a) |

serum, or saline plus serum plus ascitic fluid. Sperm production could not be induced by the addition of testicular or pituitary extracts, nor by extracts of adult *Ligula*. Still better results have been reported by Smyth (1946, 1947b, 1948, 1949, 1950) who used both *Ligula* and *Schistocephalus*. He found that one of the most important factors for inducing sexual maturation was a raise in temperature to 40°C. The worms then matured rather rapidly, though slower than in their normal habitat, and shed eggs which, however, failed to embryonate in the first series reported. It was found next that if the pH of the medium was controlled by means of calcium carbonate, thus preventing a highly detrimental acidification, and if the oxygen tension was kept low, at least a small percentage of the eggs embryonated in the case of *Ligula*, and a higher, but variable percentage in that of *Schistocephalus*. The receptaculum seminis of the worms was always sperm-free, making it probable that the development of the eggs was only parthenogenetic. Spermatogenesis did take place, but the sperms failed to reach the receptaculum. Essentially identical results were obtained whether the medium was completely inorganic (for example, $\frac{3}{4}$ Locke solution plus calcium carbonate) or whether it contained organic substances, such as serum or peptone broth. It follows, hence, that the endogenous stores of nutritive material sufficed to insure development as soon as the physicochemical environment was favorable. It must be recognized that for this reason no further insight into the actual nutritional needs have been gained so far.

## C. Growth Requirements of Trematodes

Stunkard (1940) mentioned briefly that he was able to rear metacercariae of *Plagitura parva* to sexual maturity in a bacteria-free medium which contained living yeast cells, but he has not as yet described these experiments in detail. Ferguson (1940) kept metacercariae of *Posthodiplostomum minimum* in a sterile medium consisting of diluted Tyrode solution, chicken serum, and yeast extract. During incubation at 39°C the worms developed into adults within a few days. They produced, however, only inactive sperms and the eggs were abnormal and not viable.

Ferguson found later (Ferguson, 1943) that sterile cercariae of *Diplostomum flexicaudum* remained alive for about a week in Tyrode solution with little or no development taking place. If, however, a lens of a sunfish or of a rat was added to the Tyrode, morphologically normal metacercariae developed, but they were not quite normal physiologically, proving noninfective for birds. The experiments are nevertheless of great interest since they show that the lens of the two vertebrates mentioned contained most of the required growth-promoting substances. It is noteworthy that no development took place when pieces of rabbit or bovine lens were placed into Tyrode, but that the worms did develop when frog Ringer was substituted for Tyrode. This obviously shows that the inorganic substances are of great importance in such cases.

This latter fact has also been observed by Stephenson (1947) who reported best survival of adult *Fasciola hepatica* in a medium containing NaCl 150 m$M$, KCl 10 m$M$, CaCl$_2$ 1 m$M$, sodium borate 6 m$M$, and glucose 30 m$M$ (pH 8.6). In this medium the worms survived at 36°C for about 60 hours. In view of this short survival time it is obviously not possible to speak of a culture. The worms employed in this case were not sterile and the addition of borax checked bacterial activity.

The nutritional requirements of *Schistosoma mansoni* have been studied recently by Ross and Bueding (1950). They found nearly equal survival in serum ultrafiltrate (10 to 12 days) and in whole serum (14 to 18 days), an observation indicating that the proteins and other nondialyzable substances of the serum were probably not required. In a wholly synthetic medium consisting essentially of a balanced, buffered salt solution, amino acids, carbohydrates, vitamins, and various growth factors, the worms died within 12 to 18 hours. If an aqueous extract of beef muscle or a purified fraction of protogen was added to the synthetic medium, survival was significantly increased indicating that the early death of the worms in the pure synthetic medium cannot have been due to its being toxic. A nutritional deficiency of unknown nature must be assumed. Bueding (personal communication) recently has established definitely that protogen is an essential nutritional factor for *Schistosoma mansoni*.

## D. Growth Requirements of Nematodes

Analysis has progressed farthest in the case of *Neoaplectana glaseri*, a parasite of the Japanese beetle which belongs to the family Steinernematidae. Glaser (1931, 1932) showed first that its entire life cycle could be achieved on veal infusion dextrose agar with bakers yeast growing on the surface. Yeast furnished an unidentified growth factor as evidenced by the fact that development ceased once the yeast had been consumed by the nematodes. In this way up to 32 successive generations could be obtained, but most strains died out after the 7th or 8th transfer, that is, in 14 to 16 weeks. This loss was due to a failure of reproduction since the ovaries of the worms did not develop any more. The underlying reason was apparently a nutritional deficiency, the diluting out of a necessary growth factor. Such waning cultures could be saved by several passages through living beetle larvae, or by the addition of powdered larvae, or desiccated bovine ovary to the medium every few generations, but the addition of known hormones was less satisfactory (Glaser, 1940b). All these cultures contained yeast and were hence not germ-free.

Glaser (1940a) succeeded finally in sterilizing second stage larvae and growing them under aseptic conditions on nutrient agar slants to which a piece of sterile rabbit kidney had been added. Under these conditions at least 14 transfers corresponding to approximately 50 generations were possible without any sign of weakening. Substitution of chick or mouse embryo for kidney was possible, but the cultures were then less luxuriant.

On this same medium *Neoaplectana chresima* could also be grown (Glaser, McCoy, and Girth, 1942). Both species developed well also in a medium which did not involve the addition of fresh tissue pieces. It is a semi-solid gel sterilized by autoclaving, consisting of 20 gm ground beef kidney or liver, 100 ml water, 0.5 gm sodium chloride, and 0.5 gm agar. It is noteworthy that beef muscle could not be employed instead of kidney or liver, no multiplication whatever taking place in that event.

Very little is known about the growth requirements of the Ascaridina. The larvae of *Ascaris lumbricoides* were kept alive for one week in diluted horse serum plus debris of fresh liver by Hoeppli, Feng, and Chu (1938). Fenwick (1939) studied the saline requirements of this same worm and found best survival ($5\frac{1}{2}$ days) in a purely inorganic solution of the following composition: NaCl 0.80%, KCl 0.02%, CaCl$_2$ 0.02%, MgCl$_2$ 0.01%. Deletion of any one of these components shortened survival. Ackert, Todd, and Tanner (1938) found a rather marked increase in length (53.8%) of larval *Ascaridia lineata* kept for 9 days on salt dextrose agar plates.

A considerable body of information is available concerning various species of Strongylina. The free-living stages of many species are readily cultivated in nonsterile cultures, for example in mixtures of feces and charcoal (Looss, 1896; Fülleborn, 1921) or media containing humus, sand, loam, or clay (Stoll, 1923). A combination of feces coal mixture with the agar plate technique has been used successfully (Fülleborn, 1921) and is useful not only for strongylid worms but also for such forms as *Rhabdias bufonis* (Schaake, 1931). All these cultures are of course much too complicated for an analysis of the growth requirements. Some simplification has been introduced by McCoy (1929a, b, 1930) who showed that the larvae of *Ancylostoma caninum* can be grown in unibacterial cultures. Dead bacteria or sterilized feces proved unsuitable. The larvae required oxygen for development, but were quite insensitive to pH changes, developing as they did in the pH range of 4.0 to 10.0. Similarly, Lapage (1933) was able to rear sheep and rabbit nematodes of the genera *Trichostrongylus*, *Ostertagia*, *Chabertia*, and *Graphidium* to the infective stage in unibacterial cultures.

Great progress was then made by Glaser and Stoll (1938b) with *Haemonchus contortus*. Starting from sterilized eggs a development of the larvae to the infective stage was obtained in a sterile semi-solid medium containing agar, liver extract, ground yeast, and a piece of fresh rabbit kidney. The medium was adjusted to pH 7.0 and the cultures were incubated at room temperature. The infective larvae harvested from these cultures were slightly smaller than controls grown in the customary non-sterile feces cultures, but they proved fully infective to a lamb.

On this same medium *Ancylostoma braziliense* developed to the third larval stage and it was shown that the yeast and liver extract could be omitted, the larvae developing just as far in water agar plus sterile rabbit kidney (Lawrence, 1948). This worker then experimented with various other media containing extracts of kidney or meat, the residue of such extractions, yeast preparations, and liver extract. In most media some larvae reached the infective stage and it was observed that autoclaved kidney gave as good results as fresh tissue. The conclusion was reached that some heat stable, water insoluble substance present in kidney and muscle contained the required growth promoting substances.

Weinstein (1949) experimenting with *Ancylostoma caninum, Ancylostoma duodenale,* and *Nippostrongylus muris* reared the free-living larvae to the infective stage in homogenates of fresh chick embryos or rat liver. According to his results the growth factors appear to be fairly unstable, heating of rat liver extract for 15 minutes or 1 minute respectively to 55 or 100°C almost completely inactivating them. A similar inactivation occurred by filtration through a Seitz filter. In dialyzed embryo extracts or in a Tyrode dissolved sediment of rat liver, the latter obtained by high speed centrifugation, the hookworm larvae soon died showing abnormal fat deposits and little growth. In the supernatant the larvae stayed alive for longer periods, but failed completely to grow. It does seem then that the growth factors contributed by organs must be complex and their elucidation will doubtless require a vast amount of work.

The further problem of developing the adult parasitic stages of the Strongylina *in vitro* has not yet been solved fully. A beginning has been made, however, by Glaser and Stoll (1938a) with *Haemonchus contortus.* They inoculated sterilized filariform larvae, exsheathed by means of Labarraque's solution, into a medium of the following composition: 0.5% agar in Ringer solution plus sheep liver extract, heat killed ground yeast, sheep blood, and either small pieces of sheep kidney or kidney extract. The pH was adjusted to 3.0 and the cultures were incubated at 39.5°C. It was found that in this medium development progressed to the last third of the fourth larval stage (second parasitic stage), the larvae being about 5 times as long as those used for inoculation.

Important steps in the development of strongylid worms are the periodic ecdyses occurring at the end of each stage. Lapage (1935a, b) has first shown that a convenient way of inducing exsheathing is the exposure of the larvae to various sulfur compounds. He was especially successful with Milton's solution, a solution containing sodium hypochlorite. Good results were also obtained with the similar Labarraque solution first used by Glaser and Stoll (1938a, 1940). It seems that these solutions have a solvent action on the sheath and produce an increased pressure within it. These physicochemical factors seem to be most important in expelling the larvae from the sheath, although the violent movements of the larvae probably assist materially in freeing them. Stoll (1940) investigated then in more detail the conditions governing ecdysis of the first parasitic stage of *Haemonchus contortus* in the absence of sulfur compounds. He found that it occurs spontaneously in balanced salt solutions such as Ringer's or Tyrode, hypotonic solutions ($\frac{1}{4}$ to $\frac{3}{4}$ of normal strength) being most favorable. The rates of ecdysis were favored by restricted oxygen supply and the addition of small amounts of aqueous liver extract was highly beneficial. The second preparasitic ecdysis of *Trichostrongylus retortaeformis* was studied by Crofton (1947) who found it initiated by the action of pepsin at a pH of 4 to 5.

Very little is known about the growth requirements of the Dioctophymatina. The larvae of *Eustrongylides ignotus* survive extremely well and metabolize actively *in vitro*, staying alive up to about 5 months at 37°C in Bacto broth glucose solutions and up to 4 years in Bacto proteose peptone glucose solutions at 20°C. Of all the hundreds of larvae kept isolated only one moulted into an adult (von Brand and Simpson, 1942, 1944, 1945). The reasons why bacterial contaminants are often so damaging to helminthic cultures have been studied to some extent with this species. It was shown that *Bacillus subtilis* kills the worms by producing ammonia to which they are extremely sensitive. This finding, however, cannot be generalized. Other bacterial contaminants and other worm species probably involve different mechanisms (von Brand and Simpson, 1947).

The growth requirements of the Trichinellidae are unknown. Weller (1943) succeeded in developing larvae of *Trichinella spiralis* in roller tube tissue cultures to the stage of sexual differentiation. The addition of liver or yeast extracts, of glutathione, vitamins, or various nitrogenous substances did not seem to benefit the worms.

It may be pointed out that the results obtained in trying to elucidate the growth requirements of the free-living stages of parasitic nematodes and of their parasitic stages show a certain resemblance to those reported for free-living nematodes. A detailed comparison is beyond the scope of the present account. For a historical review and new results concerning the growth requirements of free-living nematodes the reader is referred to the papers by Dougherty and Calhoun (1948) and Dougherty, Raphael, and Alton (1950).

## E. Growth Requirements of Acanthocephala

These are entirely unknown. Only a few data on the saline requirements of *Neoechinorhynchus emydis* are available. Best survival was found in a solution containing 0.5% NaCl and 0.02% CaCl₂. The addition of small amounts of KCl or MgCl₂ appeared not to benefit the worms (Gettier, 1942).

### VII. Growth Requirements of Endoparasitic Arthropods

Von Kemnitz (1916) tried to rear the larvae of *Gasterophilus intestinalis* *in vitro* without succeeding to induce pupation. Best survival, 57 days, was obtained on agar plates containing 0.5% glucose and 0.4% hydrochloric acid which were kept in an atmosphere of carbon dioxide. He stresses the point that the larvae usually die rapidly as soon as the medium assumes an alkaline reaction which happened frequently in his experiments, since they were not conducted under aseptic conditions.

LITERATURE

Ackert, J. E., Todd, A. C., and Tanner, W. A. (1938). *Trans. Am. Microscop. Soc.* **57:** 292–296.
Adler, S. (1942). *Trans. Roy. Soc. Trop. Med. Hyg.* **35:** 219–221.
Anderson, H. H., and Hansen, E. L. (1947). *In* Liber Jubilaris J. Rodhain, pp. 47–61. Goemaere, Brussels.
Anfinsen, C. B., Geiman, Q. M., McKee, R. W., Ormsbee, R. A., and Ball, E. G. (1946). *J. Exptl. Med.* **84:** 607–621.
Bass, C. C., and Johns, F. M. (1912). *J. Exptl. Med.* **16:** 567–579.
Bos, A. (1933). *Zentr. Bakt. Parasitenk. Abt. I. Orig.* **130:** 220–227.
von Brand, T., Rees, C. W., Jacobs, L., and Reardon, L. V. (1943). *Am. J. Hyg.* **37:** 310–319.
von Brand, T., and Simpson, W. F. (1942). *Proc. Soc. Exptl. Biol. Med.* **49:** 245–248.
von Brand, T., and Simpson, W. F. (1944). *J. Parasitol.* **30:** 121–129.
von Brand, T., and Simpson, W. F. (1945). *Proc. Soc. Exptl. Biol. Med.* **60:** 368–371.
von Brand, T., and Simpson, W. F. (1947). *J. Parasitol.* **33:** 71–78.
Brutsaert, P., and Henrard, C. (1938). *Compt. rend. soc. biol.* **127:** 1469–1472.
Cailleau, R. (1935). *Compt. rend. soc. biol.* **119:** 853–855.
Cailleau, R. (1936a). *Compt. rend. soc. biol.* **121:** 424–425.
Cailleau, R. (1936b). *Compt. rend. soc. biol.* **122:** 1027–1028.
Cailleau, R. (1937). *Ann. inst. Pasteur* **59:** 137–172 and 293–328.
Cailleau, R. (1938a). *Compt. rend. soc. biol.* **127:** 861–863.
Cailleau, R. (1938b). *Compt. rend. soc. biol.* **127:** 1421–1422.
Cailleau, R. (1939a). *Compt. rend. soc. biol.* **130:** 319–320.
Cailleau, R. (1939b). *Compt. rend. soc. biol.* **130:** 1089–1090.
Cailleau, R. (1939c). *Compt. rend. soc. biol.* **131:** 964–966.
Cailleau, R. (1940). *Compt. rend. soc. biol.* **134:** 32–34.
Cauthen, G. E., and Harris, M. M. (1935). *Am. J. Hyg.* **22:** 364–365.
Chang, S. L. (1947). *J. Infectious Diseases* **80:** 164–171.
Chatton, E. (1918). *Compt. rend. soc. biol.* **81:** 343–346.

Chinn, B. D., Jacobs, L., Reardon, L. V., and Rees, C. W. (1942). *Am. J. Trop. Med* **22**: 137–146.

Chung, H. (1936). *Z. Parasitenk.* **9**: 28–49.

Cleveland, L. R., and Sanders, E. P. (1930). *Science* **72**: 149–151.

Coutelen, F. R. (1927a). *Ann. parasitol. humaine et comparée* **5**: 1–19.

Coutelen, F. R. (1927b). *Ann. parasitol. humaine et comparée* **5**: 239–242.

Coutelen, F. R. (1929a). *Ann. parasitol. humaine et comparée* **7**: 399–409.

Coutelen, F. R. (1929b). *Compt. rend. soc. biol.* **100**: 619–621.

Crofton, H. D. (1947). *Parasitology* **38**: 101–103.

Dobell, C. (1947). *In* Liber Jubilaris J. Rodhain, pp. 201–211. Goemaere, Brussels.

Dougherty, E. C., and Calhoun, H. G. (1948). *Proc. Helminthol. Soc. Wash. D. C.* **15**: 55–68.

Dougherty, E. C., Raphael, J. C., and Alton, C. H. (1950). *Proc. Helminthol. Soc. Wash.* **17**: 1–10.

Epps, W., Weiner, M., and Bueding, E. (1950). *J. Infectious Diseases* **87**: 149–151.

Fairbairn, D. (1950). *J. Parasitol.* **36** Suppl.: 39.

Fairbairn, D., and Reesal, M. R. (1950). *Science* **112**: 792–793.

Fenwick, D. W. (1939). *J. Helminthol.* **17**: 211–228.

Ferguson, M. S. (1940). *J. Parasitol.* **26**: 359–372.

Ferguson, M. S. (1943). *J. Parasitol.* **29**: 319–323.

De Freitas, G., and De Castro, F. T. (1948). *O Hospital* **33**: 725–730.

Fülleborn, F. (1921). *Arch. Schiffs-u. Tropen-Hyg.* **25**: 121–123.

Geiman, Q. M. (1946). *Proc. Intern. Congr. Trop. Med. Malaria. 4th. Congr. Wash. D. C.* **1**: 618–628.

Geiman, Q. M., Anfinsen, C. B., McKee, R. W., Ormsbee, R. A., and Ball, E. G. (1946). *J. Exptl. Med.* **84**: 583–606.

Gettier, A. (1942). *Proc. Helminthol. Soc. Wash. D. C.* **9**: 75–78.

Glaser, R. W. (1931). *Science* **73**: 614–615.

Glaser, R. W. (1932). *Studies Rockefeller Inst. Med. Research* **83**: 521–550.

Glaser, R. W. (1940a). *Proc. Soc. Exptl. Biol. Med.* **43**: 512–514.

Glaser, R. W. (1940b). *J. Exptl. Zool.* **84**: 1–12.

Glaser, R. W. (1942). *J. Parasitol.* **28**: 123–126.

Glaser, R. W., and Coria, N. A. (1935). *Am. J. Hyg.* **22**: 221–226.

Glaser, R. W., McCoy, E. E., and Girth, H. B. (1942). *J. Parasitol.* **28**: 123–126.

Glaser, R. W., and Stoll, N. R. (1938a). *Science* **87**: 259–260.

Glaser, R. W., and Stoll, N. R. (1938b). *Parasitology* **30**: 324–332.

Glaser, R. W., and Stoll, N. R. (1940). *J. Parasitol.* **26**: 87–94.

Green, N. K., and Wardle, R. A. (1941). *Can. J. Research* **D19**: 240–244.

Guthrie, R. (1946). Thesis Univ. Minnesota.

Hall, M. C. (1917). *J. Am. Med. Assoc.* **68**: 772–773.

Hawking, F. (1944). *Lancet* **1944, 1**: 693–694.

Hawking, F. (1945). *Trans. Roy. Soc. Trop. Med. Hyg.* **39**: 245–263.

Hobson, A. D. (1948). *Parasitology* **38**: 183–227.

Hoeppli, R., and Chu, H. J. (1937). Festschrift B. Nocht, pp. 199–203. De Gruyter, Hamburg.

Hoeppli, R., Feng, L. C., and Chu, H. J. (1938). *Chinese Med. J. Suppl.* **2**: 343–374.

van Hoof, L. M. J. J. (1947). *Trans. Roy. Soc. Trop. Med. Hyg.* **40**: 728–754.

Jacobs, L. (1947). *Am. J. Hyg.* **46**: 172–176.

Jacobs, L. (1950). *J. Parasitol.* **36**: 128–130.

Johns, F. M., and Querens, P. L. (1914). *Am. J. Trop. Diseases* **1**: 620–624.

Johnson, E. M. (1947). *J. Parasitol.* **33**: 85.

Johnson, G., Trussell, M., and Jahn, F. (1945). *Science* **102**: 126–128.

Joyeux, C., and Baer, J. G. (1942). *Bull. mus. hist. nat. Marseille* **2**: 1 (not seen).

von Kemnitz, G. (1916). *Z. Biol.* **67**: 129–244.

Kollath, W., and Erhardt, A. (1936). *Biochem. Z.* **286**: 287–288.

Kupferberg, A. B., Johnson, G., and Sprince, H. (1948). *Proc. Soc. Exptl. Biol. Med.* **67**: 304–308.

Lamy, L. (1948). *Compt. rend.* **226**: 2021–2022.

Lapage, G. (1933). *Nature* **131**: 583–584.

Lapage, G. (1935a). *J. Helminthol.* **13**: 103–114.

Lapage, G. (1935b). *Parasitology* **27**: 186–206.

Lawrence, J. J. (1948). *Australian J. Exptl. Biol. Med. Sci.* **26**: 1–8.

Little, P. A., and Subbarow, Y. (1945). *J. Bact.* **50**: 57–60.

Lönnberg, E. (1892). *Zentr. Bakt. Parasitenk. Abt. I. Orig.* **11**: 89–92.

Looss, A. (1896). *Zentr. Bakt. Parasitenk. Abt. I. Orig.* **20**: 863–870.

Lourie, E. M. (1946). *Trans. Roy. Soc. Trop. Med. Hyg.* **40**: 4–5.

Lwoff, A. (1934). *Zentr. Bakt. Parasitenk. Abt. I. Orig.* **130**: 498–518.

Lwoff, M. (1933a). *Ann. inst. Pasteur* **51**: 55–116.

Lwoff, M. (1933b). *Ann. inst. Pasteur* **51**: 707–713.

Lwoff, M. (1935). *Compt. rend. soc. biol.* **119**: 969–971.

Lwoff, M. (1936). *Compt. rend. soc. biol.* **121**: 419–421.

Lwoff, M. (1937). *Compt. rend. soc. biol.* **126**: 771–773.

Lwoff, M. (1938a). *Compt. rend. soc. biol.* **128**: 241–243.

Lwoff, M. (1938b). *Compt. rend.* **206**: 540–542.

Lwoff, M. (1939). *Compt. rend. soc. biol.* **130**: 406–408.

Lwoff, M. (1940). Recherches sur le pouvoir de synthèse des flagellés trypanosomides. Monographie institut Pasteur, Masson et Cie. Paris.

Lwoff, M., and Ceccaldi, J. (1939). *Bull. soc. path. exotique* **32**: 721–726.

Magath, T. B. (1919). *Trans. Am. Microscop. Soc.* **38**: 49–170.

Markov, G. (1938). *Compt. rend. acad. sci. U.R.S.S.* **19**: 511–512.

McCoy, O. R. (1929a). *Science* **69**: 74–75.

McCoy, O. R. (1929b). *Am. J. Hyg.* **10**: 140–156.

McCoy, O. R. (1930). *Am. J. Hyg.* **11**: 413–448.

McKee, R. W., and Geiman, Q. M. (1948). *Federation Proc.* **7**: 172.

McKee, R. W., Geiman, Q. M., and Cobbey, T. S. (1947). *Federation Proc.* **6**: 276.

Meleney, H. E., Frye, W. W., Leathers, W. S., and Snyder, T. L. (1940). *Proc. 3d. Intern. Congr. Microbiol.*, pp. 410–411.

Mendelsohn, W. (1935). *J. Parasitol.* **21**: 417.

Noeller, W. (1928). *In* von Prowazek's Handbuch der pathogenen Protozoen. Lieferung **12**: 1815-1967. Barth, Leipzig.

Phillips, B. P. (1950). *Science* **111**: 8–9.

Phillips, B. P., and Rees, C. W. (1950). *Am. J. Trop. Med.* **30**: 185–191.

Ponselle, M. A. (1924). *Compt. rend.* **178**: 1219–1221.

von Razgha, A. (1929). *Z. Parasitenk.* **4**: 784–793.

Rees, C. W. (1937). *Am. J. Hyg.* **26**: 283–291.

Rees, C. W. (1950). *Gaz. méd. France* **57**: 835–841.

Rees, C. W., Bozicevich, J., Reardon, L. V., and Daft, F. S. (1944). *Am. J. Trop. Med.* **24**: 189–193.

Rees, C. W., and Reardon, L. V. (1944). *Trop. Med. News* **1**: 18.

Rees, C. W., Reardon, L. V., and Baernstein, H. D. (1948). *J. Parasitol.* **34** Suppl.: 11.

Rees, C. W., Reardon, L. V., and Bartgis, I. L. (1950). *Parasitology* **40**: 338–342.

Rees, C. W., Reardon, L. V., Jacobs, L., and Jones, F. (1941). *Am. J. Trop. Med.* **21:** 567–578.

Rees, C. W., Reardon, L. V., Jones, F., and Griffin, A. M. (1947). *J. Parasitol.* **33:** 385.

Rees, C. W., Reardon, L. V., Johnson, E. M., and Mayfield, M. F. (1945). *J. Parasitol.* **31** Suppl.: 7.

Reichenow, E. (1932). *Z. Parasitenk.* **4:** 784–793.

Reichenow, E. (1934). *Arch. Schiffs-u. Tropen-Hyg.* **38:** 292–302.

Reichenow, E. (1937a). *In* Fetschrift B. Nocht, pp. 487–496. De Gruyter, Hamburg.

Reichenow, E. (1937b). *Compt. rend. 12th. cong. intern. zool. Lisbonne 1935*, **3:** 1955–1968.

Reichenow, E. (1939). *Arch. Schiffs-u. Tropen-Hyg.* **43:** 197–202.

Ross, O. A., and Bueding, E. (1950). *Proc. Soc. Exptl. Biol. Med.* **73:** 179–182.

Sampath, A., and Little, P. (1949). *J. Bact.* **57:** 265.

Schaake, M. (1931). *Z. Parasitenk.* **3:** 517–648.

Shaffer, J. G., and Frye, W. W. (1948). *Am. J. Hyg.* **47:** 214–221.

Shaffer, J. G., Ryden, F. W., and Frye, W. W. (1948). *Am. J. Hyg.* **47:** 345–350.

Shaffer, J. G., Ryden, F. W., and Frye, W. W. (1949). *Am. J. Hyg.* **49:** 127–133.

Shaffer, J. G., Walton, J. G., and Frye, W. W. (1948). *Am. J. Hyg.* **47:** 222–225.

Smyth, J. D. (1946). *J. Exptl. Biol.* **23:** 47–70.

Smyth, J. D. (1947a). *Biol. Revs.* **22:** 214–238.

Smyth, J. D. (1947b). *Parasitology* **38:** 173–181.

Smyth, J. D. (1948). *Nature* **161:** 138.

Smyth, J. D. (1949). *J. Exptl. Biol.* **26:** 1–14.

Smyth, J. D. (1950). *J. Parasitol.* **36:** 371–383.

Snyder, T. L., and Meleney, H. E. (1941). *Am. J. Trop. Med.* **21:** 63–73.

Snyder, T. L., and Meleney, H. E. (1943). *J. Parasitol.* **29:** 278–284.

Stephenson, W. (1947). *Parasitology* **38:** 116–122.

Stoll, N. R. (1923). *Am. J. Hyg.* **3** July Suppl.: 1–36.

Stoll, N. R. (1940). *Growth* **4:** 383–406.

Stone, W. S., and Reynolds, F. H. K. (1939). *Science* **90:** 91–92.

Stunkard, H. W. (1932). *J. Parasitol.* **19:** 163.

Stunkard, H. W. (1940). *J. Parasitol.* **26:** 1–15.

Tobie, E. J., von Brand, T., and Mehlman, B. (1950). *J. Parasitol.* **36:** 48–54.

Tobie, E. J., and Rees, C. W. (1948). *J. Parasitol.* **34:** 162.

Trager, W. (1941). *J. Exptl. Med.* **74:** 441–461.

Trager, W. (1943). *J. Exptl. Med.* **77:** 411–420.

Trager, W. (1947). *J. Parasitol.* **33:** 345–350.

Trager, W. (1950). *J. Exptl. Med.* **92:** 349–365.

Trussell, R. E., and Plass, E. D. (1940). *Am. J. Obstet. Gynecol.* **40:** 883–890.

Van Cleave, H. J., and Williams, C. O. (1943). *J. Parasitol.* **29:** 127–130.

Vogel, H. (1934). *Zoologica* **33;** Heft 86: 1–103.

Wardle, R. A. (1937). *In* Manitoba Essays. 60th. Anniv. Commem. Vol. Univ. Manitoba: 338–364.

Weinman, D. (1944). *Proc. Soc. Exptl. Biol. Med.* **55:** 82–83.

Weinman, D. (1946). *Proc. Soc. Exptl. Biol. Med.* **63:** 456–458.

Weinstein, P. P. (1949). *J. Parasitol.* **35** Suppl.: 14.

Weiss, E. D., and Ball, G. H. (1947). *Proc. Soc. Exptl. Biol. Med.* **65:** 278–283.

Weller, T. H. (1943). *Am. J. Path.* **19:** 503–515.

Wilmoth, J. H. (1945). *Physiol. Zoöl.* **18:** 60–80.

Witte, J. (1934). *Münch. tierärztl. Wochschr.* **50:** 564–566.

Zotta, G. (1923). *Compt. rend. soc. biol.* **88:** 913–915 and 1350–1352.

# Part III

# CHEMICAL HOST–PARASITE RELATIONSHIPS

# CHAPTER 16

## NUTRITIONAL RELATIONSHIPS BETWEEN PARASITES AND HOSTS

### I. Introductory Remarks

Endoparasites live generally in surroundings abounding with readily available food. In some cases, such as the tissue parasites, the food supply is more or less constant, while in that of intestinal parasites it may be quite variable. Hence it is a legitimate question to ask whether tissue parasites react in the same way to changes in the nutritional state of the host as do intestinal parasites. Another important point is whether parasites significantly influence the nutrition of the host, and if so by what mechanisms. These and related questions will be discussed in the following sections.

### II. Nutritional Relationships in Symbiosis

A partnership between two organisms justifiably can be called a symbiosis only when both partners derive benefit from their association. This definition does not imply, however, that the breaking of the partnership must necessarily be injurious to one or both associates. It is sufficient that both derive some benefit, even if it be of minor nature. This point, which has sometimes been overlooked when the association between ruminants and their ciliate fauna has been discussed, has been correctly emphasized by Mangold (1943).

A symbiotic relationship is especially close and clear cut between the termites and their intestinal flagellates. Termites live normally on a diet of wood which they can utilize only when the protozoa are present (Cleveland, 1924; Hungate, 1938). If the termites are defaunated, for example by starvation or oxygenation (Cleveland, 1925a) they die even if they have ample opportunity to ingest wood particles. It is clear that they depend for their carbon requirements largely, if not completely, on the degradation products of cellulose produced by the intestinal fauna and it is probable that acetic acid is especially important, since this is the main endproduct of the flagellate's cellulose fermentation (Hungate, 1939, 1943).

Experimentally, however, defaunated termites can directly metabolize lower carbohydrates such as glucose, galactose, or sucrose (Cook, 1943). It has also been shown that the complex of termite plus intestinal fauna does not necessarily require wood, but that the termites at least increase in weight and remain apparently healthy on a diet containing sugar, protein, salts, and vitamins A, B, D, and G (Cook and Scott, 1933). Fundamentally then their nutritional requirements are the same as those of other insects and only the means of satisfying them are specialized. A peculiar situation exists in respect to their nitrogenous requirements and this phase needs some further discussion.

Wood, the normal food of termites, is quite poor in nitrogen (Hungate, 1940) and experimental food, such as cotton cellulose or filterpaper used successfully by Cleveland (1925b), often contains very little nitrogen, although some is always present (Hungate, 1941). A curious finding is that termite-infested wood always contains more nitrogen than sound wood. This, however, does not indicate fixation of atmospheric nitrogen by either termites or flagellates. The increase is at the expense of the nitrogen of the soil and is probably due to the action of fungi developing in the wood. Termites then can fill their essential nitrogenous requirements from this source which they not infrequently supplement by cannibalism (Hendee, 1935).

In so far as the flagellates are concerned, it has been assumed that they utilize nitrogenous waste products of the termites (Leach and Granovsky, 1938), but they certainly cannot utilize all these endproducts. This is clearly demonstrated by the relatively high nitrogen content of the termites' fecal pellets (Hungate, 1941). It is probable that the protozoa actually are nitrogen-starved most of the time. Hungate (1941) deduces this from Andrew and Light's (1929) observation that normally only few flagellates are dividing, but that a rapid rate of division occurs a few days after ecdysis. Hungate (1941) assumes that this is correlated with an increased availability of nitrogenous material to the protozoa at this period in the life cycle of the termites.

To sum up: The flagellates are benefited by finding shelter in a habitat with the required low oxygen tension and they are provided by the termites with small ingestible wood particles as well as with nitrogenous material. In return the flagellates furnish the insects degradation products of cellulose which the latter can absorb and utilize in their energy metabolism. It is obviously a case of symbiosis, even of obligatory symbiosis, either partner being in nature unable to survive in the absence of the other. The symbiosis between the roach *Cryptocercus* and its intestinal protozoa is fundamentally quite similar to the termite symbiosis; for a detailed account reference is made to the paper by Cleveland *et al.* (1934).

The relationship between ruminants and the ciliate fauna occurring in their rumen is obligatory only for the protozoa, which do not survive in any other natural habitat. The benefits derived by them from the association require no further elaboration. The hosts can be freed from these organisms by various procedures: Starvation (Mangold and Schmitt-Krahmer, 1927; Dogiel and Winogradowa-Fedorowa, 1930), feeding of milk (Eberlein, 1895; Mangold and Usuelli, 1932), or administration of copper sulfate (Becker, 1929). Such defaunated animals remain in excellent health (Becker and Everett, 1930; Falaschini, 1934; Usuelli and Fiorini, 1938) indicating obviously that the protozoa do not contribute any vital function. It has furthermore been found that the extent of food digestion is about the same in protozoa-containing and protozoa-free hosts (Wereninow, Winogradow, and Diakow, 1930; Winogradow, Winogradowa-Fedorowa, and Wereninow, 1930; Becker, Schulz, and Emmerson, 1929). It is evident that the ruminants do not depend on the cellulose-digesting powers of the ciliates in the same sense as the termites do on those of their flagellates. The rumen contains, in contrast to the termite intestine, numerous cellulose-digesting bacteria which alone are sufficient to break the plants down to compounds which the ruminant can absorb and utilize.

It is not surprising, therefore, that some doubts exist whether this association can be regarded as a true symbiosis or should be considered as a case of commensalism. The enormous number of ciliates must be emphasized in this connection. According to the determinations of Schwarz (1925), Ferber and Winogradowa (1929), and Ferber (1928) their nitrogen corresponds to 15 to 20% of all the nitrogen present in the rumen. In other words, they transform plant protoplasm at a rapid rate into animal protoplasm and it is possible that this latter is especially easily available to the host. It is well known that the rumen ciliates are immediately killed upon reaching the next compartment of the stomach and there is no reason to doubt that they are digested and that the products of this digestion can be absorbed. Mangold (1943) has also pointed out that the protozoa avidly engulf starch particles, transforming them into glycogen and thus saving the carbohydrate from bacterial fermentation and making it available to the host upon the protozoan's death. It has also been claimed that the protozoa are able to manufacture vitamin B, but in this respect the rumen bacteria are probably of much greater importance to the host (Manusardi, 1931). There is general agreement that the enormous number of protozoa may be of some significance by stirring the rumen content and thus mixing it effectively with the digestive juices of the host (Becker, 1932; Mangold, 1943; Hastings, 1944). On the whole then it would seem possible that the hosts derive some slight benefit and it is probably justified to consider the association as a symbiosis.

It is well known that a similar ciliate fauna occurs in the cecum of equids, but there is still less known about its function. It has been estimated that the protozoan protein amounts in this case to about 25% of the total protein occurring in the cecum (Schwarz and Bienert, 1926); a possible physiological function hence cannot be denied at present.

### III. EFFECT OF COMPLETE STARVATION OF THE HOST ON PARASITES

Several parasites of the intestinal tract can be completely eliminated by withholding food from the hosts. It has already been mentioned in the last section that it was possible in this way to defaunate termites and to eliminate rumen ciliates. It may be added here that the periods of starvation needed to remove the different species of termite flagellates vary. *Trichonympha* was thus lost after 6 days while *Leidyopsis* required 8 days (Cleveland, 1925a). Much longer periods, 6 and 8 weeks respectively, were required to eliminate *Lophomonas blattarum* and *Endolimax blattae* from cockroaches, while *Nyctotherus ovalis*, *Lophomonas striata*, and *Endamoeba blattae* persisted even after the roaches had been starved for 10 weeks (Armer, 1944). Apparently the trichomonads are also quite resistant; they did not disappear from rats starved for 8 days (Hegner and Eskridge, 1937b).

The exact mechanism by which starvation of the host eliminates intestinal protozoa is not well understood and, as a matter of fact, has hardly been studied. It is possible that protozoa having a high rate of metabolism, such as the termite flagellates, actually starve to death. It should not be overlooked, however, that alternate mechanisms are also possible. Mealworm gregarines can thus be eliminated from their hosts by several weeks starvation at room temperature. But in this case the impression was gained that the majority of specimens encysted and was expelled from the intestine in this dormant, though obviously living state (von Brand, unpublished observations).

Some pertinent data have also become known for intestinal helminths through the investigations of Reid (1940, 1942a, b, 1944) and Reid and Ackert (1941). They showed that the strobilae of *Railletina cesticillus* were expelled when the hosts were starved for 24 to 48 hours while the period required for the removal of *Ascaridia galli* varied between 48 and 96 hours. In both cases a very considerable decrease in glycogen content of the parasite occurred. Since this polysaccharide is probably the source for muscular energy, it is possible that under conditions of starvation a weakening of muscular activity prevents the worms from counteracting peristalsis and that they are then unable to maintain their position in the gut. It must be emphasized that in tapeworms only the strobilae were affected. The scolex and neck region remained in the host even if the latter was starved for 20 days.

If the view is correct that the high metabolic rate of these worms lies at the root of their rapid elimination, it should be expected that worms with a lower metabolic rate would withstand longer periods of host starvation. Hardly any data on this point are as yet available. According to a casual observation of Weinland (1901), some living ascarids were expelled by a dog after 4 days starvation; they still contained 1.8% glycogen. Burlingame and Chandler (1941) reported that starving rats lost in 5 days about 30% of the *Moniliformis dubius* specimens present initially.

It is extremely unlikely that tissue parasites could be killed by starving the host. The larvae of *Eustrongylides ignotus*, for example, were completely normal, both as to their appearance and their glycogen content when their hosts (*Fundulus*) were starved for 65 days (von Brand, 1938). This observation should not be interpreted as indicating that tissue parasites remain completely unaffected. It should be noted in this connection that Müller and Simons (1920) found a retarded multiplication of pathogenic trypanosomes in starving hosts. Solazzo (1929), on the other hand, reported that *Trypanosoma brucei* could be maintained for several days in starving, but not in fed pigeons. Kendall (1949) observed that much fewer cercariae of *Fasciola hepatica* developed in starving than in fed *Limnaea truncatula*.

## IV. Effects of Generally Deficient Host Diets on Parasites

It has been assumed for a long time that undernutrition or malnutrition has a profound effect on human parasitic diseases. Epidemiological surveys have thus shown that severe outbreaks of malaria often accompany or follow periods of famine or other economic stress under which the nutritional state of the population has been impaired. Hackett (1937) has presented a discussion of these aspects of the malaria problem. Another example is hookworm disease in which dietary deficiencies or concurrent diseases play an important role in the development of chronic infections (Otto, 1940; Cort and Otto, 1940).

These views have been put on a fairly secure basis by animal experimentation. It is true that the experimental evidence is contradictory in so far as malaria is concerned. Passmore and Sommerville (1940) did not find distinct differences in the course of infections with *Plasmodium cynomolgi* and *Plasmodium knowlesi* in monkeys, one group of which was kept on a well-balanced diet while the other received an ill-balanced one. Brooke (1945) came to different results with *Plasmodium relictum*, *Plasmodium cathemerium*, and *Plasmodium lophurae*. He found that birds kept on quantitatively or qualitatively insufficient diets had more severe primary attacks, showed a greater tendency to relapse, and were less resistant to superinfection. As will be shown in a following section, certain well-defined dietary components, such as biotin or ascorbic acid, have a considerable influence on the development of malarial parasites *in vivo* and it is possible that the presence or absence of one or more of such specific factors may have been responsible for the contradictory results reviewed.

Several interesting studies have been done with intestinal helminths. Foster and Cort (1931, 1932, 1935) showed that dogs receiving adequate amounts of a generally deficient diet (mainly deficient in vitamins and minerals) showed a lowered resistance to infection with *Ancylostoma caninum*. Larger numbers of worms developed in these animals and the egg production per worm was greater than in dogs kept on an optimum diet. A characteristic reduction in age immunity occurred in the experimental animals and their resistance due to previous infections was also largely broken down, especially in younger dogs. The resistance returned when the animals were again provided with a full diet. The whole situation indicates clearly that these results were due to a change in the physiological responses of the hosts rather than to a stimulating effect of the experimental diet on the worms. This applies also to the experiments of Chandler (1932) who observed that rats kept on an insufficient diet showed a diminished resistance against the development of *Nippostrongylus muris*. Porter (1935) similarly found greater numbers of the same helminth to develop in rats kept on a milk diet than in controls having access to a regular diet regardless of whether he studied primary infections or reinfections.

Similar observations, indicating that the qualitatively poor diet of the host favors in general the development of intestinal nematodes, have also been reported from larger domesticated animals, especially sheep. Fraser and Robertson (1933), Taylor (1943); Lucker and Neumayer (1947), and Gordon (1948) reported for example that lambs on poor feed were less resistant to infections with *Haemonchus, Ostertagia, Bunostomum*, or *Trichostrongylus* than were animals kept on optimal diets. Whitlock, Calloway, and Jeppeson (1943) were able to cure *Haemonchus* infections of older sheep by providing them with a corn and alfalfa diet instead of keeping them on a poor pasture. On the other hand Whitlock (1949) found that lambs on optimum diet carried heavier *Haemonchus* burdens than did pasture fed animals, although apparently the opposite held true for the smaller trichostrongylid species.

The question whether undernutrition or malnutrition materially influences parasites of invertebrates has hardly been approached. It is known, however, that the flagellates parasitizing termites and *Cryptocercus* do not survive for very long periods when their hosts are placed on a variety of cellulose-free diets (Montalenti, 1927; Lund, 1930; Cleveland, Hall, Sanders, and Collier, 1934). It has also been made probable that a positive correlation exists between the amount of blood ingested by *Aedes aegypti* and the number of oocysts of *Plasmodium gallinaceum* developing (Hovanitz, 1947).

## V. Effects of One-Sided Diets of the Host on the Parasites

A carbohydrate-rich diet has been found to benefit many intestinal parasites. Hegner and Eskridge (1937a) found it to be favorable to intestinal amoebas of rats, Sassuchin (1931) and Armer (1944) reported similar observations for cockroach parasites, as did Mowry and Becker (1930) for rumen ciliates, and Westphal (1939) for the human parasites *Chilomastix* and *Enteromonas*. Some corresponding results have also been obtained in experiments with metazoan parasites. *Hymenolepis diminuta* thrives best when the host's diet contains a high proportion of carbohydrate (Chandler, 1943), as does *Railletina cesticillus* (Reid, 1942b).

A high protein diet, on the other hand, often apparently creates conditions unfavorable to intestinal parasites. Hegner (1923), Hegner and Eskridge (1937a), Ratcliffe (1930), Kessel (1929), Kessel and Huang (1926), Sassuchin (1931), and Armer (1944) found this to be true for intestinal amoebas and flagellates of rats, monkeys, human beings, and cockroaches. Morris (1936), however, could maintain better infections with *Endamoeba blattae* in roaches kept on a high protein diet that in insects getting but little protein.

The question naturally arises as to what the mechanisms are that make a carbohydrate-rich diet often favorable and a diet high in protein often unfavorable. The situation is obviously complicated since both direct effects on the parasites and indirect effects *via* their environment are possible. It is a well-established fact that many intestinal parasites have a pronounced carbohydrate metabolism. This is especially true for forms that lead *in vivo* a predominantly anaerobic life (see Chapter 10). It is conceivable, or even probable, that they are directly benefited by carbohydrates in the host's diet by using them as food. Such an effect can, of course, become apparent only if the carbohydrate reaches the parasites in a form that can be utilized. It can thus hardly be expected that easily absorbed carbohydrates reach parasites living in the large intestine. Suggestive in this direction is Westphal's (1939) observation that carbohydrates favor the development of *Chilomastix* and *Enteromonas* only if they are given to the host in a form that is not rapidly digested and absorbed, for example in the form of lentils.

On the other hand, there can be no doubt that changes in the host's diet may have a profound influence on parasites by inducing physicochemical changes in the latter's environment. In this connection Hegner (1937) has emphasized that changes in the diet occasion changes in the hydrogen ion concentration of the intestinal contents, and changes in the bacterial flora that may be of the utmost importance to parasites. Such an indirect action is very likely in the case of the unfavorable action of one carbohydrate, lactose, or of milk on rumen ciliates (Eberlein, 1895), intestinal nematodes (Ackert and Riedel, 1946; Shorb and Spindler, 1947; Spindler, Zimmerman, and Hill, 1944), or cestodes (Hager, 1941). As Read (1950) has pointed out, a diet high in lactose changes the pH and oxidation-reduction potential of the intestinal contents, the intestinal emptying time, the vitamin synthesis by intestinal bacteria, and probably many other factors.

Similarly the breaking down of resistance to infection with certain parasites by diet may be due at least in some cases to changes in the physicochemical environment. Thus it has recently been possible to infect rabbits and guinea pigs with *Endamoeba histolytica*, although both species are ordinarily refractive to such an infection (Westphal, 1941; Tobie, 1949; Carrera and Faust, 1949). Positive results were achieved by placing the prospective hosts on a grain-bread diet, or a guinea pig dry ration, respectively, that is, on rations omitting greens. This, according to Westphal's (1941) working hypothesis, is the decisive point. The omission of green food material radically changes the fermentation processes occurring in the intestine making it, especially the cecum of herbivores, physiologically more similar to the large intestine of the normal host. Recent investigations (Greenberg and Taylor, 1950) showed that the type of dietary carbohydrate is important in experimental infections of rats with *Endamoeba histolytica;* lactose or galactose in relatively high proportions favored the infections. It must also be emphasized that Taylor *et al.* (1950) infected 75% of their guinea pigs when the latter were fed rat pellets and kale, that is, a ration containing greens.

An indirect action *via* the host must also be assumed to explain the observation (Donaldson and Otto, 1946) that rats kept on a protein-deficient diet were unable to develop the same immunity from repeated sublethal infections with *Nippostrongylus muris* as rats kept on a balanced diet. It is true that their experimental diet contained more carbohydrate than the balanced diet, but since the latter had 58% carbohydrate, a directly favoring effect of a slight surplus can hardly be assumed. Larsh (1950) used the same diet as Donaldson and Otto (1946) and found that it reduced the natural resistance and interfered with the development of acquired resistance against *Hymenolepis nana* in mice.

## VI. Influence of Single Nutritional Components on Parasites

The influence, on parasites, of vitamins in the host's diet has been studied rather extensively in recent years. The results of these experiments are not uniform as the following paragraphs will amply demonstrate. Sometimes the addition of vitamins to the diet increased the numbers of parasites in the host, while in other cases the same effect was brought about by vitamin deficiencies, and so on. It is possible, or even probable, that in some instances vitamins are actually growth requirements of certain parasites, but that in other cases vitamins in the diet increase the defense mechanisms of the host, while vitamin deficiencies may decrease them. Obviously, a multitude of possibilities exists in such a complex situation and, in most instances, it is at present impossible to decide definitely whether a certain effect was due to a direct or an indirect action of a given nutritional component of the diet.

## A. Parasitic Protozoa

Vitamins in the host's diet have a marked effect on the course of infections with *Trypanosoma lewisi*. Becker, Manresa, and Johnson (1943) showed that the addition of relatively large amounts of vitamins $B_1$ and $B_6$ to a previously dry-heated ration allowed the parasites to reach higher numbers in the blood and the infections persisted longer than usual. It must be emphasized that this ration was deficient in pantothenic acid and that the experiments were complicated by a concurrent *Bartonella* infection. Becker, Taylor, and Fuhrmeister (1947) later studied the effects of pantothenate deficiency in *Bartonella*-free rats on the same parasite. The results were the same as those reported previously, *i.e.*, higher parasite counts and prolonged multiplication period. The authors assume these effects to be indirect ones, resulting primarily from a decreased efficiency by the host in producing ablastin which in *Trypanosoma lewisi* infections controls the parasite level. Similar results were obtained with a biotin deficient diet (Caldwell and György, 1943, 1947).

Deficiency of the host in the vitamin B complex seems to enhance somewhat the resistance to *Trypanosoma equiperdum* (Reiner and Paton, 1932). On the other hand, *Trypanosoma brucei* infections could be established in pigeons, which are normally entirely refractive, if the birds were kept on a diet lacking the vitamin B complex (Solazzo, 1929).

The only other relevant studies with parasitic flagellates concern *Trichomonas hominis*. It was found to be benefited in rats by the addition of raw liver, liver powder, or liver extract to the host's diet (Ratcliffe, 1930; Hegner and Eskridge, 1937c) and in this case it is farily certain that the action was an indirect one, brought about by changes in the rat's cecum.

Extensive observations are available for *Eimeria nieschulzi*, a rat parasite. Becker and Dilworth (1941) found that vitamin $B_1$ in the host's ration had a slightly depressing action on the development of this parasite, as measured by the production of oocysts. Vitamin $B_6$, on the contrary, had a stimulating effect, but both vitamins given together had a strong inhibitory effect. This depressing action was also observed when the vitamins were administered parenterally (Becker, 1941). Pantothenic acid in the diet stimulated the parasites and nullified the growth-inhibiting action of the two combined B vitamins (Becker and Smith, 1942; Becker, Manresa, and Smith, 1943). Riboflavin inhibited the parasites while nicotinic acid did not seem to have any effect (Becker, 1942). Whether, or to what extent, these observations indicate a vitamin requirement by the coccidium is difficult to evaluate since it has not yet been grown *in vitro* and indirect actions *via* changes in the host cannot be excluded with certainty.

A somewhat more positive answer is probably justified in the case of *Plasmodium gallinaceum*. Brackett, Waletzky, and Baker (1946) have shown that blood-induced infections of this parasite are suppressed in pantothenic acid-deficient chickens, or in chickens treated with analogues, for example pantoyltauramido-4-chlorobenzene. The addition of pantothenic acid to the chickens' diet completely eliminated the activity of this and similar antagonists. Trager (1943a) has shown that calcium pantothenate prolongs the survival *in vitro* of *Plasmodium lophurae*. The entire situation favors the assumption that the reduced growth rate of *Plasmodium gallinaceum* in the deficient chicken was directly linked to an insufficient supply of pantothenate to the parasites.

It is true, however, that *Plasmodium lophurae* itself is *in vivo* not markedly influenced by lack of pantothenic acid in the host's diet and it is not influenced conspicuously by an analogue, $\omega$-methylpantothenic acid (Trager, 1943; Schinazi *et al.*, 1950). This apparent indifference of *Plasmodium lophurae in vivo* may be explained by assuming that it can mobilize sufficient pantothenic acid even in deficient hosts from the latter's tissues. Becker, Brodine, and Marousek (1949) showed that it was able to mobilize pantothenate, biotin, or both from the host. An observation of Brackett, Waletzky, and Baker (1946) points in the same direction. They found that sporozoite-induced infections of *Plasmodium gallinaceum* were insensitive to pantothenic acid deficiencies in the host's diet, in contrast to blood-induced infections. It is entirely possible that the tissue stages of this parasite are in a better position to utilize whatever pantothenate is left in the deficient hosts than are the blood stages.

A direct action is also probable in the case of riboflavin. Only much smaller numbers of *Plasmodium lophurae* developed in riboflavin-deficient hosts than in normally fed controls (Seeler and Ott, 1944).

Biotin-deficient diets, on the contrary, increased the susceptibility of the host animals to both *Plasmodium lophurae* and *Plasmodium gallinaceum* (Trager, 1943a; Seeler, Ott, and Gundel, 1944). An indirect action is probably involved, biotin being probably necessary for the synthesis of the lipid fraction of a lipoprotein in the host's blood plasma which inhibits the growth of the parasites (Trager, 1947a, b, 1949). Folic acid deficiency had a similar effect, but the mechanism involved is at present not known (Seeler and Ott, 1945).

Ball *et al.* (1945) had observed that the ascorbic acid level of monkeys infected with *Plasmodium knowlesi* was much lower than in normal animals. McKee and Geiman (1946) then found in monkeys that spontaneously showed a low ascorbic acid plasma level, an unusually slow development of parasitemia and a gradual spontaneous control of the infections. Upon administration of vitamin C the infections again took their normal course and analogous observations were made with monkeys who were made experimentally ascorbic acid deficient. A decision whether the observed effects were due to a direct or indirect action on the parasites could, however, not be made.

## B. Parasitic Worms

The effects of vitamin-deficient host diets on *Ascaridia galli* have been studied primarily by Ackert and his coworkers (Ackert, 1931, 1939; Ackert, Fisher, and Zimmerman, 1927; Ackert, McIlvaine, and Crawford, 1931; Ackert and Nolf, 1931; Ackert and Spindler, 1929). It was found that a lack of either vitamin A or the vitamin B complex favored the worms. More specimens remained in the chicken's intestine and, at least in the case of vitamin A deficiency, the worms grew longer than worms recovered from hosts kept on a normal, full diet. A lack of vitamin D, on the other hand, did not affect the worms appreciably. Ackert (1939, 1942) is, on the whole, inclined to ascribe the observed effects to changes in the host's resistance rather than to direct dietary effects on the parasites. He does point out, however, that not every diet which breaks the host's resistance down is actually favorable to the parasites. The maintainance of chickens by intramuscular injection of vitamin-free nutrient solutions or of only glucose solutions, led to the recovery of only few and small worms (Ackert and Whitlock, 1935; Ackert, Whitlock, and Freeman, 1940). Sadun, Totter, and Keith (1949) also assume a lowered resistance to *Ascaridia* in order to explain their observation that the nematodes recovered from birds kept on a diet deficient in pteroylglutamic acid were more numerous and longer than those found in controls. Further experiments with chickens kept on a purified diet containing only minimal amounts of vitamin $B_{12}$ showed a very pronounced growth retardation of the worms. Supplementing the diet with liver extract led to a better, though still subnormal growth. The authors assume that these nematodes require for normal growth a substance present in liver, perhaps vitamin $B_{12}$, or the animal protein factor.

Vitamin deficiencies also lower the resistance of mammals to infection with intestinal nematodes and this is especially true in those instances where the hosts are kept on diets deficient in vitamin A. In some cases, it has then been possible to infect normally refractive hosts: Hogs with

*Ascaris lumbricoides* of human origin (Hiraishi, 1927), or rats with *Parascaris equorum* (Clapham, 1933). Jones and Nolan (1942), on the other hand, failed to establish *Enterobius vermicularis* in vitamin A deficient rats. Other workers described a lowered resistance of vitamin A deficient normal hosts to a variety of intestinal nematodes: *Nippostrongylus muris* (Spindler, 1933), *Toxocara canis* and *Toxascaris leonina* (Wright, 1935), *Trichinella spiralis* (McCoy, 1934), and *Strongyloides ratti* (Lawler, 1941). A similar lowering of resistance was found in the case of *Syngamus trachea*, a parasite of the respiratory tract (Clapham, 1934a), but not in experiments with *Heterakis gallinae* and *Ascaris lumbricoides* (Clapham, 1933, 1934b). In general, the lowered resistance of the hosts became evident by larger numbers of worms developing and often also by a reduced immunity to superinfection. Rats, for example, are usually quite resistant to superinfection with *Trichinella;* while superinfection succeeded without difficulty in vitamin A deficient hosts. It is generally assumed that these effects are all due to an interference with the host's protective mechanisms rather than to a stimulatory effect on the parasites. Whether the same explanation holds true for Zaiman's (1940) observation that fewer *Trichinella* larvae develop in the muscles of vitamin E deficient rats remains to be studied further. A marked lowering of resistance to superinfection with *Nippostrongylus muris* has also been found when the host's diet was deficient in either thiamine or riboflavine (Watt, 1944).

Relatively little work along similar lines has been done with trematodes. Krakower, Hoffman, and Axtmayer (1944) found normal growth of *Schistosoma mansoni* in guinea pigs kept on a vitamin C deficient diet, but the eggshells produced were abnormal being reduced to granules similar to those occurring in the vitellaria. The same authors (Krakower, Hoffman, and Axtmayer, 1940) had found previously that more schistosomes developed in rats kept on a vitamin A deficient diet than on a full diet, apparently fewer juveniles being killed in the lungs and the liver in the former instance.

Beaver (1937) reported that *Echinostoma revolutum* either did not develop at all or showed at least greatly retarded development in pigeons kept on a diet that in all likelihood was deficient in vitamins A and D. This result is altogether different from those reviewed above concerning nematodes but is somewhat similar to observations on cestodes summarized below, indicating apparently that nematodes and flatworms respond in different ways to nutritional deficiencies in the host's diet. Rothschild (1939), however, did obtain full development of *Cryptocotyle lingua* in gulls deprived of vitamins.

The effects of vitamin deficient host diets on the cestode *Hymenolepis diminuta* have been studied by Hager (1941), Chandler (1943), Addis

(1946), and Addis and Chandler (1944, 1946). It was found essentially that deficiencies in vitamins A, D, and E had no effect on the growth of the worms, but that fewer worms became established. Thiamine-deficient diets had no effect. It was shown later, however, by means of radioactive thiamine administered parenterally to the hosts that *Hymenolepis* can acquire this compound from the body of the host even if the latter is kept on a thiamine-free diet (Chandler, Read, and Nicholas, 1950). If the complete vitamin B complex as present in yeast was withheld from the hosts, the worms remained stunted. This deficiency was not alleviated by the addition of nine water soluble vitamins to the diet. The deficiency effect was especially noticeable when female, immature, or castrated male rats were used as host animals, but became also apparent in noncastrated male rats when the latter were kept for longer periods on the deficient diet (Beck, 1950).

In certain contrast to these results are those reported by Larsh (1947) who studied the influence of alcohol in infections with *Hymenolepis nana* var. *fraterna*. He found that considerably more cysticercoids developed in mice regularly receiving alcohol than in nonalcoholized ones. This was due essentially to a reduced food intake of the former group as evidenced by the fact that a nonalcoholic, partially starved group of mice showed about the same degree of infection as the alcoholic group. It was concluded that the reduced resistance to infection was largely due to avitaminosis.

The outlined differences between roundworms on the one hand and flatworms on the other hand are exceedingly interesting, but they are not yet open to a definite explanation. As mentioned previously, conditions during *in vivo* experiments are so complex that a definite decision whether a certain effect is due to a direct nutritional deficiency of the parasites or to a changed reaction of the host, can hardly ever be made. Read (1950) makes this point nicely by pointing out that the experiments of Sadun, Totter, and Keith (1949) indicating a growth promoting substance in liver extract active in the case of *Ascaridia*, could, on paper at least, also be explained by assuming that its absence increased the natural resistance of the host towards the parasite.

## VII. Influence of Parasites on the Nutrition of the Host

### A. Malnutrition Due to Parasitism

Many examples could be given to illustrate the fact that the nutritional state of human beings and of animals may be seriously disturbed as a consequence of parasitic diseases. The extreme emaciation of sleeping sickness patients in the late stages of the disease, or the loss of weight during amebic dysentery could serve as examples, as could the view expressed by Gelfand (1944) that infections with such parasites as hookworms or schistosomes are largely responsible for the nutritional diseases of Africans. These and similar cases will, however, not be discussed further because no direct connections between the metabolic activities of the parasites and the nutritional disorders of the host have been established as yet.

A few more examples taken from animal infections may further illustrate the topic under discussion. Infections with *Ascaris lumbricoides* frequently lead to reduced growth of pigs and this effect is already apparent when the infections are only moderately heavy. Spindler (1947) found marked growth inhibition of the hosts during the migratory period of the larvae; normal growth during the stage of development of the worms in the intestine, followed by another period of growth retardation after the helminths had reached sexual maturity.

Stewart (1933a) and Shearer and Stewart (1933) observed a lowered digestion coefficient of crude protein and crude fiber as well as a lowering of mineral absorption in lambs heavily infected with various intestinal helminths. These results were not fully confirmed, however, by Andrews (1933) and Andrews, Kauffman, and Davis (1944), who investigated the effects of pure infections with *Cooperia curticei* and *Trichostrongylus colubriformis*. They found in the majority of their lambs approximately normal digestibility coefficients but did observe that the infected lambs were less efficient than controls in transforming food into body substance. Andrews (1939) ascribed this primarily to a nervous excitation due to irritation and inflammation of the intestinal mucosa.

Distorted growth patterns of lambs infected with trichostrongyles have also been reported by Whitlock (1949) who observed not infrequently an "overcompensation" effect, that is, an initial period of excessive growth followed by a period of slowed growth. It is of interest to remember in this connection that excessive growth is sometimes a consequence of parasitism in invertebrates. Rothschild (1941) described gigantism of the snail *Peringia ulvae* infected with larval trematodes and similar observations on fresh water snails have been reported by Wesenberg-Lund (1934).

An interference with the nutrition of the host occurs also among parasitized cold blooded vertebrates. As an example for this group the growth retarding influence of heavy trematode infections on perch may be mentioned (Cross, 1935).

## B. The Role of the Parasites' Food Consumption

The view that parasites influence adversely the nutritional state of their hosts by withdrawal of food has not rarely been held in the past. Characteristic is the expression "gargantuan appetite" of the parasites used by Robson (1911) in discussing the effect of sacculinids on crustacea. Extreme caution is indicated in this question, however. Before the above view can be accepted, a number of points would have to be clarified, the most important ones being the proportion in weight between parasites and host, the metabolic intensity of both, and their actual rates of food consumption. It should, for example, be obvious that the food required by even a large tapeworm is quantitatively insignificant when compared with the average daily food consumption of man. If it is true that some persons harboring tapeworms suffer from excessive appetite and if it can be proved that this is not merely a coincidence, a mechanism other than food robbery must be involved.

Occasionally unusually heavy parasite burdens occur. Hall (1917) described a case in which an individual harbored 11 lbs. of *Ascaris*. It can be calculated from the data available on this worm's metabolism that they would have consumed in this instance only about 8% of a normal 2500-calorie diet (von Brand, 1948). Even this figure is actually probably too high since *Ascaris* excretes lower fatty acids that conceivably can be absorbed and utilized by the host. It should be remembered in this connection that bacterial decomposition of carbohydrates to volatile fatty acids and their subsequent absorption accounts for a large proportion of carbohydrate utilization by ruminants (McAnally and Phillipson, 1944; Marshall and Phillipson, 1945; Barcroft, 1945). Similarly, the withdrawal of sugar from the host by pathogenic trypanosomes has often been regarded as an important factor in explaining the injuries sustained by the host. Harvey (1949) has justifiedly pointed out that pyruvic acid, the main endproduct of the flagellates' metabolism, ought to be readily metabolized by the host. The greater part (approximately 80% or more) of the energy of the sugar molecule may thus still be available to the host.

The proportion between weight of parasite and host is more in favor of the parasite in some parasitized invertebrates than in vertebrates. The dry substance of the external sac of *Peltogaster* for example may reach values of 12%, or in some instances probably even more, of the total dry substance of the parasitized crabs and an undetermined amount would have to be added to the parasite substance for its internal root system (Reinhard and von Brand, 1944). In snails infected with larval trematodes so much host tissue is frequently replaced by parasite tissue that the latter should amount to a sizeable proportion of the former. However, the other factors bearing on the question of food robbery have not yet been determined sufficiently in these cases. Metabolic determinations on normal *Australorbis* and snails parasitized by *Schistosoma mansoni* are not favorable to the view that food robbery is an important factor (von Brand and Files, 1947).

On the whole then, there is at present little justification in assuming that food robbery of the parasites causes malnutrition of the host by inducing a state of partial starvation. A different question is whether the consumption by parasites of trace elements, vitamins, or similar microconstituents of a balanced diet may not cause nutritional disorders of the host. This possibility may deserve serious consideration, but cannot be discussed more fully because experimental evidence is lacking.

## C. The Role of Antienzymes

Antienzymes, that is, enzymes inhibiting the activity of the digestive enzymes of the host, are widespread in intestinal worms. They have been studied primarily in ascarids and tapeworms (Weinland, 1903; Dastre and Stassano, 1903; Hamill, 1906; Fetterolf, 1907; Tallqvist, 1907; Mendel and Blood, 1910; Harned and Nash, 1932; Sang, 1938; von Bonsdorff, 1939, 1948; Collier, 1941), but have also been found in smaller nematode species (Stewart, 1933b; Bushnell and Erwin, 1949). Shearer and Stewart (1933) assumed that the antienzymatic activity of stomach worms of sheep was pronounced enough to explain the nutritional disorders evidenced by parasitized sheep, a view which has subsequently not been substantiated, however (Andrews, 1939).

The antienzymes extracted from helminths are usually either antitryptic or antitryptic and antipeptic but only little is known about their chemical constitution. The most detailed investigation has been done by Collier (1941) who isolated a polypeptide from *Ascaris* very similar to the trypsin inhibitor occurring in beef pancreas (Kunitz and Northrop, 1936).

It has been assumed that the antienzymes play a role in protecting parasites from being digested by the digestive juices of the host. It has been shown that both intestinal nematodes and cestodes withstand tryptic digestion *in vitro* (Fredericq, 1878; Burge and Burge, 1915; De Waele, 1933) as long as they are living and intact but that they are digested when dead or when their cuticle is injured. This resistance is, however, not confined to helminths. It is a property which they have in common with the mucosa of the intestinal tract itself and many free-living organisms (Fermi, 1910; Northrop, 1926). It is hence difficult to ascribe to the antienzymes the primary role in protecting helminths from digestion, although they may be of some significance in this respect. It is probable that at least two more factors are involved: The impermeability of living cells to digestive enzymes, and the impermeability of the external cuticle. Bueding (1949) has emphasized that our present knowledge is insufficient to assess the relative importance of these three factors as protective mechanisms. In so far as intestinal protozoa are concerned, it is difficult to see how they could secrete sufficient antienzymes to protect themselves if this were the only important mechanism. They, in general, do not have a thick cuticle. It is possible, therefore, that here the impermeability of living membranes may be of prime importance.

## D. Concluding Remarks

The review presented in the preceding sections shows that the reasons why parasites interfere frequently with the nutritional state of the host cannot as yet be answered satisfactorily in the majority of the cases. There can be no doubt that not a single cause exists, but that a variety of mechanisms is involved, depending in part on the location of the parasites, their mechanical and toxic action at the site of absorption, their influence on the metabolism of the host, their possible interference with the nervous regulations of the body, and probably other factors. It would seem that a more detailed study of this field may lead to rewarding results.

### LITERATURE

Ackert, J. E. (1931). *Arch. zool. ital.* **16**: 1369–1379.
Ackert, J. E. (1939). *Proc. World's Poultry Congr., 7th. Congr. Cleveland, Ohio.* pp. 265–267.
Ackert, J. E. (1942). *J. Parasitol.* **28**: 1–24.
Ackert, J. E., Fisher, M. L., and Zimmerman, N. B. (1927). *J. Parasitol.* **13**: 219–220.
Ackert, J. E., McIlvaine, M. F., and Crawford, N. Z. (1931). *Am. J. Hyg.* **13**: 320-336.
Ackert, J. E., and Nolf, L. O. (1931). *Am. J. Hyg.* **13**: 337–344.
Ackert, J. E., and Riedel, B. B. (1946). *J. Parasitol.* **32** Suppl.: 15.
Ackert, J. E., and Spindler, L. A. (1929). *Am. J. Hyg.* **9**: 292–307.
Ackert, J. E., and Whitlock, J. H. (1935). *J. Parasitol.* **21**: 428.
Ackert, J. E., Whitlock, J. H., and Freeman, E. A. (1940). *J. Parasitol.* **26**: 17–32.
Addis, C. J. (1946). *J. Parasitol.* **32**: 574–580.
Addis, C. J., and Chandler, A. C. (1944). *J. Parasitol.* **30**: 229–236.
Addis, C. J., and Chandler, A. C. (1946). *J. Parasitol.* **32**: 581–584.
Andrew, B. J., and Light, S. F. (1929). *Univ. Calif. (Berkeley) Pubs. Zool.* **31**: 433–440 (not seen).
Andrews, J. S. (1939). *J. Agr. Research* **57**: 349–362.
Andrews, J. S., Kauffman, W., and Davis, R. E. (1944). *Am. J. Vet. Research* **5**: 22–29.
Armer, J. M. (1944). *J. Parasitol.* **30**: 131–142.
Ball, E. G., Anfinsen, C. B., Geiman, Q. M., McKee, R. W., and Ormsbee, R. A. (1945). *Science* **101**: 542–544.
Barcroft, J. (1945). *Proc. Nutrition Soc. (Engl. and Scot.)* **3**: 247–251.
Beaver, P. C. (1937). *Univ. Illinois Bull.* **34** No. 74: 1–96.
Beck, J. W. (1950). Dissertation Rice Inst. (not seen).
Becker, E. R. (1929). *Proc. Natl. Acad. Sci. U. S.* **15**: 435–438.
Becker, E. R. (1932). *Quart. Rev. Biol.* **7**: 282–297.
Becker, E. R. (1941). *Proc. Soc. Exptl. Biol. Med.* **46**: 494–495.
Becker, E. R. (1942). *Proc. Iowa Acad. Sci.* **49**: 503–506.
Becker, E. R., Brodine, C. E., and Marousek, A. A. (1949). *J. Infectious Diseases* **85**: 230–238.
Becker, E. R., and Dilworth, R. I. (1941). *J. Infectious Diseases* **68**: 285–290.
Becker, E. R., and Everett, R. C. (1930). *Am. J. Hyg.* **11**: 362–370.
Becker, E. R., Manresa, M., and Johnson, E. M. (1943). *Iowa State Coll. J. Sci.* **17**: 431–441.
Becker, E. R., Manresa, M., and Smith, L. (1943). *Iowa State Coll. J. Sci.* **17**: 257–262.

Becker, E. R., Schulz, J. A., and Emmerson, M. A. (1929). *Proc. Natl. Acad. Sci. U. S.* **15:** 691–693.

Becker, E. R., and Smith, L. (1942). *Iowa State Coll. J. Sci.* **16:** 443–449.

Becker, E. R., Taylor, D. J., and Fuhrmeister, C. (1947). *Iowa State Coll. J. Sci.* **21:** 237–243.

von Bonsdorff, B. (1939). *Acta Med. Scand.* **100:** 459–482.

von Bonsdorff, B. (1948). *Blood* **3:** 91–102.

Brackett, S., Waletzky, E., and Baker, M. (1946). *J. Parasitol.* **32:** 453–462.

von Brand, T. (1938). *J. Parasitol.* **24:** 445–451.

von Brand, T. (1948). *Proc. Intern. Congr. Trop. Med. Malaria. 4th. Congr. Wash. D. C.* **2:** 984–991.

von Brand, T., and Files, V. S. (1947). *J. Parasitol.* **33:** 476–482.

Brooke, M. M. (1945). *Am. J. Hyg.* **41:** 81–108.

Bueding, E. (1949). *Physiol. Revs.* **29:** 195–218.

Burge, W. E., and Burge, G. L. (1915). *J. Parasitol.* **1:** 179–183.

Burlingame, P. L., and Chandler, A. C. (1941). *Am. J. Hyg.* **33** Sect. D: 1–21.

Bushnell, L. D., and Erwin, L. E. (1949). *Physiol. Zoöl.* **22:** 178–181.

Caldwell, F. E., and György, P. (1943). *Proc. Soc. Exptl. Biol. Med.* **53:** 116–119.

Caldwell, F. E., and György, P. (1947). *J. Infectious Diseases* **81:** 197–208.

Carrera, G. M., and Faust, E. C. (1949). *Am. J. Trop. Med.* **29:** 647–667.

Chandler, A. C. (1932). *Am. J. Hyg.* **16:** 750–782.

Chandler, A. C. (1943). *Am. J. Hyg.* **37:** 121–130.

Chandler, A. C., Read, C. P., and Nicholas, H. O. (1950). *J. Parasitol.* **36:** 523–535.

Clapham, P. A. (1933). *J. Helminthol.* **11:** 9–24.

Clapham, P. A. (1934a). *Proc. Roy. Soc. London* **B115:** 18–29.

Clapham, P. A. (1934b). *J. Helminthol.* **12:** 165–176.

Cleveland, L. R. (1924). *Biol. Bull.* **46:** 177–227.

Cleveland, L. R. (1925a). *Biol. Bull.* **48:** 309–326.

Cleveland, L. R. (1925b). *Biol. Bull.* **48:** 289–293.

Cleveland, L. R., Hall, S. R., Sanders, E. P., and Collier, J. (1934). *Mem. Am. Acad. Arts Sci.* **17:** 185–342.

Collier, H. B. (1941). *Can. J. Research* **B19:** 90–98.

Cook, S. F. (1943). *Physiol. Zoöl.* **16:** 123–128.

Cook, S. F., and Scott, K. G. (1933). *J. Cellular Comp. Physiol.* **4:** 95–110.

Cort, W. W., and Otto, G. F. (1940). *Rev. Gastroenterol.* **7:** 2–14.

Cross, S. X. (1935). *J. Parasitol.* **21:** 267–273.

Dastre, A., and Stassano, H. (1903). *Compt. rend. soc, biol.* **55:** 131–132.

DeWaele, A. (1933). *Bull. classe sci. Acad. Roy. Belg. Ser. 5* **19:** 649–660 (not seen).

Dogiel, V. A., and Winogradowa-Fedorowa, T. V. (1930). *Tierernähr. u. Tierzucht* **3:** 172–188.

Donaldson, A. W., and Otto, G. F. (1946). *Am. J. Hyg.* **44:** 384–400.

Eberlein, R. K. (1895). *Z. wiss. Zool.* **59:** 233–304.

Falaschini, A. (1934). *Ann. ist. super. agr., Milano* **1:** 2 (not seen).

Ferber, K. A. (1928). *Z. Tierzücht. Züchtungsbiol.* **12:** 31–63.

Ferber, K. A., and Winogradowa, T. V. (1929). *Biol. Zentr.* **49:** 321–328.

Fermi, C. (1910). *Zentr. Bakt. Parasitenk. Abt. I. Orig.* **56:** 55–85.

Fetterolf, D. W. (1907). *Univ. Penn. Med. Bull.* **20:** 94–96.

Foster, A. O., and Cort, W. W. (1931). *Science* **73:** 681–683.

Foster, A. O., and Cort, W. W. (1932). *Am. J. Hyg.* **16:** 241–265.

Foster, A. O., and Cort, W. W. (1935). *Am. J. Hyg.* **21:** 302–318.

Fraser, A. H., and Robertson, D. (1933). *Empire J. Exptl. Agr.* **1:** 17–21.
Fredericq, L. (1878). *Bull. classe sci. Acad. Roy. Belg. Ser. 2* **46:** 213–228 (not seen).
Gelfand, M. (1944). The Sick African. A Clinical Study. Lewis, Cape Town. (not seen).
Gordon, H. McL. (1948). *Australian Vet. J.* **24:** 17–45.
Greenberg, J., and Taylor, D. J. (1950). *J. Parasitol.* **36** Suppl.: 21.
Hackett, L. W. (1937). Malaria in Europe. Oxford University Press, London.
Hager, A. (1941). *Iowa State Coll. J. Sci.* **15:** 127–153.
Hall, M. C. (1917). *In* Musser, J. H., and Kelly, T. C. (1917). A Handbook of Practical Treatment. W. B. Saunders, Philadelphia, Vol. 4, 389–419.
Hamill, J. M. (1906). *J. Physiol.* **33:** 479–492.
Harned, B. K., and Nash, T. P. (1932). *J. Biol. Chem.* **97:** 443–456.
Harvey, S. C. (1949). *J. Biol. Chem.* **179:** 435–453.
Hastings, E. G. (1944). *Bact. Revs.* **8:** 235–254.
Hegner, R. (1923). *Am. J. Hyg.* **3:** 180–200.
Hegner, R. (1937). *J. Parasitol.* **23:** 1–12.
Hegner, R., and Eskridge, L. (1937a). *J. Parasitol.* **23:** 105–106.
Hegner, R., and Eskridge, L. (1937b). *J. Parasitol.* **23:** 225–226.
Hegner, R., and Eskridge, L. (1937c). *Am. J. Hyg.* **26:** 127–134.
Hendee, E. C. (1935). *Hilgardia* **9:** 499–525.
Hiraishi, T. (1927). *Japan. Med. World* **7:** 80.
Hovanitz, W. (1947). *Am. J. Hyg.* **45:** 67–81.
Hungate, R. E. (1938). *Ecology* **19:** 1–25.
Hungate, R. E. (1939). *Ecology* **20:** 230–245.
Hungate, R. E. (1940). *Botan. Gaz.* **102:** 382–392.
Hungate, R. E. (1941). *Ann. Entomol. Soc. Am.* **34:** 467–489.
Hungate, R. E. (1943). *Ann. Entomol. Soc. Am.* **36:** 730–739.
Jones, M. F., and Nolan, M. O. (1942). *Proc. Helminthol. Soc. Wash. D. C.* **9:** 63–65.
Kendall, S. B. (1949). *J. Helminthol.* **23:** 179–190.
Kessel, J. F. (1929). *Proc. Soc. Exptl. Biol. Med.* **27:** 113–118.
Kessel, J. F., and Huang, K. K. (1926). *Proc. Soc. Exptl. Biol. Med.* **23:** 388–391.
Krakower, C. A., Hoffman, W. A., and Axtmayer, J. H. (1940). *Puerto Rico J. Pub. Health Trop. Med.* **16:** 269–391.
Krakower, C. A., Hoffman, W. A., and Axtmayer, J. H. (1944). *J. Infectious Diseases* **74:** 178–183.
Kunitz, M., and Northrop, J. H. (1936). *J. Gen. Physiol.* **19:** 991–1007.
Larsh, J. E. (1947). *J. Parasitol.* **33:** 339–344.
Larsh, J. E. (1950). *J. Parasitol.* **36** Suppl.: 45–46.
Lawler, H. J. (1941). *Am. J. Hyg.* **34** Sect. D: 65–72.
Leach, J. G., and Granovsky, A. A. (1938). *Science* **87:** 66–67.
Lucker, J. T., and Neumayer, E. M. (1947). *Am. J. Vet. Research* **8:** 400–412.
Lund, E. E. (1930). *Univ. Calif. (Berkeley) Pubs. Pub. Zool.* **36:** 81–96.
Mangold, E. (1943). *Ergeb. Biol.* **19:** 1–81.
Mangold, E., and Schmitt-Krahmer, C. (1927). *Biochem. Z.* **191:** 411–422.
Mangold, E., and Usuelli, F. (1932). *Tierernähr. u. Tierzucht.* **3:** 189–201.
Manusardi, L. (1931). *Boll. zool. agrar. bachicolt. univ. Milano* **4:** 140–148.
Marshall, R. A., and Phillipson, A. T. (1945). *Proc. Nutrition Soc. (Engl. and Scot.)* **3:** 238–243.
McAnally, R. A., and Phillipson, A. T. (1944). *Biol. Revs.* **19:** 41–54.
McCoy, O. R. (1934). *Am. J. Hyg.* **20:** 169–180.

McKee, R. W., and Geiman, Q. M. (1946). *Proc. Soc. Exptl. Biol. Med.* **63**: 313–315.

Mendel, L. B., and Blood, A. F. (1910). *J. Biol. Chem.* **8**: 177–213.

Montalenti, G. (1927). *Rend. reale accad. nazl. Lincei* [Ser. 6] **6**: 529–532.

Morris, S. (1936). *J. Morphol.* **59**: 225–263.

Mowry, H. A., and Becker, E. R. (1930). *Iowa State Coll. J. Sci.* **5**: 35–60.

Müller, J., and Simons, H. (1920). *Z. Biol.* **70**: 231–244.

Northrop, J. H. (1926). *J. Gen. Physiol.* **9**: 497–502.

Otto, G. F. (1940). *Proc. Intern. Congr. Microbiol. 3rd. Congr.* 1939, pp. 476–477.

Passmore, R., and Sommerville, T. (1940). *J. Malaria Inst. India* **3**: 447–455.

Porter, D. A. (1935). *Am. J. Hyg.* **22**: 467–474.

Ratcliffe, H. L. (1930). *Am. J. Hyg.* **11**: 159–167.

Read, C. P. (1950). *Rice Inst. Pamphlet* **27**: [No. 2] 1–94.

Reid, W. M. (1940). *J. Parasitol.* **26** Suppl.: 16.

Reid, W. M. (1942a). *Poultry Sci.* **21**: 220–229.

Reid, W. M. (1942b). *J. Parasitol.* **28**: 319–340.

Reid, W. M. (1944). *J. Parasitol.* **30** Suppl.:12.

Reid, W. M., and Ackert, J. E. (1941). *J. Parasitol.* **27** Suppl.: 35.

Reiner, L., and Paton, J. B. (1932). *Proc. Soc. Exptl. Biol. Med.* **30**: 345–348.

Reinhard, E. G., and von Brand, T. (1944). *Physiol. Zoöl.* **17**: 31–41.

Robson, G. C. (1911). *Quart. J. Microscop. Sci.* **57**: 267–278.

Rothschild, M. (1939). *Novitates Zool.* **41**: 178–180.

Rothschild, M. (1941). *Parasitology* **33**: 406–415.

Sadun, E. H., Totter, J. R., and Keith, C. K. (1949). *J. Parasitol.* **35** Suppl.: 13-14.

Sang, J. H. (1938). *Parasitology* **30**: 141–155.

Sassuchin, D. N. (1931). *Arch. Protistenk.* **70**: 681–686.

Schinazi, L. A., Drell, W., Ball, G. H., and Dunn, M. S. (1950). *Proc. Soc. Exptl. Biol. Med.* **75**: 229–234.

Schwarz, C. (1925). *Biochem. Z.* **156**: 130–137.

Schwarz, C., and Bienert, G. (1926). *Arch. ges. Physiol.* **213**: 556–562.

Seeler, A. O., and Ott, W. H. (1944). *J. Infectious Diseases* **75**: 175–178.

Seeler, A. O., and Ott, W. H. (1945). *J. Infectious Diseases* **77**: 82–84.

Seeler, A. O., Ott, W. H., and Gundel, M. E. (1944). *Proc. Soc. Exptl. Biol. Med.* **55**: 107–109.

Shearer, G. D., and Stewart, J. (1933). *Univ. Cambridge, Inst. Animal Path., Rept. Director* **3**: 87–97.

Shorb, D. A., and Spindler, L. A. (1947). *Proc. Helminthol. Soc. Wash. D. C.* **14**: 30–34.

Solazzo, G. (1929). *Z. Immunitätsforsch.* **60**: 239–246.

Spindler, L. A. (1933). *J. Parasitol.* **20**: 72.

Spindler, L. A. (1947). *Proc. Helminthol. Soc. Wash. D. C.* **14**: 58–63.

Spindler, L. A., Zimmerman, H. E., and Hill, C. H. (1944). *Proc. Helminthol. Soc. Wash. D. C.* **11**: 9–12.

Stewart, J. (1933a). *Univ. Cambridge, Inst. Animal Path., Rept. Director* **3**: 58–76.

Stewart, J. (1933b). *Univ. Cambridge, Inst. Animal Path., Rept. Director* **3**: 77–86.

Tallqvist, T. W. (1907). *Z. klin. Med.* **61**: 421–532.

Taylor, D. J., Greenberg, J., Highman, B., and Coatney, G. R. (1950). *Am. J. Trop. Med.* **30**: 817–828.

Taylor, E. L. (1943). *Vet. Record* **55**: 117–119.

Tobie, J. E. (1949). *Am. J. Trop. Med.* **29**: 859–870.

Trager, W. (1943a). *J. Exptl. Med.* **77**: 411–420.

Trager, W. (1943b). *J. Exptl. Med.* **77:** 557–582.
Trager, W. (1947a). *J. Exptl. Med.* **85:** 663–683.
Trager, W. (1947b). *Proc. Soc. Exptl. Biol. Med.* **64:** 129–134.
Trager, W. (1949). *Bact. Revs.* **13:** 105–110.
Usuelli, F., and Fiorini, P. (1938). *Boll. soc. ital. biol. sper.* **13:** 11–14.
Watt, J. Y. C. (1944). *Am. J. Hyg.* **39:** 145–151.
Weinland, E. (1901). *Z. Biol.* **42:** 55–90.
Weinland, E. (1903). *Z. Biol.* **44:** 1–15 and 45–60.
Wereninow, A., Winogradow, M., and Diakow, M. (1930). *Biochem. Z.* **226:** 387–394.
Wesenberg-Lund, C. (1934). *Kgl. Danske Videnskab. Selskabs. Skrifter Naturvidenskab. math. Afdel.* [9] **5** No. 3: 1–223.
Westphal, A. (1939). *Z. Hyg. Infektionskrankh.* **122:** 146–158.
Westphal, A. (1941). *Deut. Trop. Med. Z.* **45:** 653–657.
Whitlock, J. H. (1949). *Cornell Vet.* **39:** 146–182.
Whitlock, J. H., Calloway, H. P., and Jeppeson, Q. E. (1943). *J. Am. Vet. Med. Assoc.* **102:** 34–35.
Winogradow, M., Winogradowa-Fedorowa, T., and Wereninow, A. (1930). *Zentr. Bakt. Parasitenk. Abt. II.* **81:** 230–244.
Wright, W. H. (1935). *J. Parasitol.* **21:** 433.
Zaiman, H. (1940). *J. Parasitol.* **26** Suppl.: 44.

# CHAPTER 17

# THE PHYSIOLOGICAL BASIS AND METABOLIC CONSEQUENCES OF PARASITIC ANEMIAS

## I. Anemias due to Blood Parasites

Anemia is caused by the destruction of erythrocytes at a rate exceeding replacement and is a frequent and important symptom in many diseases due to blood parasites. The reasons for the destruction of red cells during infection with such parasites as *Bartonella*, *Anaplasma*, *Babesia*, malarial parasites, or pathogenic trypanosomes are rather obscure and the mechanisms involved are not always uniform.

The greatest amount of experimental evidence is available for malaria and it will therefore be taken up first. The parasitized red cells are destroyed in this disease at sporulation time and some parasitized and nonparasitized cells are also removed by phagocytosis. In addition, however, intravascular hemolysis of nonparasitized erythrocytes occurs and assumes spectacular dimensions in blackwater fever. The reasons for this hemolysis are still under debate despite a great amount of work devoted to the problem. Its present status has recently been reviewed by Maegraith (1948) and the following account is a brief condensation of his discussion.

Maegraith (1948) points out that a circulating hemolysin has been identified neither in simple malaria nor in blackwater fever and that changes in saline fragility of the erythrocytes also do not seem to be important. Fragility has sometimes been found increased (Barrenscheen and Glaessner, 1923; Potapenko, 1929; Shen, Fleming, and Castle, 1946), sometimes unchanged (Dudgeon, 1920; Ross, 1928, 1932; Garin, 1930), and sometimes even decreased (Matsunobu, 1937). However, unchanged saline fragility does not necessarily indicate insensitivity to other lytic agents. Foy and Kondi (1943) thus observed in blackwater fever an increased fragility of erythrocytes towards a lysolecithin system despite unchanged saline fragility.

The occurrence of spherocytosis (Gear, 1946) may have a bearing on the problem, since spherocytes have a tendency to obstruct circulation in small vessels, and changes in the surface properties of the red cells may also be of significance. A reduction in electrical charge has been observed in avian malaria (Brown, 1933), pronounced changes in membrane permeability have been recorded both in simian and human malaria (Overman, 1948; Overman, Hill, and Wong, 1949), and the red cells may become sticky (Knisely, Eliot, and Bloch, 1945; Knisely *et al.*, 1945). These factors may well contribute to hemolysis, but they appear insufficient to account for large scale destruction of red cells; it is hence not surprising that other mechanisms have been considered.

Lytic factors are normally present in animal tissues, but they are held in check by naturally occurring inhibitors. Some evidence was adduced to the effect that in blackwater fever the balance between the two types of factors is shifted to the lytic side (Maegraith, Martin, and Findlay, 1943). Whether this lytic agent is lysolecithin, as suggested by Ponder (1944), or the nitrogen- and phosphorus-free compound described by Laser and Friedmann (1945) is not clear.

A splenic factor may also be involved. It has been suggested that the spleen may, during contractions, force autohemolysin into the circulation and that this may unleash the sudden hemolysis characteristic for black-water fever (Foy and Kondi, 1943; Gear, 1946). The relative stagnation of the blood in an enlarged malarial spleen may have an influence on the amount of Fåhraeus' (1939) stabilizing factor, which is probably related to lysolecithin (Vint, 1941). Another suggestion is that the malarial parasites may possess an RH-like substance that may sensitize RH-negative persons; relapses in the infection would then cause a hemolytic reaction (Butts, 1945).

There is some probability that hemolysis may at least in part be due to immune reactions involving antigen-antibody complexes and possibly complement (Coggeshall, 1937; Gear, 1946). Gear (1946) assumes that parasitized red cells become autoantigenic and that as a consequence an antibody or hemolysin is produced in the spleen or the reticuloendothelial system in general. The antibody or hemolysin would accumulate in the congested spleen and would on occasion be forced in relatively large amounts into the circulation.

Further possible mechanisms of hemolysis, such as increased acidity of the blood plasma, lytic action of malarial pigment, or toxin production by the parasites are not considered as important by Maegraith (1948) because in malaria at most small changes in alkaline reserve occur (Ross, 1932; Fairley and Bromfield, 1933; Wakeman, 1929), and because Morrison and Anderson's (1942) experiments disprove an important role of the malarial pigment, and because there is no definite evidence for the production of toxins.

There is still less definite information available concerning the mechanism of erythrocyte destruction in infections with other blood parasites. No mechanical destruction comparable to the bursting of erythrocytes during sporulation of malarial parasites occurs in infections with bartonellas or pathogenic trypanosomes. In these latter infections the fragility of the red cells appears to be materially increased (Weinman, 1938; Ikejiani, 1946c). Two mechanisms have been considered as contributing factors: Acidosis and increased blood potassium (Ikejiani, 1946c).

Acidosis, as evidenced by an increased lactic acid level of the blood, a lowered pH, or a lowered alkaline reserve has been observed both in infections with *Bartonella* (von Brand, Regendanz, and Weise, 1932) and pathogenic trypanosomes (Kligler and Geiger, 1928; Scheff, 1928; Kligler, Geiger, and Comaroff, 1929; Dominici, 1930; Linton, 1930; Andrews, Johnson, and Dormal, 1930; Krijgsman, 1933). It is more pronounced than in malaria, but whether it is sufficiently severe to account for such a large scale erythrocyte destruction as occurs in bartonellosis, is very dubious.

An increase in the potassium level of the blood serum has also been observed in both infections (Kessler and Zwemer, 1944; Zwemer and Culbertson, 1939; Ikejiani, 1946a, b). It appears somewhat earlier and is more pronounced in the trypanosome than in the *Bartonella* infections despite the fact that during the latter the red cells are destroyed at a much faster rate than in the former. This would seem to make potasium unlikely as a rather unspecific main cause for erythrocyte destruction and obviously more work is necessary to solve the problem. This is especially true also for infections with *Babesia, Theileria*, and *Nuttalia* where only the fact of blood cell destruction is known, but where not even a beginning of an analysis of the mechanisms involved has been made.

Large scale destruction of erythrocytes and insufficient replacement leads obviously to a diminution of the functioning hemoglobin. Malarial parasites also destroy the hemoglobin of still circulating red cells. The resulting anemia can therefore reach extreme degrees. In *Plasmodium falciparum* infections the red cell count can drop as low as 0.44 million/mm³ (Carducci, 1907), in *Plasmodium vivax* infections to 0.56 million/mm³ (Amy, 1934), but in most instances the decline is not quite as pronounced. In average *vivax* infections the red cell counts vary between 2.2 and 4.9 million/mm³ (Fairley and Bromfield, 1933). In *Anaplasma* infections counts as low as 0.76 million/mm³ have been reported (Rees and Hale, 1936) and in infections with *Bartonella muris* the red cells may drop from 10 to 11 million/mm³ to about 2 million (Ford and Eliot, 1928).

One of the unavoidable consequences of pronounced red cell destruction is a lowering of the oxygen-carrying capacity of the blood; in anaplasmosis for instance it can fall as low as 18% of normal (Rees and Hale, 1936). Determinations of the oxygen-carrying capacity of the blood alone do not give a complete picture of the seriousness of an anemic condition in parasitic diseases, however. Frequently factors are operative that, within the lungs, tend to hinder the oxygen saturation of those red cells that are left. In rats infected with pathogenic trypanosomes the oxygen content of the blood may thus drop from a normal level of 16 to 18 volume% to 2.6 volume %, a reduction that is much greater than the corresponding loss of hemoglobin (Andrews, Johnson, and Dormal, 1930). Another example hinting at undersaturation is the fact that the venous blood of *Anaplasma* infected cattle has on occasion been found to be practically oxygen-free (Rees and Hale, 1936). As to the mechanisms involved, it has been suggested that the agglomeration of trypanosomes in the vessels of the heart and lungs may have prevented proper aeration of the blood (Andrews, Johnson, and Dormal, 1930). In malaria, pulmonary edema seems to occur frequently (Spitz, 1946) and intravascular agglomeration of red cells obstructs the free flow of blood, a fact observed in avian, simian, and human malaria (Lack, 1942; Knisely, 1943; Knisely, Eliot, and Bloch, 1945; Knisely *et al.*, 1947).

It is obvious then that a severe strain is placed on the circulatory system in order to compensate for the deficiencies in the vascular mechanism of freely securing oxygen and this strain will be especially heavy in those instances where fever increases the oxygen demand of the tissues. During malarial rigor, for instance, the heat production may be increased by about 200% (Du Bois, 1922).

To what extent the compensating mechanisms suffice in achieving an approximately normal oxygen supply of the tissues is frequently difficult to decide. It has been found that the oxygen consumption of trypanosome-infected rats is somewhat raised in the terminal stages of the disease (von Fenyvessy, 1926; von Brand, 1951), this increase being due in part to a slight rise in body temperature, in part to the oxygen consumption of the flagellates. It does not seem justified, however, to assume with Scheff and Rabati (1938) that the parasites kill their hosts by asphyxiation. During the greater part of the infection both the temperature and the oxygen consumption of the infected animals stay normal (Kligler, Geiger, and Comaroff, 1929; von Brand, 1951), indicating probably that at least during this period the oxygen supply of the tissues was normal. The possibility cannot be excluded that in heavily infected small laboratory animals localized tissue anoxemia develops when parasites agglomerate in small blood vessels. It is unlikely, however, that such a mechanism could be operative in human trypanosomiasis where the parasites develop only in small numbers.

In all malarias, on the other hand, anoxia and changes in circulation are of the utmost importance. A vast literature is available on this phase which space does not permit to review here. It has been summarized in a most stimulating manner by Maegraith (1948). He points out that general circulatory disturbances occur which offer essentially the picture of shock associated with anoxemia and also local circulatory disturbances in almost any organ of the body. These then produce a variety of symptoms and their genesis is somewhat variable from organ to organ. Changes in the endothelial cells of the blood vessels and changes in the blood flow are however the most important factors and of general occurrence. What appears to be a fundamental problem for further research is expressed by Maegraith (1948) in the following words: "The anoxemia created by the loss of red cells and changes in pulmonary circulation is probably in itself insufficient in most cases of malaria to initiate the tissue changes and the host's response to the invasion. There must be other factors involved, about which at present there is very little information." He emphasizes in this connection that no specific toxin has been identified but that there is very strong evidence for the existence of "some circulating diffusable agent."

## II. Anemias due to Intestinal Parasites

In heavy infections with coccidia large scale destructions of host tissues occur with resulting severe hemorrhages. Bloody stools are a well known symptom of intestinal coccidiosis in cattle, poultry, and other animals (literature in Becker, 1934; Brackett and Bliznick, 1950). The mechanism involved, mechanical damage to the tissues, offers little physiological interest and these cases are therefore only mentioned incidentally.

Of greater physiological interest is the anemia produced by intestinal nematodes, especially *Necator*, *Ancylostoma*, and *Haemonchus*. It has been shown that *Ancylostoma* withdraws large amounts of blood from the host, estimated as high as 0.84 ml/worm/day (Wells, 1931; Nishi, 1933). This figure is probably a maximal one and the average blood withdrawal may well be appreciably smaller (Foster and Landsberg, 1934). Hahn and Offutt (1949) showed recently that moderately infected dogs lost within 16 to 27 days an amount of blood corresponding to the total initial amount. The blood sucking activities of the worms are certainly pronounced enough to produce an anemic condition in their hosts, the severity of which depends on the number of worms present and the nutritional state of the host. *Haemonchus* seems to withdraw considerably smaller amounts of blood per worm. According to Martin and Ross' (1934) calculation, 4000 specimens, as are often found in the stomach of a sheep, would ingest daily about 60 ml blood, still an appreciable amount for a daily occurrence. Andrews (1942) found that two lambs lost, within 10 days, during a fatal infection with *Haemonchus*, 1942 and 2380 ml of blood, respectively, that is, 1.6 to 2.5 times the entire original blood volume.

Hookworm anemia is a microcytic hypochromic anemia, that is, an anemia similar in every respect to that produced by chronic loss of blood regardless of the latter's etiology. Foster and Landsberg (1934) could simulate the blood picture of hookworm anemia by simple periodic bleeding of dogs and the *Haemonchus* anemia could be reproduced by blood withdrawal in sheep (Fourie, 1931; Andrews, 1942). It is hence not necessary, as was done originally, to assume that toxins produced by the worms play a significant role by damaging either the circulating blood corpuscles directly, or the blood-forming organs (Fülleborn and Kikuth, 1929; Landsberg, 1939). Just as in other microcytic anemias, the anemia due to hookworms in man and dog responds well generally to iron therapy (Cruz, 1932, 1934, 1948; Rhoads, *et al.*, 1934; Suarez, 1933; Hill and Andrews, 1942; Foster and Landsberg, 1934). It must be stressed, however, that iron therapy alone prevents the anemia only when the hosts are on a generally well balanced diet and, as a matter of fact, striking reticulocyte responses have been observed even in acute fatal hookworm infections of dogs when the latter did not receive iron (Landsberg, 1937). If, however, the hosts are on suboptimal diets, especially on diets deficient in protein, the response of the hemopoietic system to iron therapy is only transitory (Payne and Payne, 1940; Otto and Landsberg, 1940); anemia does then develop and in experimental animals its appearance is not even significantly delayed.

If it is conceded that the withdrawal of blood by the parasites lies at the root of the hookworm anemia, a correlation to the physiological requirements of the parasites becomes probable. It is generally assumed that the amount of blood sucked by the hookworm is much larger than its need for organic food material. This was emphasized first by Wells (1931) and the question naturally arose as to the biological significance of this excessive blood consumption. While the exact rate of oxygen consumption of the hookworm has not yet been established, it does appear to be high (Harwood and Brown, 1934). The oxygen contained in the ingested blood should be ample to supplement the rather small amounts of that gas which these worms encounter in their normal habitat (von Brand and Jahn, 1941). Fundamentally then, the hookworm anemia would seem to be due to the oxygen requirements of the parasites and related to a rather unusual method of securing this gas.

The anemia produced by *Diphyllobothrium latum* is, in contrast to the hookworm anemia, a macrocytic anemia corresponding in most hematological and clinical details to a typical pernicious anemia although a few minor deviations occur. These have been summarized by Birkeland (1932) and von Bonsdorff (1948b), but their review lies beyond the scope of the present account.

Various theories have been proposed to account for the origin of the tapeworm anemia. A specific toxin, or various toxic fractions, one of them apparently an albumose fraction, were incriminated especially by Seyderhelm (1918), Becker, Helander, and Simola (1925), and Nyfeldt (1927), but their leads seem not to have been followed up further, apparently because it was felt that their fractions contained bacterial rather than helminth toxins (Kingisepp, 1933).

Another assumption was that oleic acid present in the worms and absorbed by the host upon disintegration of proglottids within the intestine was the hemolytic factor responsible (Tallqvist, 1907; Faust and Tallqvist, 1907). This view also has not been generally accepted because the amounts of pure oleic acid of nonworm origin necessary to produce anemia in experimental animals is very large, larger than one would expect as possible to be derived from a worm. Tötterman (1938) has pointed out, however, that the lipids of the worm may sensitize a person and thus, under certain conditions, precipitate anemia. It is also of interest to note that more recently Wardle and Green (1941) reported the unsaturated fraction of the *Moniezia* ether extract as the most potent one in reducing the number of red cells in experimental animals. It is also worthwhile recalling that higher fatty acids are excreted by tapeworms (see Chapter 3) thus perhaps indicating the possibility of a chronic intoxication. Von Brand (1948) has pointed out that, if the fatty acids should play a role in the etiology of this anemia, its physiological basis would rest on the inability of the large tapeworms to secure large amounts of oxygen in their normal habitat. Therefore it would have just an opposite basis from that mentioned above for the hookworm anemia.

Other mechanisms must however also be considered and they may well be the more important ones. Saltzman (1935) has first expressed the view that the tapeworm may interfere with the production or absorption of the antianemic factor, or with the production of its components. In other words he proposes a mechanism that is assumed to lead to pernicious types of anemia in sprue and some other disorders. Experimental studies along this line have been done primarily by von Bonsdorff who has recently summarized his experiences (von Bonsdorff, 1948b).

It was found that the gastric juice of patients with tapeworm anemia contained the intrinsic factor, but a decreased secretion of this factor may at least facilitate the anemia (von Bonsdorff, 1940; Helander, 1945). A lack of extrinsic factor (vitamin $B_{12}$), which is usually contained in the proteins of the diet, does not seem to be responsible, although a relative deficiency such as occurs during times of economic distress may be a contributing factor (von Bonsdorff, 1943, 1948b). Fairly good evidence was adduced to the effect that the worm prevents the necessary interaction between extrinsic and intrinsic factors. Thus Castle's antianemic factor is probably not produced and this may well be the real precipitating cause of the anemia, once the normal stores of antianemic factor in the body have become exhausted. A mixture of gastric juice and meat was very effective in bringing about remission of cryptogenetic pernicious anemia, but in cases of *Diphyllobothrium* anemia the mixture was effective only after the parasite had been expelled (von Bonsdorff, 1947a). It is of great interest that the interaction was prevented only by the living worm. The admixture of freshly minced or of dried worm substance to the diet did not interfere with the production of the antianemic factor (von Bonsdorff, 1947b). It is also important to note that intestinal absorption as such is not impaired, but nevertheless the antianemic factor is more or less completely depleted in the liver in patients suffering from pernicious tapeworm anemia.

Folic acid is apparently not destroyed by the worms, since patients harboring them respond very well to folic acid treatment. However, there is a possibility, as yet unproved, that the infection may interfere with the conjugase system which normally releases folic acid from pteroylheptaglutamic acid. In a normal diet folic acid usually occurs in the conjugated form (von Bonsdorff, 1948a).

Of course only a minority of persons infested with *Diphyllobothrium* develop a pernicious type of anemia, which may be due to one more factor—the localization of the worm within the intestine. It seems that anemia develops only when the tapeworms are localized high up in the intestine; the critical border line seems to lie approximately at the junction of jejunum and ileum (von Bonsdorff, 1947c, d). It is conceivable that only worms so localized are in a position to prevent the interaction between extrinsic and intrinsic factor (von Bonsdorff, 1948b).

## LITERATURE

Andrews, J. S. (1942). *J. Agr. Research* **65:** 1–18.
Andrews, J., Johnson, C. M., and Dormal, V. J. (1930). *Am. J. Hyg.* **12:** 381–400.
Amy, A. C. (1934). *J. Roy. Army Med. Corps* **62:** 318–329.
Barrenscheen, H. K., and Glaessner, K. (1923). *Wien. Arch. klin. Med.* **5:** 409–418.
Becker, E. R. (1934). Coccidia and Coccidiosis of Domesticated, Game and Laboratory Animals and of Man. Collegiate Press, Ames, Iowa.
Becker, G., Helander, E., and Simola, P. (1925). *Z. ges. exptl. Med.* **48:** 204–225.
Birkeland, I. W. (1932). *Medicine* **11:** 1–139.
von Bonsdorff, B. (1940). *Acta Med. Scand.* **105:** 540–557.
von Bonsdorff, B. (1943). *Acta Med. Scand.* **116:** 77–95.
von Bonsdorff, B. (1947a). *Acta Med. Scand. Suppl.* **196:** 456–477.
von Bonsdorff, B. (1947b). *Acta Med. Scand.* **129:** 59–76.
von Bonsdorff, B. (1947c). *Acta. Med. Scand.* **129:** 142–155.
von Bonsdorff, B. (1947d). *Acta Med. Scand.* **129:** 213–233.
von Bonsdorff, B. (1948a). *Acta Med. Scand. Suppl.* **213:** 82–90.
von Bonsdorff, B. (1948b). *Blood* **3:** 91–102.
Brackett, S., and Bliznick, A. (1950). The Occurrence and Economic Importance of Coccidiosis in Chicken. Lederle Laboratory Division, American Cyanamid Co.
von Brand, T., (1948). *Proc. Intern. Congr. Trop. Med. Malaria. 4th Congr. Wash. D. C.* **2:** 984–991.

von Brand, T. (1951). *Exptl. Parasitol.* **1:** 60–65.
von Brand, T., and Jahn, T. L. (1941). *In* Christie, J. R. (1941). An Introduction to Nematology. Sect. 2, Part 2, 356–371. Chitwood, Babylon, N. Y.
➤ von Brand, T., Regendanz, P., and Weise, W. (1932). *Zentr. Bakt. Parasitenk. Abt. I. Orig.* **125:** 461–468.
Brown, H. C. (1933). *Trans. Roy. Soc. Trop. Med. Hyg.* **26:** 515–522.
Butts, D. C. A. (1945). *Am. J. Trop. Med.* **25:** 417–420.
Carducci, A. (1907). *Atti soc. studi. malar.* **8:** 225 (not seen).
Coggeshall, L. T. (1937). *Am. J. Trop. Med.* **17:** 605–617.
Cruz, W. O. (1932). *Compt. rend. soc. biol.* **111:** 483–485.
Cruz, W. O. (1934). *Mem. ist. Oswaldo Cruz* **29:** 427–485.
Cruz, W. O. (1948). *Proc. Intern. Congr. Trop. Med. Malaria. 4th. Congr. Wash. D. C.* **2:** 1045–1052.
Dominici, A. (1930). *Boll. ist. sieroterap. milan.* **9:** 438–441.
DuBois, E. F. (1922). *In* Barker, L. F. (1922). Endocrinology and Metabolism. D. Appleton, New York, Vol. 4, pp. 94–151.
Dudgeon, L. S. (1920). *J. Hyg.* **19:** 208–244.
Fåhraeus, R. (1939). *Lancet* **237:** 630–634.
Fairley, N. H., and Bromfield, R. J. (1933). *Trans. Roy. Soc. Trop. Med. Hyg.* **27:** 289–314.
Faust, E. S., and Tallqvist, T. W. (1907). *Arch. exptl. Path. Pharmakol.* **57:** 367–385.
von Fenyvessy, B. (1926). *Biochem. Z.* **173:** 289–297.
Ford, W. W., and Eliot, C. P. (1928). *J. Exptl. Med.* **48:** 475–492.
Foster, A. O., and Landsberg, J. W. (1934). *Am. J. Hyg.* **20:** 259–290.
Fourie, P. J. J. (1931). *Union S. Africa, Dept. Agr. Repts. Director Vet. Services Animal Ind., Onderstepoort* **17:** 495–572.
Foy, H., and Kondi, A. (1943). *Trans. Roy. Soc. Trop. Med. Hyg.* **37:** 1–18.
Fülleborn, F., and Kikuth, W. (1929). *Arch. Schiffs-u. Tropen-Hyg.* **33** (3): 171–188.
Garin, C. P. (1930). *Rev. prat. mal. pays chauds* **10:** 55–62 (not seen).
Gear, J. (1946). *Trans. Roy. Soc. Trop. Med. Hyg.* **39:** 301–314.
Hahn, P. F., and Offut, E. P. (1949). *Science* **110:** 711–713.
Harwood, P. D., and Brown, H. W. (1934). *J. Parasitol.* **20:** 128.
Helander, E. V. (1945). *Acta Med. Scand. Suppl.* **155:** 1–115.
Hill, A. W., and Andrews, J. (1942). *Am. J. Trop. Med.* **22:** 499–506.
Ikejiani, O. (1946a). *J. Parasitol.* **32:** 374–378.
Ikejiani, O. (1946b). *J. Parasitol.* **32:** 379–382.
Ikejiani, O. (1946c). *J. Parasitol.* **32:** 383–386.
Kessler, W. R., and Zwemer, R. L. (1944). *J. Infectious Diseases* **75:** 134–137.
Kingisepp, G. (1933). *Arch. exptl. Path. Pharmakol.* **170:** 733–743.
Kligler, I. J., and Geiger, A. (1928). *Proc. Soc. Exptl. Biol. Med.* **26:** 229–230.
Kligler, I. J., Geiger, A., and Comaroff, R. (1929). *Ann. Trop. Med. Parasitol.* **23:** 325–335.
Knisely, M. H. (1943). *J. Am. Med. Assoc.* **121:** 885.
Knisely, M. H., Bloch, E. H., Eliot, T. S., and Warner, L. (1947). *Science* **106:** 431–440.
Knisely, M. H., Eliot, T. S., and Bloch, E. H. (1945). *Arch. Surg.* **51:** 220–236.
Knisely, M. H., Stratman-Thomas, W. K., Eliot, T. S., and Bloch, E. H. (1945). *J. Natl. Malaria Soc.* **4:** 285–300.
Krijgsman, B. J. (1933). *Z. Parasitenk.* **6:** 1–22 and 438–477.
Lack, A. R. (1942). *Science* **96:** 520–521.

Landsberg, J. W. (1937). *Am. J. Hyg.* **26:** 60–71.

Landsberg, J. W. (1939). *J. Am. Vet. Med. Assoc.* **94 (2):** 389–397.

Laser, H., and Friedmann, E. (1945). *Nature* **156:** 507.

Linton, R. W. (1930). *J. Exptl. Med.* **52:** 103–111.

Maegraith, B. (1948). Pathological Processes in Malaria and Blackwater Fever. Charles C Thomas, Springfield, Ill.

Maegraith, B., Martin, N. H., and Findlay, G. M. (1943). *Brit. J. Exptl. Path.* **24:** 58–65.

Martin, C. J., and Ross, I. C. (1934). *J. Helminthol.* **12:** 137–142.

Matsunobu, M. (1937). *J. Formosan Med. Assoc.* **36:** 1002 (German summary).

Morrison, D. B., and Anderson, W. A. D. (1942). *U. S. Pub. Health Service. Pub. Health Repts.* **57:** 161–174.

Nishi, M. (1933). *J. Formosan Med. Assoc.* **32:** 677–691.

Nyfeldt, A. (1927). Experimentelle undersøgelser over den perniciøse anaemi's pathogenese. J. Lund, Copenhagen.

Otto, G. F., and Landsberg, J. W. (1940). *Am. J. Hyg.* **31:** Sect. D: 37–47.

Overman, R. R. (1948). *Am. J. Physiol.* **152:** 113–121.

Overman, R. R., Hill, T. S., and Wong, Y. T. (1949). *J. Natl. Malaria Soc.* **8:** 14–31.

Payne, G. C., and Payne, F. K. (1940). *Am. J. Hyg.* **32** Sect. D: 125–132.

Ponder, E. (1944). *J. Gen. Physiol.* **27:** 483–512.

Potapenko, N. A. (1929). *Russ. J. Trop. Med.* **7:** 234 (not seen).

Rees, C. W., and Hale, M. W. (1936). *J. Agr. Research* **53:** 477–492.

Rhoads, C. P., Castle, W. B., Payne, G. C., and Lawson, H. A. (1934). *Medicine* **13:** 317–375.

Ross, G. R. (1928). *Ann. Trop. Med. Parasitol.* **22:** 5–16.

Ross, G. R. (1932). *Mem. London School Hyg. Trop. Med.* **6:** 1–262.

Saltzman, F. (1935). *Finska Laek. Saellsk. Handl.* **77:** 589 (not seen).

Scheff, G. (1928). *Biochem. Z.* **200:** 309–330.

Scheff, G., and Rabati, F. (1938). *Biochem. Z.* **298:** 101–109.

Seyderhelm, R. (1918). *Deut. Arch. klin. Med.* **126:** 95–147.

Shen, S. C., Fleming, E. M., and Castle, W. B. (1946). *Proc. Soc. Exptl. Biol. Med.* **63:** 419–422.

Spitz, S. (1946). *Military Surgeon* **99:** 555–572.

Suarez, R. M. (1933). *Puerto Rico J. Pub. Health Trop. Med.* **8:** 299–337.

Tallqvist, T. W. (1907). *Z. klin. Med.* **61:** 421–532.

Tötterman, G. (1938). *Acta Med. Scand.* **96:** 267–288.

Vint, F. W. (1941). *E. African Med. J.* **18:** 162–174.

Wakeman, A. M. (1929). *W. African Med. J.* **2:** 169 (not seen).

Wardle, R. A., and Green, N. K. (1941). *Trans. Roy. Soc. Can. Sect. V* [3] **35:** 85–97.

Weinman, D. (1938). *J. Infectious Diseases* **63:** 1–9.

Wells, H. S. (1931). *J. Parasitol.* **17:** 167–182.

Zwemer, R. L., and Culbertson, J. T. (1939). *Am. J. Hyg. Sect. C* **29:** 7–12.

# CHAPTER 18

# METABOLIC DISTURBANCES IN PARASITIC INFECTIONS

## I. INORGANIC SUBSTANCES

### A. Protozoan Infections

Increases in the potassium content of the blood plasma are pronounced especially during the febrile periods of human malaria (Pinelli, 1929; Andriadse, 1929; Zwemer, Sims, and Coggeshall, 1940), in avian malaria (Velick and Scudder, 1940), simian malaria (Zwemer, Sims, and Coggeshall, 1940; McKee *et al.*, 1946), in the terminal stages of trypanosomiasis (Zwemer and Culbertson, 1939; Ikejiani, 1946a, b), and bartonellosis (Kessler and Zwemer, 1944). The sources from which the potassium is derived are probably not uniform. A certain fraction unquestionably comes from destroyed red blood cells. In malaria, changes in permeability of the membrane of nonparasitized erythrocytes lead to a potassium depletion of the cells and hence to its increase in the plasma (Overman, 1948; Overman, Hill, and Wong, 1949). It is probable, however, that these two factors alone are insufficient to explain the potassium accumulation. It is likely that another source must be sought in damaged body cells other than erythrocytes. There are strong indications that in malaria the adrenal cortex, perhaps due to anoxia, may be involved in this release of potassium (Zwemer, Sims, and Coggeshall, 1940; Maegraith, 1948).

It has been assumed that the potassium accumulation together with shifts in other ions may lead to severe metabolic disturbances since an excess of potassium is very toxic and it has even been incriminated as responsible for death in malaria (Overman, 1947) and trypanosomiasis (Zwemer and Culbertson, 1939). This latter view is somewhat extreme, however. The potassium accumulation is well below the fatal level in malaria (Maegraith, 1948) and trypanosome-infected rats die at the same rate regardless of whether they have been made, prior to infection, resistant to potassium or not (Scheff and Thatcher, 1949).

Concomitant with the drop in potassium, the sodium and chlorine content of the erythrocytes increases in malaria (Overman, 1948), while the sodium content of the blood plasma is lowered, at least during the paroxysms (Flosi, 1944; Overman, Hill, and Wong, 1949). The plasma chlorine is usually normal; significant reductions have been observed only in cases with renal involvement (Lahille, 1915; Wakeman, 1929; Miyahara, 1936;

Ross, 1932; Fairley and Bromfield, 1934). No significant changes in blood chlorine seem to occur in *Leishmania* infections (Stein and Wertheimer, 1942), or in trypanosomiasis (Linton, 1930; Hudson, 1944), but a lowering of the chlorine content of the cerebrospinal fluid has been reported from human sleeping sickness cases (Sicé, 1930a). In chickens infected with *Eimeria tenella*, on the contrary, a marked rise in blood chlorine has been observed (Waxler, 1941a). The excess chlorine was in this case apparently derived from the tissues where a small decrease was found. Corresponding changes could be induced by artificial hemorrhage.

Very little is known about other ions. The inorganic blood phosphate has been found approximately normal in uncomplicated malaria but increased in blackwater fever (Ross, 1932; Wats and Das Gupta, 1934; Fairley and Bromfield, 1934). Lowered inorganic phosphate has, on the other hand, been described from human patients during paroxysms (Gall and Steinberg, 1947), and the inorganic phosphate of both red cells and plasma is lowered in simian malaria (McKee *et al.*, 1946). Normal blood calcium was found in experimental leishmaniasis (Stein and Wertheimer, 1942) and in malaria (Ross, 1932; Fairley and Bromfield, 1934; Wats and Das Gupta, 1934) in which also no significant changes in magnesium have been observed (Gall and Steinberg, 1947). Somewhat low serum iron values have been found, although not regularly, in infantile visceral leishmaniasis (Cacioppo, 1947).

## B. Helminth Infections

Changes in the inorganic blood constituents occurring as a consequence of helminthic infections have received but little attention. The available data have been summarized in Table 38 and indicate that, in general, no changes or only minor abnormalities have been reported. In no case have the latter been connected as yet with any specific pathological process or with any specific biological activity of the parasites.

Shearer and Stewart (1933) studied the mineral metabolism of young lambs infected with intestinal nematodes. They found a normal potassium and sodium balance but an abnormally low phosphorus and calcium retention. The calcium balance was in some cases even negative, that is, more calcium was excreted than absorbed. On the basis of these observations they assume a probable interference with skeletal growth. However, Andrews (1938) was unable to confirm these results. He emphasized that the mineral content of bones of normal and infected lambs did not show significant differences.

Very definite fluctuations of abnormal magnitude in phosphorus and calcium metabolism occur during trichinosis. According to Rogers' (1942) observations the excretion of inorganic phosphorus falls off markedly during

TABLE 38. Changes in inorganic constituents of the blood plasma or blood serum during infections with helminths

| HOST | PARASITE | K | Na | Ca | P | S | Cl | Fe | AUTHOR |
|---|---|---|---|---|---|---|---|---|---|
| Man<br>Rabbit<br>Rabbit<br>Cattle, sheep | Schistosoma mansoni<br>S. japonicum<br>Clonorchis sinensis<br>Fasciola hepatica | | | Normal<br>Decreased<br>Decreased | Normal<br>Increased<br>Increased | Increased<br>Increased | Normal<br><br>Slightly increased | | Pons (1937)<br>Hiromoto (1939)<br>Shigenobu (1932)<br>Balian (1940); Usuelli and Balian (1938) |
| Man | Diphyllobothrium latum | Irregular variations | | | | | | Usually normal, sometimes increased or decreased | Becker (1926); Hirvonen (1941) |
| Man, dog, guinea pig | Trichinella spiralis | | | Normal, rarely increased | Normal, rarely increased | | Normal | | Pierce et al. (1939); Hartman, Foote, and Pierce (1940); Beahm and Jorgensen (1941); Carrick (1944) |
| Man | Hookworms | Somewhat increased | Increased | Normal | Normal | | | | Villela and Teixeira (1929) |
| Sheep<br>Sheep | Haemonchus contortus<br>Trichostrongylus colubriformis | | | Normal or decreased | Normal<br>Normal or decreased | | | | Weir et al. (1948)<br>Franklin, Gordon, and Macgregor (1946) |

the initial stages of the infection, but rises to two or three times the normal level about 4 weeks after infection. The assimilation of calcium is decreased shortly after infection; it then rises, only to fall off again about 3 weeks after infection.

### C. Arthropod Infections

Drilhon (1936) presented data on the mineral content of the hemolymph of normal *Carcinus maenas* and of crabs infected by *Sacculina*. He found in the infected specimens a normal sodium and potassium content, but a rather marked increase in calcium and magnesium. He points out that these changes are somewhat similar to those occurring in normal crabs at the time of moulting.

## II. Carbohydrates

### A. Protozoan Infections

Disturbances in the carbohydrate metabolism seem to occur rather frequently in protozoan diseases. The main aspects studied are the blood sugar and the carbohydrate reserves. A comparative view of the relevant findings has been presented in Table 39.

Many studies have been done on experimental animals infected with pathogenic trypanosomes, the reason being that a rather acrimonious controversy arose as to the origin and significance of the terminal hypoglycemia and the lowered glycogen reserves as soon as the first papers dealing with these topics were published (Schern, 1925; Regendanz and Tropp, 1927). It gave rise to numerous subsequent studies.

It had been originally suggested that the pathogenic trypanosomes consume so much sugar in the blood stream of their hosts that the carbohydrate reserves of the latter would become exhausted. Such a severe strain would be put on the liver that its function would break down and the animals would in the end die of glycopryvic intoxication. In other words it was assumed that practically the entire pathological picture would be due directly to the sugar consumption of the parasites. This view, first proposed by Schern (1925, 1928) and subsequently accepted by several workers (von Fenyvessy, 1926; Scheff, 1928, 1932; Knowles and Das Gupta, 1927/28; Schern and Artagaveytia-Allende, 1936; Hoppe and Chapman, 1947), is not sufficient to explain the pathogenesis of the metabolic disturbance. While it is true that the pathogenic trypanosomes have an exceedingly high rate of sugar consumption (see Chapter 10), this theory is disproved by the following facts: 1. The terminal hypoglycemia cannot be due to a total exhaustion of the carbohydrate reserves, since it can be relieved temporarily by injections of adrenalin (Regendanz, 1929b; Regendanz and Tropp, 1927; Krijgsman, 1933) and since the blood sugar returns to a normal level even

TABLE 39. Blood sugar and glycogen reserves in parasitic infections

| HOST | PARASITE | BLOOD SUGAR | LIVER GLYCOGEN | MUSCLE GLYCOGEN | AUTHOR |
|---|---|---|---|---|---|
| Man | *Leishmania donovani* | Hypoglycemia in adults, hyperglycemia in children | | | Banerjee and Saha (1923); Auricchio (1924) |
| Dog | *L. donovani* | Normal | | | Stein and Wertheimer (1942) |
| Rat | Trypanosomes of the *lewisi* group | Usually normal, occasionally terminal hypoglycemia | | Normal (total body glycogen) | Regendanz and Tropp (1927); Regendanz (1929a); Linton (1929); Molomut (1947); von Brand et al. (1949) |
| Various small and large warm-blooded animals | Trypanosomes of the *evansi, brucei,* and *congolense* groups | Usually normal during greater part of infection with pronounced terminal hypoglycemia; rarely hyperglycemia during part of infection | Terminally usually very low, occasionally total depletion | Usually somewhat lowered; sometimes normal or even increased | Schern (1925, 1928); von Fenyvessy (1926); Regendanz and Tropp (1927); Dubois and Bouckaert (1927); Cordier (1927); Bruynoghe, Dubois, and Bouckaert (1927); Knowles and Das Gupta (1927/28); Zotta and Radacovici (1929a, b); Scheff (1928, 1932); Regendanz (1929b); Linton (1930a); Locatelli (1930); von Brand and Regendanz (1931); Tubangui and Yutue (1931); von Brand, Regendanz, and Weise (1932); Krijgsman (1933); von Jancsó and von Jancsó (1935a, b); Poindexter (1935); Browning (1938); French (1938d); Hudson (1944); Hoppe and Chapman (1947) |
| Man | *Trypanosoma gambiense* | Normal | | | Walravens (1931); Wormall (1932) |
| Man | *Plasmodium vivax, P. malariae, P. falciparum* | Frequently hyperglycemia in pyrexial stages, sometimes normal in all stages, sometimes hypoglycemia | | | De Langen and Schut (1917); Yoshida and Ko (1920); Massa (1927); Ruge (1929, 1935); Petersen (1926); Rudolf and Marsh (1927); Sinton and Hughes (1924); Williams (1927); Hughes and Malik (1930); Sinton and Kehar (1931); Zaun (1935); Gall and Steinberg (1947) |
| Monkey | *P. knowlesi* | Hypoglycemia | Decreased | | Fulton (1939) |
| Duck | *P. lophurae* | Terminal hypoglycemia | | | Marvin and Rigdon (1945) |
| Chicken | *Eimeria tenella* | Pronounced hyperglycemia | Normal or increased | Normal or decreased | Pratt (1940, 1941); Waxler (1941b) |

250

| Rat | *Bartonella muris* | Pronounced terminal hypoglycemia | | Linton (1929); Regendanz (1929a); Hoffenreich (1932); von Brand, Regendanz, and Weise (1932) |
|---|---|---|---|---|
| Rabbit | *Clonorchis sinensis* | Sometimes hyperglycemia, sometimes hypoglycemia | | Uyeno (1935a); Kawai (1937) |
| Sheep | *Fasciola hepatica* | Normal | | Balian (1940) |
| Man | *Schistosoma mansoni* | Usually normal, occasionally hyper- or hypoglycemia | | Day (1924); Erfan and Camb (1933); Pons (1937); Seife and Lisa (1950) |
| *Australorbis glabratus* | *S. mansoni* | | Decreased (total body glycogen) | von Brand and Files (1947) |
| *Physa occidentalis* | *Echinostoma revolutum* | | Decreased (total body glycogen) | Hurst (1927) |
| Man, dog, rabbit | *Trichinella spiralis* | Usually normal, occasionally hypoglycemia | | Augustine (1936); Harwood *et al.* (1937); Pierce *et al.* (1939); Hartman, Foote, and Pierce (1940); Hatieganu and Fodor (1942) |
| Man | *Ascaris lumbricoides* | Occasionally hypoglycemia | | Frank (1944) |
| Man | Hookworms | Normal | | Donomae (1927) |
| Dog | *Ancylostoma caninum* | | Normal | von Brand and Otto (1938) |

in fasting animals after the administration of trypanocidal drugs (Scheff, 1932). 2. Identical symptoms, terminal hypoglycemia and lowered glycogen reserves, occur in small laboratory animals like rats where the parasites reach levels of 2 to 3 billion per ml blood and in rabbits where so few organisms develop that they can be found frequently only with difficulty in the peripheral blood (von Brand and Regendanz, 1931). 3. The feeding of sugar to trypanosome-infected animals does perhaps slightly prolong the lives of the hosts, but only for short periods and does not prevent the development of the typical terminal hypoglycemia (Cordier, 1927; Angolotti and Carda, 1929; Bruynoghe, Dubois, and Bouckaert, 1927; Hoppe and Chapman, 1947).

It must be admitted that the actual mechanism responsible for the disturbance in carbohydrate metabolism during trypanosomiasis is not definitely established. It is possible that a toxic action is involved, as assumed by several investigators (Regendanz and Tropp, 1927; Zotta and Radacovici, 1929a; Locatelli, 1930; Krijgsman, 1933, 1936; von Brand, 1938; French, 1938d). It must be realized, however, that it has so far not been possible to demonstrate trypanosome toxins in a convincing manner (see Chapter 7).

There can be no doubt that the liver is involved. It has been shown that trypanosome-infected animals form considerably less glycogen from orally administered sugar than normal ones (von Brand and Regendanz, 1931) and that starving infected animals form little, or in the late stages of the disease, no glycogen at all from body proteins under the influence of cortisone (von Brand, Tobie, and Mehlman, 1951). It has furthermore been shown that the alimentary blood sugar curve of infected animals is abnormal (von Brand and Regendanz, 1931; Scheff, 1932; Bell and Jones, 1946) and that the utilization of fructose is impaired (Schern and Citron, 1913). In human infections no gross disturbance of the carbohydrate metabolism has been noted (Walravens, 1931; Wormall, 1932), but the patients studied were not in the last stage of the disease. Further progress concerning the question of the mechanism responsible for the disturbed carbohydrate metabolism will probably have to wait for studies on the cellular level. It does seem possible that changes in the enzymatic complex of the liver may be involved, or that regulatory, perhaps hormonal influences are at work.

In malaria, the evidence concerning disturbances of the carbohydrate metabolism of the host parallels to some extent that summarized for trypanosomiasis, with the difference that much fewer animal studies have been done. However, much more evidence involving human cases is available. As indicated in Table 39, the behavior of the blood sugar in humans is somewhat variable, but an appreciable rise of the sugar level during the pyrexic stages has been observed so often that its occurrence cannot be doubted. Definite indications exist also to the effect that the carbohydrate functions of the liver are impaired. Abnormalities in the blood sugar curve after administration of glucose or fructose have been described (Williams, 1927; Sinton and Hughes, 1924; Hughes and Malik, 1930), while, on the other hand, galactose tolerance tests gave approximately normal results in most cases (Lippincott et al., 1946).

It has been suggested that the rise in blood sugar during malarial paroxysms is due to an excessive breakdown of liver glycogen (Sinton and Kehar, 1931). The underlying cause, if indeed a primary damage of the liver is involved, may be anoxia. Maegraith (1948) pointed out in this connection that anoxia induced by low oxygen content of the ambient atmosphere induces in rats a transient hyperglycemia which is followed by hypoglycemia. This is due to an initial stimulation of the adrenals resulting in the release of an excess of adrenalin which raises the blood sugar if enough liver glycogen is available, but may lead to hypoglycemia when the glycogen stores are exhausted. This sequence of events bears a marked similarity to that assumed by Sinton and Kehar (1931) as explaining similar phenomena in malaria.

Experiments both on monkeys and ducks have shown that in the late stages of malarial infections a pronounced hypoglycemia occurs and that at least in monkeys the glycogen stores of the liver become largely exhausted (Fulton, 1939; Marvin and Rigdon, 1945), observations exactly parallelling those reported from trypanosome-infected animals and those found in bartonellosis (Table 39). Further comparative work is indicated in order to establish whether the mechanisms producing these identical symptoms are actually different, or whether they will ultimately be led back to a common cause which by necessity would then have to be rather unspecific.

The disturbance in carbohydrate metabolism occurring in infections of chickens with *Eimeria tenella* offers a somewhat different picture, since the most striking symptom is in this case a very pronounced hyperglycemia (Pratt, 1940; Waxler, 1941b) associated with a decrease in glycogen stores (Pratt, 1941). It had originally been assumed that the rise in blood sugar was a simple consequence of the severe hemorrhage characteristic for this disease. This explanation is probably far too simple. Daugherty (1950) recently has shown that homogenates from ceca of infected chickens inhibited glycolysis of chicken brain *in vitro*, but did not interfere with this tissue's degradation of fructose-1,6-phosphate. They did, in contrast to homogenates of uninfected ceca, interfere with the esterification of inorganic phosphate. On the basis of these observations it seems probable that some phases of the intermediate carbohydrate metabolism, especially the phosphorylative steps, are disturbed in coccidiosis. Whether a similar disturbance occurs in cases of liver coccidiosis has not yet been studied. In one unpublished experiment the present author observed that the blood sugar of a rabbit infected with *Eimeria stiedae* rose to an abnormal height after oral administration of sugar.

## B. Helminth Infections

Helminths do not seem to interfere as often or as severely as protozoa with the carbohydrate metabolism of their hosts. The most pronounced changes in blood sugar have been found in cases of parasitism involving the liver (*Clonorchis, Schistosoma*, see Table 39). Curiously enough, the glycogen picture seems not to have been studied yet in these diseases. In view of the fact that the sugar tolerance of rabbits infected with *Clonorchis* has been found abnormal (Uyeno, 1935a, Kawai, 1937), such a study seems worthwhile. This applies especially to schistosomiasis where the eggs of schistosomes produce extensive necrotic lesions. Therefore disturbances in the hepatic functions, including glycogen synthesis and detoxication mechanisms, should be expected to occur in severe cases. Glycosuria and even frank diabetes mellitus have been described from some human infections and the alimentary blood sugar curve was then highly abnormal (Day, 1924; Erfan and Camb, 1933; Seife and Lisa, 1950). It is evident that these conditions are due not only to liver damage, but to pancreas involvement. An infiltration of helminth eggs into the pancreas occurs (Seife and Lisa, 1950), but this alone cannot explain the diabetic conditions, since the latter ceases rapidly after anthelminthic medication (Day, 1924; Erfan and Camb, 1933).

Slight abnormalities in sugar tolerance have been described from humans parasitized by hookworms and there were some indications pointing towards a lowered sugar absorption (Saito, 1933; Firki and Ghalioungi, 1937). Minor irregularities in the galactose test were observed, though not in all cases, in human infections with *Schistosoma japonicum* (Lippincott *et al.*, 1947). A *Trichinella* infection, on the other hand, seems not to interfere materially with the carbohydrate metabolism of the host (Table 39); a normal sugar tolerance curve has been found in infected rabbits (Augustine, 1936). A curious observation which cannot as yet be assessed as to its true significance, is Lewis' (1928) finding that *Trichinella* larvae invade primarily glycogen-poor muscles.

## C. Arthropod Infections

*Carcinus* specimens parasitized by *Sacculina* seem not to store appreciable amounts of glycogen in their subcutaneous tissues as do normal crabs, at least before a moult. Smith (1913) assumes that this failure is responsible for the inability of sacculinized crabs to moult but whether this assumption is completely justified, remains to be seen. It should be remembered that in insects at least the moulting process is governed by hormonal processes. Smith (1913) furthermore found that normal animals kept the glycogen content of their hepato-pancreas fairly constant even during prolonged starvation, while in sacculinized specimens a progressive depletion occurred. He assumes that the former replenish the liver glycogen from the subcutaneous stores, but that the latter are unable to do so. The influence of the purely ectoparasitic *Gyge* on the glycogen stores of its host, *Upogebia*, apparently is of a different nature. Somewhat more glycogen was found in parasitized specimens than in normal ones (Hughes, 1940).

## III. Lipids

### A. Protozoan Infections

Abnormalities in lipid metabolism seem to occur in some trypanosome infections. Linton (1930a, b) reported normal cholesterol and lecithin content of the blood in *Trypanosoma lewisi* infections, while in rats infected with *Trypanosoma equiperdum* only the cholesterol was within normal limits. The lecithin level was increased in this case and in Surra infections of horses (Randall, 1934). Launoy and Lagodsky (1937) found an increased cholesterol level in the blood of rabbits infected with *Trypanosoma annamense*, while Scheff (1932), on the other hand, found in guinea pigs infected with *Trypanosoma equiperdum* normal cholesterol and phospholipid levels in the blood, but a rather considerable increase in neutral fat content. Exactly corresponding findings have been reported for the liver where a tenfold increase in neutral fat with normal cholesterol and phospholipid content was found (Scheff and Horner, 1932; Scheff and Csillag, 1936). Increases in the cholesterol, phospholipid, and fatty acid blood levels occur also in *Leishmania* infections of hamsters (Ada and Fulton, 1948).

The cholesterol and phospholipid level of the blood has been determined very often on malaria-infected human beings. The results of these studies are somewhat difficult to evaluate since there is no complete unanimity of opinion as to what exactly constitutes a normal cholesterol level. Much depends therefore on the base line selected for comparison. On the whole it does seem that the cholesterol of the blood of malarial patients is often abnormally low (Crespin and Zaky, 1919; Fairley and Bromfield, 1933; McQuarrie and Stoesser, 1932; Kopp and Solomon, 1943), but some authors reported approximately normal values (Ross, 1932; Greig, Hendry, and van Rooyen, 1934). Similarly, both normal and subnormal values have been encountered in simian malaria (Krishnan, Ghosh, and Bose, 1936; Kehar, 1937).

Variable findings have been reported concerning the phospholipid content of the blood of malarious humans and monkeys with a preponderance of low values (Kopp and Solomon, 1943; Whitmore and Roe, 1929; Kehar, 1937). There can be no doubt that the variations both in cholesterol and phospholipid blood levels are greater in malaria than during health and it is probable that they indicate a disturbance in lipid metabolism. It is possible that liver damage, perhaps due to anoxia, lies at its root (Maegraith, 1948).

### B. Helminth Infections

A definite disturbance in lipid metabolism occurs in infections with *Clonorchis sinensis*. Shigenobu (1932) found an increased cholesterol level in the blood of an infected rabbit and Uyeno (1935b) showed that liver homogenates of infected rabbits had a reduced hydrolyzing action on tributyrin (pH 8.04, 38°C). He reported also that extracts of such livers interfered with the fat splitting action of the pancreas lipase of cattle.

A raised blood cholesterol was found in rabbits infected with *Schistosoma japonicum* (Hiromoto, 1939) and in humans afflicted with filariasis (Boyd and Roy, 1930). Human beings and dogs infected with *Trichinella spiralis*, on the other hand, showed normal values (Pierce *et al.*, 1939; Hartman, Foote, and Pierce, 1940). The evidence is somewhat contradictory in so far as ancylostomiasis is concerned. Donomae (1927) reported a decrease in the fatty acid, lecithin, and cholesterol content of the blood serum, but an increase of all these fractions in the blood cells. Villela and Teixeira (1929), on the contrary, found an increased blood cholesterol level in ancylostomiasis patients.

### C. Arthropod Infections

Smith (1911, 1913) and Robson (1913) observed that the hepato-pancreas of *Carcinus* and *Inachus* parasitized by *Sacculina neglecta* was abnormally rich in fat and they also assumed an excess of fat in the blood of the host animals without, however, proving this latter point by chemical analysis. An increased fat content of the liver of male but not of female *Upogebia* parasitized by the ectoparasitic *Gyge branchialis* was also reported by Hughes (1940). Pierre (1935), on the other hand, found less fat in the liver of *Diogenes* infested by *Septosaccus cuenoti*, as did Reinhard and von Brand (1944) in that of *Pagurus* infected by *Peltogaster paguri*. In this latter case a generalized fat depletion in the entire body was establised definitely by quantitative determinations of the ether extract. No significant changes in fat content were found in *Pagurus* infected by the ectoparasitic *Stegophryxus hyptius* (Reinhard, von Brand, and McDuffie, 1947).

It appears then that various species of parasitic crustacea have a different influence on the fat content and presumably on the lipid metabolism of their hosts. The mechanism of this interference is rather obscure and its full elucidation will have to wait for metabolic studies. Smith (1911, 1913) and Robson (1913) are of the opinion that an alleged fat consumption of the parasites is responsible for the changes they observed. Reinhard and von Brand (1944), on the other hand, are inclined to incriminate the toxic action of sacculinids which has been demonstrated rather conclusively by Lévy (1923, 1924).

Only one observation is available which indicates abnormalities in fat metabolism of parasitized insects. Male *Thelia bimaculata* parasitized by *Aphelopus theliae* contain according to Kornhauser (1919) 47% more lipids than normal males.

## IV. NITROGENOUS SUBSTANCES

### A. Protozoan Infections

One of the most characteristic abnormal symptoms involving proteins concerns changes in the blood proteins. As the data summarized in Table 40 indicate, the changes in total protein content of the blood plasma are in most instances not very conspicuous, but considerable shifts in the various nitrogenous fractions occur. The albumin fraction usually is markedly reduced in infections with leishmanias, trypanosomes, and malarial parasites while the globulin fraction may be either increased, approximately normal, or occasionally even somewhat decreased. But even if below the norm, it is relatively less lowered than the albumin fraction. Even in this case, therefore, the albumin/globulin ratio is changed in favor of globulin. The lack of corresponding changes in the blood of monkeys infected with *Plasmodium inui* is understandable because this is, clinically, a very mild type of infection.

In so far as details of these changes are concerned, it has been observed that in kala-azar the euglobulin or $\alpha$-globulin was predominantly increased (Lloyd and Paul, 1928a, b; Most and Lavietes, 1947; Ada and Fulton, 1948). This has also been reported for malaria (Lloyd and Paul, 1929). Dole and Emerson (1945), using electrophoretic methods, found that the increase in the globulin fraction during a malarial attack was due to an increase in fibrinogen and gamma globulin. An increase in fibrinogen was also observed by Radosavljevic and Ristic (1926), while Kopp and Solomon (1943) found a decrease in fibrinogen. Dole and Emerson (1945) concluded that these changes are nonspecific and that hence diagnostic methods based on blood proteins such as those of Henry (1927) or Proske and Watson (1939) are unreliable. In view of this finding a reinvestigation of Lloyd and Paul's (1928b) claim that proteinographs in kala-azar are so characteristic as to be of diagnostic value, would seem indicated.

It is clear that a reduction in blood proteins, especially albumin, entails a lowering of the osmotic pressure of the blood and a consequence may be a loss of fluid from the capillaries leading to local edema. Such edemas do occur occasionally in malaria. Attempts to explain them on the basis of changes in concentration of the blood proteins have not been entirely successful (Boyd and Proske, 1941; Kopp and Solomon, 1941). The latter authors assume that the anemia developing in such cases may be a contributing factor. This is a very plausible explanation since, as Maegraith (1948) pointed out, the effects of anoxia on permeability of the endothelia of smaller vessels have been well established by physiologists.

Changes in proteins in principle similar to those described for the blood plasma occur in the cerebrospinal fluid during the later stages of human sleeping sickness. The protein content is then usually increased and this is due largely to an increase in the globulin fraction (Sicé, 1930b; Zschucke, 1932; Fairbairn, 1934). Hill (1948) has emphasized that the data concerning the total protein content of the cerebrospinal fluid during trypanosomiasis are difficult to evaluate accurately since various methods give quite different results and different authors report different results from normal persons with one and the same method.

The nonprotein nitrogen and the urea content of the blood appear usually approximately normal in protozoan infections. In the terminal stages of trypanosomiasis, where many vital functions fail, an increase in nonprotein nitrogen and urea occurs, while usually normal values are found during the earlier stages (Scheff, 1928; Linton, 1930a; Jones, 1933; Randall, 1934; Launoy and Lagodsky, 1936, 1937; French, 1938b, c). In malaria, these blood constituents show a sharp increase frequently in cases of partial or complete anuria, a natural consequence of nitrogen retention, which is especially frequent in blackwater fever (Lahille, 1915; Patrick, 1922; Owen and Murgatroyd, 1928). Cases of increased blood urea have, however, also been reported from malarial patients who showed no obvious signs of renal involvement and this has been interpreted as being due to an increased tissue catabolism (Driver, Gammel, and Karnosh, 1926).

In so far as the overall nitrogen metabolism is concerned, it has been established that trypanosome-infected animals show an increased urinary nitrogen excretion, while the fecal nitrogen stays within normal limits or is sometimes lower than normal. The general nitrogen balance is usually negative, especially in the late stages of the infections (Staehelin, 1904; Fellmer, 1909; Scheff, 1928; French, 1938a). These findings are probably related to the fact that the temperature of infected animals is somewhat raised. It is well known that similar changes occur under diverse febrile conditions so that they are not specific for trypanosomiasis.

## B. Helminth Infections

Changes in blood proteins have been observed especially in schistosomiasis and ancylostomiasis (Table 40). It is evident that they are essentially similar to those described in the previous section. Just as in leishmaniasis or malaria, the increase in globulin is due essentially to an increase in the euglobulin fraction (Faust and Meleney, 1924; Faust and Jones, 1934; Khalil and Hassan, 1932; Villela and Teixeira, 1929, 1930), leading to the same characteristic changes in the albumin/globulin ratio. In all these diseases, therefore, a disturbance of the synthesis ability of the liver must be assumed.

It has been assumed that in helminthic infections the lowered albumin content of the blood plasma plays an important part in causing edema, and this view has been expressed with a greater emphasis than in protozoan infections. Salah (1938) has emphasized the point for mixed cases of schistosomiasis and ancylostomiasis and Villela and Teixeira (1937) for ancylostomiasis. Salah (1938), however, conceded that the anemic condition of his patients may have been a contributing factor. It should be recognized, however, that this concept cannot be applied indiscriminately to all edemas of verminous origin. Filarial elephantiasis, for example, is due largely to an obstruction of the lymphatic vessels. Drinker *et al.* (1934) could produce marked edemas in dogs by blocking the lymphatics.

Ohta and Nishizaki (1936) found an increased urinary excretion of ammonia, amino acids, and purine compounds in rabbits infected with *Schistosoma japonicum*, indicating a generalized disorder of the protein metabolism and more specifically a faulty liver function. Further evidence to this effect is the observation that minced livers of infected rabbits formed only about one-quarter to one-third as much allantoin than did livers from normal animals when incubated aerobically with uric acid at pH 7.4 at 38°C (Nishizaki, 1938). The same author (Nishizaki, 1940) correlated an increased excretion of urinary amino nitrogen with disturbed deamination in the liver of rabbits infected with *Clonorchis sinensis*.

Interesting observations are available on the nitrogen metabolism during trichinosis. Flury and Groll (1913) found a nitrogen retention during the period of development of the larvae in the muscles. As soon as the capsules were formed, an increased nitrogen excretion began which was interpreted as resulting from the elimination of substances originating from destroyed muscle fibers. These studies were then amplified by Rogers (1941, 1942). According to his findings the protein digestion of infected rats fell to a low point 8 to 12 days after infection, possibly due to the secretion of antienzymes by the worms and to mechanical damage to the mucosa. The urinary nitrogen and urea output rose immediately after infection, fell off then and rose again sharply beginning about 13 days after infection. These changes were attributed to a toxic action of the parasites, since they occurred before a large scale invasion of the muscle fibers occurred. Urinary creatine and creatinine were markedly increased only after about 13 days, while the excretion of these compounds was abnormally low during the

TABLE 40. Changes in nitrogenous components of the blood plasma or blood serum during parasitic infections

| HOST | PARASITE | TOTAL PROTEINS | ALBUMIN | GLOBULIN | NONPROTEIN NITROGEN | UREA | AUTHOR |
|---|---|---|---|---|---|---|---|
| Man, dog | *Leishmania donovani* | Usually increased | Decreased | Increased | Usually normal, sometimes increased | | Sia and Wu (1921); Wu (1922); Lloyd and Paul (1928a, b); Giraud, Ciaudo, and Bernard (1935); Stein and Wertheimer (1942); Cooper, Rein, and Beard (1946); Most and Lavietes (1947) |
| Syrian hamster | *L. donovani* | Normal | Normal or decreased | Normal or increased | | | Stein and Wertheimer (1942); Gellhorn *et al.* (1946); Ada and Fulton (1948) |
| Man, small and large mammals | Various species of pathogenic trypanosomes | Usually normal | Often somewhat decreased | Increased | Usually normal, terminally increased | Usually normal, terminally increased | Wiechmann and Horsters (1927); Scheff (1928, 1932); Sicé *et al.* (1931); Linton (1930a); Trensz and Jardon (1933); Krijgsman (1933); Randall (1934); Launoy and Lagodsky (1936, 1937); French (1938a, b, c); Wilde and French (1945); Ikejiani (1946c) |
| Man | *Plasmodium vivax, P. malariae, P. falciparum* | Usually decreased | Usually decreased | Often increased, rarely decreased | Usually normal, sometimes increased | Usually normal, sometimes increased | Achard and Saint-Girons (1912); Patrick (1922); Boulay and Bédier (1924); Driver, Boulay and Karnosh (1926); Owen and Murgatroyd (1928); Wakeman and Morrell (1929); Lloyd and Paul (1929); Ross (1932); James (1939); Kopp and Solomon (1941); Boyd and Proske (1941); Kopp (1942); Dole and Emerson (1945); Glenn *et al.* (1946); Overman, Hill, and Wong (1949) |
| Monkey | *Plasmodium knowlesi* | Decreased | Decreased | Increased | | | Ghosh and Sinton (1935); Kehar (1936) |
| Monkey | *P. inui* | Normal | Normal | Normal | | | Ghosh and Sinton (1935) |
| Man | *Schistosoma haematobium* | Approx. normal | Decreased | Increased | Approx. normal | | Khalil and Hassan (1932) |

260

| Host | Parasite | | | | Reference |
|---|---|---|---|---|---|
| Man, rabbit | *S. japonicum* | Decreased | Increased | Increased | Faust and Meleney (1924); Hiromoto (1939) |
| Cattle, sheep | *Fasciola hepatica* | Slightly decreased | . | | Balian (1940) |
| Dog, rabbit | *Trichinella spiralis* | Decreased | Increased | Normal | Hartman, Foote, and Pierce (1940); Wright and Oliver-Gonzalez (1943) |
| Man | Hookworms | Usually decreased | Normal or slightly increased | Normal | Donomae (1927); Villela and Teixeira (1929, 1930, 1937) |
| Sheep | *Haemonchus contortus* | Decreased | | | Weir *et al.* (1948) |

first 4 to 12 days. This finding parallells somewhat the observation of Markowicz and Bock (1931) who reported a similar decrease in infected humans during the acute febrile stage, while in all fatal cases a sharp increase in output occurred before death. As in other conditions leading to extended lysis of necrotic tissues, guanidine or guanidine derivatives are at abnormally high levels in the blood of animals dying of trichinosis and it has been suggested that guanidinemia may be an important factor in producing many of the symptoms described for this infection (Harwood et al., 1937).

## C. Arthropod Infections

Damboviceanu (1928) and Drilhon (1936) both found that the total proteins of the hemolymph of sacculinized crabs was abnormally high and the former investigator states that this increase is due to a rise in the pseudoglobulin fraction.

### LITERATURE

Achard, C., and Saint-Girons, F. (1912). *Bull. mém. soc. méd. hôp. Paris* **28**: 749–758.
Ada, G., and Fulton, J. D. (1948). *Brit. J. Exptl. Path.* **29**: 524–529.
Andrews, J. S. (1938). *J. Agr. Research* **57**: 349–362.
Andriadse, N. (1929). Nachr. trop. Med. **2**: 704 (not seen).
Angolotti, E., and Carda, P. (1929). *Med. paises calidos* **2**: 431–435.
Augustine, D. L. (1936). *Am. J. Hyg.* **24**: 170–176.
Auricchio, L. (1924). *Pediatria* **32**: 704–711.
Balian, B. (1940). *Nuova Veterinaria* **18**, No. 6: 14–22, and No. 7: 10–16.
Banerjee, D. N., and Saha, J. C. (1923). *Calcutta Med. J.* **17**: 109–114.
Beahm, E. H., and Jorgensen, M. N. (1941). *Proc. Soc. Exptl. Biol. Med.* **47**: 294–299.
Becker, G. (1926). *Acta Soc. Med. Fennicae Duodecim* **7**: No. 9: 1–8.
Bell, F. R., and Jones, E. R. (1946). *Ann. Trop. Med. Parasitol.* **40**: 199–208.
Boulay, A., and Bédier, E. (1924). *Bull. soc. path. exotique* **17**: 282–284.
Boyd, M. F., and Proske, H. O. (1941). *Am. J. Trop. Med.* **21**: 245–260.
Boyd, T. C., and Roy, A. C. (1930). *Indian J. Med. Research* **17**: 949–951.
von Brand, T. (1938). *Quart. Rev. Biol.* **13**: 41–50.
von Brand, T., and Files, V. S. (1947). *J. Parasitol.* **33**: 476–482.
von Brand, T., and Otto, G. F. (1938). *Am. J. Hyg.* **27**: 683–689.
von Brand, T., and Regendanz, P. (1931). *Biochem. Z.* **242**: 451–468.
von Brand, T., Regendanz, P., and Weise, W. (1932). *Zentr. Bakt. Parasitenk. Abt. I. Orig.* **125**: 461–468.
von Brand, T., Tobie, E. J., Kissling, R. E., and Adams, G. (1949). *J. Infectious Diseases* **85**: 5–16.
von Brand, T., Tobie, E. J., and Mehlman, B. (1951). *Am. J. Hyg.* **54**: 76–81.
Browning, P. (1938). *J. Path. Bact.* **46**: 323–329.
Bruynoghe, R., Dubois, A., and Bouckaert, J. P. (1927). *Bull. acad. Roy. méd. Belg. Ser. 5* **7**: 142–156.
Cacioppo, F. (1947). *Boll. soc. ital. biol. sper.* **23**: 150–152.
Carrick, L. (1944). *Am. J. Clin. Path.* **14**: 24–27.
Cooper, G. R., Rein, C. R., and Beard, J. W. (1946). *Proc. Soc. Exptl. Biol. Med.* **61**: 179–183.

Cordier, G. (1927). *Compt. rend. soc. biol.* **96:** 971–973.

Crespin, J., and Zaky, A. (1919). *Compt. rend. soc. biol.* **82:** 216–218.

Damboviceanu, A. (1928). *Compt. rend. soc. biol.* **98:** 1633–1635.

Daugherty, J. W. (1950). *J. Parasitol.* **36** Suppl.: 42.

Day, H. B. (1924). *Trans. Roy. Soc. Trop. Med. Hyg.* **18:** 121–130.

De Langen, C. D., and Schut, H. (1917). *Geneesk. Tijdschr. Nederland.-Indie* **57:** 330 (not seen).

Dole, V. P., and Emerson, K. (1945). *J. Clin. Invest.* **24:** 644–647.

Donomae, I. (1927). *Japan. J. Med. Sci. Part 8* **1:** 385–412.

Drilhon, A. (1936). *Compt. rend.* **202:** 981–982.

Drinker, C. K., Field, M. E., Heim, J. W., and Leigh, O. C. (1934). *Am. J. Physiol.* **109:** 572–586.

Driver, J. R., Gammel, J. A., and Karnosh, L. J. (1926). *J. Am. Med. Assoc.* **87:** 1821–1827.

Dubois, A., and Bouckaert, J. P. (1927). *Compt. rend. soc. biol.* **96:** 431–433.

Erfan, M., and Camb, H. (1933). *J. Trop. Med. Hyg.* **36:** 348–349.

Fairbairn, H. (1934). *Trans. Roy. Soc. Trop. Med. Hyg.* **27:** 471–490.

Fairley, N. H., and Bromfield, R. J. (1933). *Trans. Roy. Soc. Trop. Med. Hyg.* **27:** 289–314.

Fairley, N. H., and Bromfield, R. J. (1934). *Trans. Roy. Soc. Trop. Med. Hyg.* **28:** 307–334.

Faust, E. C., and Jones, C. A. (1934). *Proc. Soc. Exptl. Biol. Med.* **31:** 478–479.

Faust, E. C., and Meleney, H. E. (1942). *Am. J. Hyg. Monogr. Ser.* **3:** 1–339.

Fellmer, T. (1909). *Z. Immunitätsforsch.* **3:** 474–477.

von Fenyvessy, B. (1926). *Biochem. Z.* **173:** 289–297.

Firki, M. M., and Ghalioungi, P. (1937). *Lancet* **232:** 800–802.

Flosi, A. Z. (1944). *Rev. Clin. São Paulo* **16:** 1–6.

Flury, F., and Groll, H. (1913). *Arch. exptl. Path. Pharmakol.* **73:** 214–232.

Frank, L. L. (1944). *Am. J. Digestive Diseases* **11:** 195–197.

Franklin, M. C., Gordon, H. McL., and Macgregor, C. H. (1946). *J. Council Sci. Ind. Research* **19:** 46–60.

French, M. H. (1938a). *J. Comp. Path. Therap.* **51:** 23–35.

French, M. H. (1938b). *J. Comp. Path. Therap.* **51:** 36–41.

French, M. H. (1938c). *J. Comp. Path. Therap.* **51:** 42–45.

French, M. H. (1938d). *J. Comp. Path. Therap.* **51:** 269–281.

Fulton, J. D. (1939). *Ann. Trop. Med. Parasitol.* **33:** 217–227.

Gall, E. A., and Steinberg, A. (1947). *J. Lab. Clin. Med.* **32:** 508–525.

Gellhorn, A., van Dyke, H. B., Pyles, W. J., and Tupikova, N. A. (1946). *Proc. Soc. Exptl. Biol. Med.* **61:** 25–30.

Giraud, P., Ciaudo, P., and Bernard, R. (1935). *Bull. soc. path. exotique* **28:** 922–929.

Ghosh, B. N., and Sinton, J. A. (1935). *Records Malaria Survey India* **5:** 173–202.

Glenn, P. M., Kaplan, L. I., Read, H. S., and Becker, F. T. (1946). *Am. J. Med. Sci.* **212:** 197–206.

Greig, E. D. W., Hendry, E. B., and van Rooyen, C. E. (1934). *J. Trop. Med. Hyg.* **37:** 289–295.

Hartman, E., Foote, M., and Pierce, H. B. (1940). *Am. J. Hyg.* **31:** Sect. D: 74–75.

Harwood, P. D., Spindler, L. A., Cross, S. X., and Cutler, J. T. (1937). *Am. J. Hyg.* **25:** 362–371.

Hatieganu, J., and Fodor, O. (1942). *Wien. klin. Wochschr.* **55:** 807–809.

Henry, A. F. X. (1927). *Gaz. hebd. sci. med.* **48:** 311.

Hill, K. R. (1948). *Trans. Roy. Soc. Trop. Med. Hyg.* **41:** 641–644.

Hiromoto, T. (1939). *Mitt. med. Ges. Okayama* **51:** 1637 (German summary).

Hirvonen, M. (1941). *Acta Med. Scand.* **108:** 63–72.

Hoffenreich, F. (1932). *Arch. Schiffs-u. Tropen-Hyg.* **36:** 141–144.

Hoppe, J. O., and Chapman, C. W. (1947). *J. Parasitol.* **33:** 509–516.

Hudson, J. R. (1944). *J. Comp. Path. Therap.* **54:** 108–119.

Hughes, T. A., and Malik, K. S. (1930). *Indian J. Med. Research* **18:** 249–257.

Hughes, T. E. (1940). *J. Exptl. Biol.* **17:** 331–336.

Hurst, C. T. (1927). *Univ. Calif. (Berkeley) Pubs. Zool.* **29:** 321–404.

Ikejiani, O. (1946a). *J. Parasitol.* **32:** 374–378.

Ikejiani, O. (1946b). *J. Parasitol.* **32:** 379–382.

Ikejiani, O. (1946c). *J. Parasitol.* **32:** 369–373.

James, C. S. (1939). *Med. J. Australia* **1939 I:** 759–761.

von Jancsó, N., and von Jancsó, H. (1935a). *Z. Immunitätsforsch.* **84:** 471–504.

von Jancsó, N., and von Jancsó, H. (1935b). *Z. Immunitätsforsch.* **86:** 1–30.

Jones, E. R. (1933). *Vet. Record* **13:** 1062–1063.

Kawai, T. (1937). *J. Formosan Med. Assoc.* **36:** 604–605 (English summary).

Kehar, N. D. (1936). *Records Malaria Survey India* **6:** 499–509.

Kehar, N. D. (1937). *Records Malaria Survey India* **7:** 117–129.

Kessler, W. R., and Zwemer, R. L. (1944). *J. Infectious Diseases* **75:** 134–137.

Khalil, M., and Hassan, A. (1932). *Bull. soc. path. exotique* **25:** 149–167.

Knowles, R., and Das Gupta, B. M. (1927/28). *Indian J. Med. Research* **15:** 997–1057.

Kopp, I. (1942). *J. Lab. Clin. Med.* **27:** 1054–1062.

Kopp, I., and Solomon, H. C. (1941). *Am. J. Med. Sci.* **202:** 861–886.

Kopp, I., and Solomon, H. C. (1943). *Am. J. Med. Sci.* **205:** 90–97.

Kornhauser, S. I. (1919). *J. Morphol.* **32:** 531–636.

Krijgsman, B. J. (1933). *Z. Parasitenk.* **6:** 1–22.

Krijgsman, B. J. (1936). *Z. vergleich. Physiol.* **23:** 663–711.

Krishnan, K. V., Ghosh, B. M., and Bose, P. N. (1936). *Records Malaria Survey India* **6:** 1–12.

Lahille, A. (1915). *Bull. mém. soc. méd. hôp. Paris* **31:** 905–917.

Launoy, L. L., and Lagodsky, H. (1936). *Compt. rend. soc. biol.* **122:** 1055–1058.

Launoy, L. L., and Lagodsky, H. (1937). *Bull. soc. pathol. exotique* **30:** 57–68.

Lévy, R. (1923). *Bull. soc. zool. France* **48:** 291–294.

Lévy, R. (1924). *Bull. soc. zool. France* **49:** 333–336.

Lewis, J. H. (1928). *Zentr. Bakt. Parasitenk. Abt. I. Orig.* **107:** 114–126.

Linton, R. W. (1929). *Ann. Trop. Med. Parasitol.* **23:** 307–313.

Linton, R. W. (1930a). *J. Exptl. Med.* **52:** 103–111.

Linton, R. W. (1930b). *J. Exptl. Med.* **52:** 695–700.

Lippincott, S. W., Marble, A., Ellerbrook, L. D., Hesselbrock, W. B., Engstrom, W. W., and Gordon, H. H. (1946). *J. Lab. Clin. Med.* **31:** 991–998.

Lippincott, S. W., Paddock, F. K., Rhees, M. C., Hesselbrock, W. B., and Ellerbrook, L. D. (1947). *Arch. Internal Med.* **79:** 62–76.

Lloyd, R. B., and Paul, S. N. (1928a). *Indian J. Med. Research* **17:** 583–610.

Lloyd, R. B., and Paul, S. N. (1928b). *Indian J. Med. Research* **16:** 529–535.

Lloyd, R. B., and Paul, S. N. (1929). *Indian J. Med. Research* **17:** 583–610.

Locatelli, P. (1930). *Compt. rend. soc. biol.* **105:** 449–451.

Maegraith, B. (1948). Pathological Processes in Malaria and Blackwater Fever. Charles C Thomas, Springfield, Ill.

Markowicz, W., and Bock, D. (1931). *Z. ges. exptl. Med.* **79:** 301–310.

Marvin, H. N., and Rigdon, R. H. (1945). *Am. J. Hyg.* **42:** 174–178.

Massa, M. (1927). *Pathologica* **19:** 535–541.

McQuarrie, I., and Stoesser, A. V. (1932). *Proc. Soc. Exptl. Biol. Med.* **29:** 1281–1283.
McKee, R. W., Ormsbee, R. A., Anfinsen, C. B., Geiman, Q. M., and Ball, E. G. (1946). *J. Exptl. Med.* **84:** 569–582.
Miyahara, H. (1936). *J. Formosan Med. Assoc.* **35:** 1092 (not seen).
Molomut, N. (1947). *J. Immunol.* **56:** 139–141.
Most, H., and Lavietes, P. H. (1947). *Medicine* **26:** 221–284.
Nishizaki, B. (1938). *Mitt. med. Ges. Okayama* **50:** 1418–1423.
Nishizaki, B. (1940). *Mitt. med. Ges. Okayama* **52:** 17–24.
Ohta, T., and Nishizaki, B. (1936). *Mitt. med. Ges. Okayama* **48:** 442–463.
Overman, R. R. (1947). *Federation Proc.* **6:** 174–175.
Overman, R. R. (1948). *Am. J. Physiol.* **152:** 113–121.
Overman, R. R., Hill, T. S., and Wong, Y. T. (1949). *J. Natl. Malaria Soc.* **8:** 14–31.
Owen, D. U., and Murgatroyd, F. (1928). *Ann. Trop. Med. Parasitol.* **22:** 503–530.
Patrick, A. (1922). *Ann. Trop. Med. Parasitol.* **16:** 451–455.
Petersen, W. F. (1926). *Proc. Soc. Exptl. Biol. Med.* **23:** 753–574.
Pierce, H. B., Hartman, E., Simcox, W. J., Aitken, T., Meservey, A. B., and Farnham, W. B. (1939). *Am. J. Hyg.* **29:** Sect. D: 75–81.
Pierre, M. (1935). *Trav. stat. biol. Roscoff* Fasc. **13:** 179–208.
Pinelli, L. (1929). *Riv. malariol.* **8:** 310–314.
Poindexter, H. A. (1935). *J. Parasitol.* **21:** 292–301.
Pons, J. A. (1937). *Puerto Rico J. Pub. Health Trop. Med.* **13:** 171–254.
Pratt, I. (1940). *Trans. Am. Microscop. Soc.* **59:** 31–37.
Pratt, I. (1941). *Am. J. Hyg.* **34** Sect. C: 54–61.
Proske, H. O., and Watson, R. B. (1939). *U. S. Pub. Health Service. Pub. Health Repts.* **54:** 158–172.
Radosavljevic, A., and Ristic, L. (1926). *Z. ges. exptl. Med.* **51:** 48–80.
Randall, R. (1934). *Philippine J. Sci.* **53:** 97–105.
Regendanz, P. (1929a). *Ann. Trop. Med. Parasitol.* **23:** 523–527.
Regendanz, P. (1929b). *Arch. Schiffs-u. Tropen-Hyg.* **33:** 242–251.
Regendanz, P., and Tropp, C. (1927). *Arch. Schiffs-u. Tropen-Hyg.* **31:** 376–385.
Reinhard, E. G., and von Brand, T. (1944). *Physiol. Zoöl.* **17:** 31–41.
Reinhard, E. G., von Brand, T., and McDuffie, S. F. (1947). *Proc. Helminthol. Soc. Wash. D. C.* **14:** 69–73.
Robson, G. C. (1911). *Quart. J. Microscop. Sci.* **57:** 267–278.
Rogers, W. P. (1941). *J. Helminthol.* **19:** 87–104.
Rogers, W. P. (1942). *J. Helminthol.* **20:** 139–158.
Ross, G. R. (1932). *Mem. London School Hyg. Trop. Med.* **6:** 1–262.
Rudolf, G. deM., and Marsh, R. G. B. (1927). *J. Trop. Med. Hyg.* **30:** 57–63.
Ruge, H. (1929). *Arch. Schiffs-u. Tropen-Hyg.* **33:** 567–587.
Ruge, H. (1935). *Arch. Schiffs-u. Tropen-Hyg.* **39:** 14–19.
Saito, W. (1933). *Mitt. med. Ges. Okayama* **45:** 2709 (not seen).
Salah, M. (1938). *Trans. Roy. Soc. Trop. Med. Hyg.* **31:** 431–436.
Scheff, G. (1928). *Biochem. Z.* **200:** 309–330.
Scheff, G. (1932). *Biochem. Z.* **248:** 168–180.
Scheff, G., and Csillag, Z. (1936). *Arch. exptl. Path. Pharmakol.* **183:** 467–477.
Scheff, G., and Horner, E. (1932). *Biochem. Z.* **248:** 181–188.
Scheff, G., and Thatcher, J. S. (1949). *J. Parasitol.* **35:** 35–40.
Schern, K. (1925). *Zentr. Bakt. Parasitenk. Abt. I. Orig.* **96:** 356–365 and 440–454.
Schern, K. (1928). *Biochem. Z.* **193:** 264–268.
Schern, K., and Artagaveytia-Allende, R. (1936). *Z. Immunitätsforsch.* **89:** 21–63.
Schern, K., and Citron, H. (1913). *Deut. med. Wochschr.* **39:** 1356–1357.

Seife, M., and Lisa, J. R. (1950). *Am. J. Trop. Med.* **30:** 769–772.

Shearer, G. D., and Stewart, J. (1933). *Univ. Cambridge, Inst. Animal Path., Rept. Director* **3:** 87–97.

Shigenobu, T. (1932). *Mitt. med. Ges. Okayama* **44:** 1099–1112.

Sia, R. H. P., and Wu, H. (1921). *Chinese Med. J.* **35:** 527–532.

Sicé, A. (1930a). *Bull. soc. path. exotique* **23:** 640–650.

Sicé, A. (1930b). *Bull. soc. path. exotique* **23:** 77–79, 222–243, and 307–331.

Sicé, A., Boisseau, R., Provost, J., and Deniel, L. (1931). *Bull. soc. path. exotique* **24:** 181–184.

Sinton, J. A., and Hughes, T. A. (1924). *Indian J. Med. Research* **12:** 409–422.

Sinton, J. A., and Kehar, N. D. (1931). *Records Malaria Survey India* **2:** 287–304.

Smith, G. (1911). *Quart. J. Microscop. Sci.* **57:** 251–265.

Smith, G. (1913). *Quart. J. Microscop. Sci.* **59:** 267–295.

Staehelin, R. (1904). *Arch. Hyg.* **50:** 77–96.

Stein, L., and Wertheimer, E. (1942). *Ann. Trop. Med. Parasitol.* **36:** 17–37.

Trensz, F., and Jardon, M. (1933). *Bull. soc. path. exotique* **26:** 442–444.

Tubangui, M. A., and Yutuc, L. M. (1931). *Philippine J. Sci.* **45:** 93–107.

Usuelli, F., and Balian, B. (1938). *Boll. soc. ital. biol. sper.* **13:** 45–46.

Uyeno, H. (1935a). *Mitt. med. Ges. Okayama* **47:** 673–691.

Uyeno, H. (1935b). *Mitt. med. Ges. Okayama* **47:** 1094–1108.

Velick, S. F., and Scudder, J. (1940). *Am. J. Hyg.* **31** Sect. C: 92–94.

Villela, G. G., and Teixeira, J. C. (1929). *Mem. inst. Oswaldo Cruz, Suppl.* **6:** 62–68.

Villela, G. G., and Teixeira, J. C. (1930). *Mem. inst. Oswaldo Cruz* **23:** 50–58.

Villela, G. G., and Teixeira, J. C. (1937). *J. Lab. Clin. Med.* **22:** 567–572.

Wakeman, A. M. (1929). *W. African Med. J.* **2:** 169.

Wakeman, A. M., and Morrell, C. A. (1929). *W. African Med. J.* **3:** 6–7.

Walravens (1931). *Ann. soc. belg. méd. trop.* **11:** 213–218.

Wats, R. C., and Das Gupta, B. M. (1934). *Indian J. Med. Research* **21:** 475–481.

Waxler, S. H. (1941a). *Am. J. Physiol.* **134:** 19–25.

Waxler, S. H. (1941b). *Trans. Am. Microscop. Soc.* **60:** 453–460.

Weir, W. C., Bahler, T. L., Pope, A. L., Phillips, P. H., Herrick, C. A., and Bohstedt, G. (1948). *J. Animal Sci.* **7:** 466–474.

Whitmore, E. R., and Roe, J. H. (1929). *Rept. Med. Dept. United Fruit Co.* **18:** 59 (not seen).

Wiechmann, E., and Horsters, H. (1927). *Deut. Arch. klin. Med.* **155:** 177–185.

Wilde, J. K. H., and French, M. H. (1945). *J. Comp. Path. Therap.* **55:** 206–228.

Williams, R. G. (1927). *Lancet* **213:** 1071–1073.

Wormall, A. (1932). *Biochem. J.* **26:** 1777–1787.

Wright, G. G., and Oliver-Gonzalez, J. (1943). *J. Infectious Diseases* **72:** 242–245.

Wu, H. (1922). *J. Biol. Chem.* **51:** 33–39.

Yoshida, T., and Ko, K. (1920). *J. Formosan Med. Assoc.* No. 206 and 207 (not seen).

Zaun, F. (1935). *Arch. Schiffs-u. Tropen-Hyg.* **39:** 363–373.

Zotta, G., and Radacovici, E. (1929a). *Compt. rend. soc. biol.* **102:** 129–130.

Zotta, G., and Radacovici, E. (1929b). *Arch. roumaines path. exptl. microbiol* **2:** 55–80.

Zschucke, J. (1932). *Z. Hyg. Infektionskrankh.* **114:** 464–500.

Zwemer, R. L., and Culbertson, J. T. (1939). *Am. J. Hyg.* **29** Sect C: 7–12.

Zwemer, R. L., Sims, E. A. H., and Coggeshall, L. T. (1940). *Am. J. Trop. Med.* **20:** 687–701.

# CHAPTER 19

# ENDOCRINOLOGICAL RELATIONSHIPS

## I. INFLUENCE OF PARASITES ON THE INTERNAL SECRETIONS OF THEIR HOSTS

Parasites localize occasionally in glands of internal secretion and it is quite probable that functional disturbances may occur. *Echinococcus* cysts have thus been found in the suprarenals and the thyroid (literature in Braun and Seifert, 1926), and microfilariae of *Dirofilaria immitis* have been observed accumulated in the anterior lobe of the pituitary (Hashimoto, 1939). A closer search through the literature would probably have revealed more such cases. It is, however, obvious that the situation offers only a modest physiological interest when mechanical damages to an innersecretory gland alone are involved and therefore no effort has been made to compile a complete list of such instances. Of greater interest are those cases where functional changes of innersecretory glands occur that are not due to mechanical interference and we will consider in the following sections primarily two glands, the suprarenals and the gonads.

### A. Suprarenals

Signs of insufficiency of the adrenal glands frequently have been reported from malaria, *e.g.*, asthenia, peripheral vascular failure, hypotension, and, in the algid form of pernicious malaria, lowered body temperature. In some chronic cases even pigmentation abnormalities of the skin and the mucous membranes similar to those of Addison's disease have been observed (Paisseau and Lemaire, 1916; Junior and Brandao, 1937; Marañon, 1939). Furthermore, many of the biochemical changes described in the preceding chapter, such as changes in the potassium, sodium, or sugar content of the blood could be due to adrenal insufficiency, but other mechanisms are just as possible. They have been mentioned previously. Pathological lesions of various kinds have been found in the adrenals of human malaria patients (Paisseau and Lemaire, 1916; Dudgeon and Clarke, 1917; Natali, 1934) and in some cases of simian malaria (Natali, 1934), although here they are not of regular occurrence (Rigdon and Stratman-Thomas, 1942). The cause of these lesions is not definitely known; anoxia alone may be responsible in many cases (Maegraith, 1948).

While it does seem probable that adrenal involvement may play a significant role in producing some of the symptoms in malaria, it is almost impossible to state so definitely in a given clinical case. Maegraith (1948) in this connection has pointed to Rigdon's (1942) and Kean and Taylor's (1946) work which has shown that in malaria a condition independent of adrenal damage can develop which simulates traumatic shock. It's symptoms, however, resemble very much those of adrenal insufficiency.

In chickens infected with *Plasmodium gallinaceum*, a hypertrophy of the adrenals has been observed (Nadel *et al.*, 1949) which reached its maximum about one day after the parasites had attained their highest level. It was due to an actual increase in tissue and not only to an increase in tissue fluid. Chemically, these suprarenals showed a normal percentage of ascorbic acid; the latter's absolute amounts, therefore, were actually increased (Josephson *et al.*, 1949). This seems to be a clear contrast to human and simian malaria where the entire body becomes depleted of ascorbic acid (Gerdjikoff, 1939; Wozonig, 1945; Sorce and Mutolo, 1946; McKee and Geiman, 1946; McKee, Cobbey, and Geiman, 1947).

Whether the adrenals are significantly impaired during trypanosomiasis is not known. It has been established that the ascorbic acid content of the adrenals is markedly reduced in rats infected with *Trypanosoma hippicum* (Nyden, 1948) and it may be significant that injections of adrenocorticotropic hormone do not relieve the terminal hypoglycemia of rats parasitized by *Trypanosoma equiperdum*, but this finding is not conclusive since cortisone also failed to raise the blood sugar (von Brand, Tobie, and Mehlman, 1951).

## B. Gonads

The problem of the influence of parasites on the gonads of their hosts is actually a dual one. First, the question arises, by what mechanism do the parasites damage the sex glands proper and, second, what are the consequences, if any, in respect to the internal secretions of the host. That is, in essence, how are the secondary sexual characters affected? We shall consider these questions for various groups of hosts.

*1. Worms.* Sollas (1911) found the male gonads of *Lumbricus herculeus* destroyed by parasites while the ovaries remained intact and in these specimens no clitellum had been formed. It seemed therefore justified to look upon the clitellum as a secondary sexual character subject to the influence of a hormone produced by the male glands. Subsequent surgical castration experiments, however, led to somewhat contradictory results (literature in von Buddenbrock, 1950). This case is mentioned only in passing since it is questionable whether animal parasites were responsible for the atrophy of the testes. Sollas (1911) is inclined to ascribe the castration to bacteria, but newer reviewers of the problem, such as Koller (1938), incriminate the protozoon *Monocystis* sp., which was also present in Sollas' worms. Whether this is justified, appears somewhat questionable.

*2. Snails.* The effects of trematode infections on the sex glands of snails vary with different species of parasites. In *Stagnicola emarginata angulata*, for instance, an infection with *Cercaria yogena* did not materially change the structure of the ovotestis. If the snail was parasitized by *Cercaria laruei* or *Diplostomum flexicaudum* the ovotestis was not completely destroyed, but no developing eggs could be found, while in infections with *Plagiorchis muris* the ovotestis completely disappeared (Pratt and Barton, 1941). Other examples of more or less complete parasitic castration of terrestrial and aquatic snails by larval trematodes can be found in the literature (Garnault, 1889; Szidat, 1924; Hurst, 1927; and others).

Little analysis of the effects of parasitic castration of snails has been done as yet; the best analysis available concerns *Bulimus tentaculatus* parasitized by *Pleurogenes medians* which has been studied by Neuhaus (1940, 1949). Large scale or even complete reduction of the gonads is brought about in this instance even by light infections. A starvation effect, incriminated by Szidat (1941), could be excluded by studies of the effects of prolonged starvation, as could mechanical destruction. The most probable mechanism is secretion of toxic substances by the parasites.

Little is known as to the effects of parasitism on the endocrine secretion of the snails, which is none too surprising in view of the paucity of information available concerning the role endocrine secretions play in the life of snails. Neuhaus (1940) has found that such secondary sex characters as the penis of *Bulimus* do not fully develop if juvenile specimens are attacked by the parasites. No reduction in the size of the penis occurred when adults became infected and this was somewhat unexpected since in some snails at least the secondary sex characters show marked variations in size depending upon the breeding cycle. This has been demonstrated especially for *Littorina* by Linke (1934). In these latter snails, parasitic castration by unspecified larval trematodes led to a reduction in size of the penis and such other accessory organs as the vesicula seminalis or the prostatic gland. It is hence probable that the gonads of snails do produce true sex hormones. This has been pointed out by von Buddenbrock (1950).

There is little evidence that parasitization of snails by trematodes leads to true sex reversal. Wesenberg-Lund (1931) did find that the female elements of the ovotestis of *Succinea putris* disappeared first while spermatogenesis proceded for some time after, but such a simple time interval in atrophy does not seem significant for the question at hand. More suggestive are the observations by Krull (1935) and Rothschild (1938) on the dioecious snail *Peringia ulvae*. In isolated cases females were found that had developed a penis, but so far there is no indication available pointing to a change in the primary sex characters. No evidence whatever of sex reversal was found in *Littorina* parasitized by several species of larval trematodes (Lysaght, 1943).

*3. Crustacea.* An extensive literature exists on the influence of rhizocephalan and epicaridean parasites on their crustacean hosts. Bibliographies on this subject will be found in the papers by Brinkmann (1936); Reverberi (1944/45); Veillet (1945), and Baffoni (1949). Only the most important observations and their implications can be discussed here.

Starting from Giard's (1886) initial observations that sacculinid parasites cause a "parasitic castration" of their hosts, subsequent information shows that the effects of the parasites on the sex characteristics of their hosts can be quite different, both as far as primary and secondary sex characters are concerned. The differences are unquestionably in part due to a different action of various species of parasites, but differences in reaction of different hosts to the same parasite also occur. Some parasites lead to a more or less complete atrophy of the male and female gonads of their hosts; an example is *Peltogaster curvatus* which castrates *Pagurus meticulosus* and *Pargurus prideauxii* (Potts, 1906). In other instances only the ovaries are destroyed, while the gonads of male specimens remain normal; an example for this possibility is *Pagurus pubescens* parasitized by *Peltogaster paguri* (Reinhard, 1942). Finally, cases exist in which the gonads of both sexes stay essentially unaltered. This, for instance, happens in *Munida sarsi* infested with *Triangulus boschmai* (Brinkmann, 1936).

When the gonads are not completely destroyed, changes in their structure and possibly function may occur. Of some interest here is the observation that male gonads not too rarely assume characteristics of ovaries. What is probably the most pronounced example along this line has been reported by Okada and Miyashita (1935) who found several specimens of *Eriocheir sinensis* parasitized by *Sacculina* in which the testicular tissue had been replaced almost completely by ovarian tissue. Von Buddenbrock (1950) classifies this as a case of complete sex reversal. Some caution is necessary in stating categorically that this effect was due exclusively to the parasites. It is well known that, especially in decapods, ovarian elements appear rather frequently in the testes of nonparasitized specimens (examples in Brinkmann, 1936; Forsman, 1938; and Baffoni, 1948).

In so far as secondary sex characters are concerned, changes occur especially on the pleopods and the abdomen. A bewildering multitude of alterations has been described and, just as in the case of the primary sex characters, different combinations exist. Good examples are the modifications occurring in pagurids under the influence of rhizocephala and epicaridea. Reinhard and Buckeridge (1950) have pointed out that four possibilities exist, ranging from modifications in both sexes to no change in either sex (Table 41).

When a male crustacean is affected, the changes are usually those

TABLE 41. Effect of rhizocephala and epicaridea on the secondary sex characters of hermit crabs (essentially after Reinhard and Buckeridge, 1950)

| CATEGORY | PARASITE | HOST | MALE PLEOPODS | FEMALE PLEOPODS | AUTHOR |
|---|---|---|---|---|---|
| I | *Peltogaster paguri*<br>*P. curvatus*<br>*Athelges paguri* | *Pagurus cuanensis*<br>*P. prideauxii*<br>*P. bernhardus* | Modified<br>Modified<br>Modified | Not modified<br>Not modified<br>Not modified | Nilsson-Cantell (1926)<br>Baffoni (1947)<br>Giard (1887) |
| II | *Peltogaster curvatus*<br>*P.* sp. | *Pagurus meticulosus*<br>*P. samuelis* | Modified<br>Modified | Modified<br>Modified | Potts (1906)<br>Shiino (1931) |
| III | *Peltogaster paguri*<br>*Paguritherium alatum* | *Pagurus bernhardus*<br>*P. longicarpus* | Not modified<br>Not modified | Modified<br>Modified | Giard (1887)<br>Reinhard and Buckeridge (1950) |
| IV | *Peltogaster paguri*<br>*P. paguri*<br>*Stegophryxus hyptius*<br>*Athelges prideauxii* | *Anapagurus chiroacanthus*<br>*Pagurus pubescens*<br>*P. longicarpus*<br>*P. prideauxii* | Not modified<br>Not modified<br>Not modified<br>Not modified | Not modified<br>Not modified<br>Not modified<br>Not modified | Nilsson-Cantell (1926)<br>Reinhard (1942)<br>Thompson (1901)<br>Baffoni (1947) |

characteristic for femininization: Female pleopods appear, the shape of the abdomen approaches that of the female, and so on. The modifications appearing in female hosts are not as pronounced as those found in males and they never appear as masculinization. Symptoms of hyperfemininization may be found, such as the precocious assumption of the mature abdomen in juvenile females of *Callinectes sapidus* parasitized by *Loxothylacus texanus*. Other changes, however, especially the changes in the pleopods appearing in this case are best interpreted as due to suppressed development (Reinhard, 1950).

Various theories have been advanced in order to account for all these different effects. Smith (1911, 1913) rejected the idea that sex hormones were involved. He assumed that sacculinid parasites act as an accessory ovary withdrawing so much food, especially fat, from the host as to force it to elaborate more and more of this "yolk" material, thus changing the whole metabolism of a parasitized male crab to that characteristic for a female. This shift in metabolism would be responsible for the atrophy of the gonads and would bring about the alterations of the secondary sex characters. However, Brinkmann (1936) invalidated this theory by showing that in *Munida* parasitized by *Triangulus munidae* the host's gonads atrophy while the parasite is still internal and shows no signs of active fat resorption.

Biedl (1913) suggested that the femininization of parasitized male crabs may be due to female sex hormones elaborated by the parasites, an explanation which has not found favor because the rhizocephala are hermaphrodites. Von Buddenbrock (1950) pointed out that this theory could be saved if the parasites were protandric, as hermaphrodites belonging to many other groups are. It is difficult to see, however, how in that case immature parasites could be responsible for the initiation of the changes.

Lipschütz (1924) and van Oordt (1928) developed the idea that the castrated males correspond to neutral individuals, the neutral form resembling the female crab morphologically. This view, however, completely neglects the hyperfemininization phenomena observed in parasitized females and it seems quite impossible to explain them on this assumption.

The most versatile explanation is unquestionably due to Goldschmidt (1931). According to his theory of intersexuality both sexes contain genes producing masculinizing and femininizing substances, the quantitative balance between the two deciding the sex of an individual. Imbalance between the substances would result in intersexuality and he considers the parasitized male crabs as intersexes. Reinhard (1950) has pointed out that Goldschmidt disregards the modified females in this explanation, but that hyperfemininization phenomena could well result either from a strengthening of the female reaction or a depression of the male reaction.

Reverberi (1944/45) considered it as possible that the parasite itself could produce a femininizing substance, a concept somewhat reminiscent of Biedl's (1913) view. Reinhard (1950) has emphasized that Goldschmidt's concept fails to account for the alteration in the pleopods of females. He assumes that their development is controlled by an ovarian hormone which obviously would fail to function properly in castrated animals, and he emphasizes that the production of ovarian hormones in crustaceans has been made very probable according to studies of Haemmerli-Boveri (1926), Le Roux (1931a, b), and Callan (1940). In summing up then, it does seem that the intersexuality hypothesis fits the observations best.

A case of parasitic castration of a crustacean by a worm has been studied by Le Roux (1931a, b). He found that the acanthocephalan, *Polymorphus minutus*, does not interfere with the normal function of the testes of *Gammarus pulex*, but that in the female gammarids the ovaries are arrested, showing juvenile characteristics. Some changes in the secondary sexual characteristics of the female host, especially the oostegites, were observed, but an attempt to analyze the nature of these changes by means of artificial castration was not entirely successful. No ovaries were found in a *Leander* parasitized by a larval gordiacean of the genus *Nectonema* (Nouvel and Nouvel, 1935).

Protozoa have been incriminated with greater or lesser emphasis for the parasitic castration of crustacea. Smith (1905) found destruction of the testes and femininization of the external characteristics of *Inachus dorsettensis* parasitized by *Aggregata eberthi*. Quite similar findings were reported by Forsman (1938) for a *Diastylis* specimen whose testes had been destroyed by an unidentified sporozoon. On the other hand, infestation with *Amallocystis fasciatus* appears to have no influence on male *Gnatophausia zoea* and *Gnatophausia ingens*, but arrests the development of the oostegites in females (Fage, 1940). Finally, Baffoni (1950) observed that an *Aggregata* species produced a measurable reduction in size of the ovaries of *Leander squilla*, but had no influence on the male gonads.

*4. Insects.* The reproductive system of insects is frequently severely affected by parasitic nematodes or parasitic insects. It is characteristic that the female hosts are often more deeply altered than the males, although some exceptions to this rule exist. On the whole, however, a certain contrast to the crustacea is evident in this respect where, as shown in the preceding section, the males are in most cases more profoundly changed than are the females.

The influence of parasitic nematodes on insects will be considered first. Cases exist where only the female hosts are sterilized, while the gonads of the males remain more or less normal. Examples are *Hylemia antiqua* parasitized by *Heterotylenchus aberrans* (Bovien, 1937), or various species of grasshoppers attacked by *Agamermis decaudata* or *Mermis subnigrescens* (Christie, 1936, 1937). In other instances the gonads of both male and female hosts are destroyed as in *Oscinella frit* or *Sciara coprophila* under the influence of *Tylenchinema oscinellae* and *Tetradonema plicans*, respectively (Goodey, 1931; Hungerford, 1919). No case seems to be on record in which only the male gonads were destroyed.

The external appearance of the insects mentioned shows little, if any change, under the influence of parasitic nematodes. The situation is entirely different in ants infected by mermithids. An extensive literature on this subject exists which cannot be reviewed fully. Some more recent papers giving further references are those by Wheeler (1928), Vandel (1930, 1934), Gösswald (1929, 1930, 1938), and Kloft (1949). The effects of this type of parasitism are complicated and variable. On the one hand parasitized males, females, workers, and soldiers are found that are hardly modified externally, and such findings are especially frequent in the case of male ants. In other instances infected females occur which, on the whole, resemble normal specimens, but are easily recognized by such characters as a smaller head, shorter wings, and a distended gaster. The term mermithogynes is applied to this type of modification. In still other cases the afflicted ants exhibit externally mixed characters of males, workers, and soldiers; they are then called intercastes. Vandel (1930) distinguished two, Wheeler (1928) five different types of such intercastes. The extent of the above modifications seems to depend, according to Gösswald (1938), mainly on the following three factors: 1. The varying disposition of different species of ants, 2. The size of the afflicted specimens, usually only the large castes being readily modifiable, and 3. the time of infection, the modifications becoming the more pronounced the younger the ant was at the time of infection. Internally, first the flight muscles become reduced, followed by the abdominal fat body and the gonads. Kloft (1949) who established this sequence credits toxic excretions by the parasites only with an acceleration of the destruction of the germ cells, but he seems on the whole inclined to put the chief responsibility on an increased energy demand of the parasitized organism.

Interesting also is another instance of *Mermis* parasitism, the parasitic castration of *Chironomus*. Especially important here is the observation reported by Rempel (1940) that the internal sex organs of the female hosts are completely destroyed. However, in their stead male characteristics, especially frequently internal male genital ducts, and occasionally even testes, appear, while the external female genitalia or other external sex differentiating characters remain unaffected. In some of the insects the external genitalia were masculinized. Rempel (1940) considers his chironomids as intersexes.

Turning to insects parasitized by other insects, the best known case is that of stylopization. Under this term the parasitism of *Stylops* and related species of strepsiptera especially in hymenoptera is known, although many parasitic insects occur in a variety of other groups of insects as well. Some of these will be mentioned below.

The consequences of stylopization both on the primary and secondary sex characters of the hosts vary. In *Andrena*, for example, the ovaries are usually reduced to such an extent that egg production is prevented while the testes are not seriously interfered with (Smith and Hamm, 1914). In *Polistes*, on the other hand, the gonads of both sexes remain often approximately normal, although the size of the ovaries is frequently abnormally small (Rabaud and Millot, 1929). The secondary sex characters may remain entirely unchanged, such as in *Polistes, Vespa*, and others, while in different species, *e.g. Andrena*, more or less pronounced alterations are induced. They consist especially in changes in pigmentation of the head which in normal specimens shows a pronounced sexual dimorphism, changes in pigmentation of the mandibles, antennae, legs, and abdomen, or in female bees in the loss or at least the reduction of the hairs on the hind legs used in pollen collecting. This last morphological change is interestingly enough accompanied by a loss of the instinct of pollen collecting (Pérez, 1886; Smith and Hamm, 1914). On the whole such parasitized bees and wasps resemble intersexes (Vandel, 1933).

Various views have been expressed as to the cause of these changes. Salt (1927, 1931) is of the opinion that hymenoptera feeding their larvae in closed cells, such as *Andrena, Odynerus, Sphex*, or *Chlorion*, show changes upon parasitization because the parasite utilizes part of the limited food supply for itself, thus exposing the host larvae to partial starvation. In *Polistes, Belonogaster*, or *Vespa*, on the contrary, the larvae are fed in open cells where the food supply can be replenished when need arises. Hence no distinct state of starvation is produced and the animals remain more or less normal.

Similarly a metabolic, rather than a hormonal, disturbance is cited by Kornhauser (1919) to account for the changes observed by him in the cicada, *Thelia bimaculata*, infected with *Aphelopus theliae*. In this case the external appearance, especially the pigmentation, of the male was changed indicating an external femininization, despite the fact that the testes remained essentially unchanged.

It is, however, questionable whether it is justified to disregard sex hormones completely. Von Buddenbrock (1950) has emphasized that at least one observation exists which seems to indicate the involvement of sex hormones, *i.e.* Buchner's (1925) findings concerning *Euacanthus*. The gonads of this cicada are completely destroyed when parasitized by fly larvae. The female host possesses mycetomes which have so-called "Infektionshügel," that is, structures indispensable for the hereditary transmission of the symbionts and hence justifiedly classified amongst the secondary sex characters. In parasitized specimens these specific structures are atrophied while the mycetomes proper are otherwise entirely normal. It is, however, to be admitted that the entire question of sex hormones in insects is still controversial, many authors vehemently denying their existence. A review of this question is beyond the scope of the present account; the interested reader is referred to von Buddenbrock (1950) for a recent review.

A very interesting case is that of the squash bug, *Anasa tristis*, parasitized by the tachinid fly, *Trichopoda pennipes*, studied by Beard (1940). A second instar parasite damages only that gonad of the host lying on the side of attachment of the parasite, while the opposite one still operates normally. The latter becomes affected only when the parasite reaches the third instar. Beard (1940) emphasizes that no mechanical destruction occurs; the atrophy must be due to an indirect action which "is not in the nature of a systemic effect, nutritional or otherwise." This is indicated by the fact that both gonads do not degenerate simultaneously. Beard (1940) does not offer a definite explanation; one could think of a slowly diffusing toxic substance produced by the parasite.

Numerous observations by various authors, summarized by Varley and Butler (1933) indicate that parasites belonging to the Stylopidae, Tachinidae, Braconidae, and Chalcididae frequently accelerate the development of their hosts. This is indicated by the fact that parasitized larvae pupate prematurely and this phenomenon is especially pronounced when larvae pupate instead of undergoing diapause. Apparently two mechanisms are involved. In some instances, for example *Lucilia*, the sting of the ovipositing insect induces a shock breaking the diapause and inducing pupation. Other hosts, *e.g. Liparia* or *Urophora*, do not show any sign of shock upon being stung and pupation occurs only some time after parasitization. Since it is well known that pupation of many insects has a hormonal basis, it might be of interest to test whether the parasites produce such a hormone. Strictly speaking these last observations do not belong in the section dealing with the influence of sex hormones; they are mentioned on this occasion, however, simply to keep the observations on insect parasitism together.

5. *Vertebrates.* Flukes of the genus *Prosthogonimus* live in the oviduct and the bursa Fabricii of birds, especially ducks, hens, and pheasants. The infection results in a severe curtailment of egg production or complete stoppage of the latter even in nonfatal cases (Kotlan and Chandler, 1925; Macy, 1940; Wehr and Christensen, 1942). Whether, or to what extent, an interference with the host's sex hormones occurs is questionable; suggestive pathological changes in the ovary have been described.

Some interference with the internal secretions of the gonads due to parasitism has also been observed in man. It is a well-established fact that heavy hookworm infections delay puberty. In such infections adult males can become totally or partially impotent, and amenorrhea is frequent in women. Some such cases were described recently by Chang and Tong (1949). These symptoms are due probably to the general debilitating influence of the infection rather than to a specific influence of the parasites on the sex hormones and hence are not of particular interest for the present discussion.

## C. Miscellaneous Observations

Chagas (1911, 1916) has assumed that *Trypanosoma cruzi* was responsible for the endemic goiter frequently found in some areas of Brazil. Subsequent work (Kraus, 1926 and others; see literature in Yorke, 1937) disproved this assumption and at present there is no inclination to ascribe to this parasite any influence on the thyroid gland.

Whether changes in the internal secretions of the pancreas are induced by parasites has not been decided definitely. Hermann (1934) made histological observations showing changes in the islets of Langerhans of chickens infected with coccidia, unspecified nematodes, and *Davainea*. *Hymenolepis* and *Drepanidotaenia* produced little, if any, changes. Hermann (1934) states that infected animals show convulsions that could be caused by hypoglycemia since at least temporary relief is achieved by subcutaneous administration of sugar. He has not, however, demonstrated the hypoglycemia by actual blood sugar determinations and, as shown in a previous chapter, coccidial infections lead usually to hyper- rather than hypoglycemia.

It has been observed rather frequently that snails infected by larval trematodes are larger than usual (Risbec, 1930; Rothschild, 1936, 1941; Rothschild and Rothschild, 1939; Wesenberg-Lund, 1934; Linke, 1934). This, however, is no general rule as the studies of Cort *et al.* (1940), Lysaght (1943), and Ihm (1951) have shown. What causes gigantism of infected snails, such as *Peringia ulvae*, which is the best authenticated case, is obscure. These observations are mentioned here only because in many animals innersecretory glands have a profound influence on growth. It might be worthwhile to reinvestigate the parasitized snails from this standpoint.

## II. Influence of the Host's Internal Secretions on Parasites

### A. Gonads

Sex differences occur in infections with parasitic protozoa. It is well known that *Trichomonas foetus* and *Trichomonas vaginalis* are primarily parasites of the female genital tract. They are, however, not exclusively so; infections of bulls with the former parasite are largely responsible for the dissemination of the infection among cattle, although nonveneral infections also occur (Andrews and Miller, 1936). The same situation prevails in principle in the case of *Trichomonas vaginalis*, although nonveneral transmission seems in that case to be of greater importance. In any event there is at present no indication that the sex hormones of the host play a role in the development of the parasites. This is also true in the case of mosquitoes infected with malarial parasites. Only female mosquitoes are infected, simply because they alone are blood suckers and hence become exposed to the infection.

There remain, however, a few infections where hormonal influences may be of importance. Hauschka (1947) found male mice more susceptible to infections with *Trypanosoma cruzi* than females as evidenced by the intensity of the blood- and tissue infections, the loss of weight, and the survival time. But it is not yet known whether this difference is due to a direct influence of the sex hormones of the hosts on the parasites, or to a response of the latter to metabolic sex differences of the hosts. Young female chickens are slightly more susceptible than males to *Plasmodium gallinaceum*, more of the former's erythrocytes becoming parasitized, and the exoerythrocytic stages appear earlier in their tissues. A direct action of sex hormones appears unlikely since administration of male or female sex hormones did not alter the difference in reaction (Bennison and Coatney, 1948). Sexually mature, egg-laying ducks, on the other hand, are in general much more resistant to *Plasmodium lophurae* than males, although exceptions occur (Trager, 1948). This resistance depends in part at least on some substance present in the blood plasma which has an antiplasmodial effect (Trager and McGhee, 1950), but the situation is so complex that a complete analysis has not yet succeeded (Trager, Stauber, and BenHarel, 1950).

Chernin (1950) found that chronic *Leucocytozoon simondi* infections of ducks relapsed when the birds began egg-laying, regardless of whether they did so under normal physiological conditions or whether the onset of sexual maturity was changed by different illumination of the birds. The exact mechanism has not been elucidated, but it is quite possible that it is hormonal. This is also true in the case of the protozoa living in the rectum of frogs. It is known that they show a definite sexual cycle which depends on the sexual cycle of their hosts. Bieniarz (1950) thinks it probable that gonadotropin released from the anterior pituitary may play a role. He could show experimentally that the injection of human pregnancy urine into the cloaca of a male frog induced the beginning of the sexual cycle of *Nyctotherus*. No similar effect was obtained, however, *in vitro*. The chorionic gonadotropin of the urine cannot, therefore, alone have been responsible.

In so far as invertebrate hosts are concerned, Burtt's (1946) observations may be mentioned. He found during transmission experiments that fewer female than male *Glossina morsitans* became infected with *Trypanosoma rhodesiense*. The mortality rate of the females was, however, appreciably higher than that of the males and doubts must therefore remain whether this difference was real, especially since Duke (1930, 1933) previously had found rather a slight preponderance of infections in female flies.

Social habits resulting in differential exposure, can be made responsible for sex differences in some human helminth infections. They are obviously of as little physiological interest as the differences in parasitic incidence due to various eating habits and will therefore not be reviewed here. Similar explanations cannot apply to some observations available for animal infections. Whitlock (1937) found more female than male partridges infected with *Syngamus trachea* and he assumes that the strain of egg production may have lowered the resistance of the female birds. Clapham (1939) confirmed Whitlock's (1937) observation on a larger scale but she does not concur with his explanation, since the infections occurred primarily in immature birds.

The case of *Cysticercus fasciolaris* has been analyzed somewhat more fully. It has been well established (Curtis, Dunning, and Bullock, 1933; Campbell, 1939; Campbell and Melcher, 1940) that male rats are more susceptible to the infection with this worm than females and there is good evidence indicating that the sex hormones of the host are involved. Campbell and Melcher (1940) showed that castration increased the degree of infection in female hosts, while decreasing it in males. Administration of an androgen to castrated females lowered their resistance still farther while the injection of estrogen into castrated males had the opposite effect.

Relevant data are also available for *Hymenolepis diminuta*. Chandler (1943) and Addis and Chandler (1944) observed that the absence of an unidentified growth factor contained in brewers yeast from the diet of rats resulted in growth retardation of the tapeworms in female but not in male rat hosts. Addis (1946) then found that castration of male hosts retarded the growth of the worms. Administration of testosterone or progesterone to castrated rats resulted in normal sized worms regardless of whether the hosts were kept on a normal or a deficient diet and these results were closely parallelled when noncastrated but immature males were used instead of castrated adults. Beck and Chandler (1950) more recently stated that the same factors influenced the egg production of *Hymenolepis*, testosterone and progesterone increasing the egg production of the worms developed in castrated males or in females kept on a deficient diet. Gonadotropic hormone stimulated the egg production of worms both in male and female hosts after it had been depressed by a deficient host diet.

Few corresponding data are available as yet for other groups of worms. Ackert and Dewhirst (1950) reported recently that the injection of diethylstilbestrol enhanced the resistance of chickens to *Ascaridia galli*, significantly fewer worms developing in the injected than in the noninjected host animals. Similarly, Sadun (1948) had observed that the injection of testosterone or alpha-estradiol into immature male or female chickens, respectively, increased the resistance of the birds against *Ascaridia*. Estradiol seemed to cause an initial growth retardation, but later a faster than normal growth of the worms, while exactly the opposite held true for testosterone.

Of considerable interest are the observations of Goodey (1931) on *Tylenchinema oscinella*, a nematode parasite of the frit fly, *Oscinella frit*. Normally, the parasite sterilizes the host, but in a few cases the latter's gonads remain normal. The remarkable point is that then, and only then, the parasites remain small, are more or less degenerate, and produce either no larvae at all or only a few. More male than female flies appear able to check the parasite in this manner and while the mechanism involved has not been elucidated, one could visualize it as hormonal.

A most extraordinary case was described by Currie (1937) concerning the association of the fly, *Fergusonina nicholsonia*, and the nematode, *Fergusobia currei*. The fly larvae and the nematodes both develop side by side in galls of *Eucalyptus* trees. Only when a fly larva is ready to pupate does it become parasitized and invariably so by only two fertilized female nematodes, while a male fly is never parasitized. When the female fly hatches, larval nematodes which developed in the body cavity enter the oviduct and accompany each egg that is laid into a new flower bud, thus ensuring the perpetuation of the cycle.

Steidle (1930) found in unspecified species of tapeworms and roundworms substances producing estrus upon injection into castrated female mice. The significance of this finding and its bearing on the problem under consideration is not clear inasmuch as substances giving the same effect are widely distributed in various free-living animals and even in certain plants.

In so far as parasitic arthropods are concerned, it has been found that *Peltogaster paguri* occurs more commonly on female than male hermit crabs (Pérez, 1927, 1931a; Reinhard, 1942) and the same situation prevails in the case of *Munida sarsi* parasitized by *Triangulus munidae* (Brinkmann, 1936), while on the other hand *Gemmosaccus* infects more male than female pagurids (Pérez, 1931b). No definite reasons have so far been adduced for these differences; the speculations advanced by various authors have been summarized by Brinkmann (1936).

## B. Thyroid

Some evidence is beginning to accumulate showing that the state of the host's thyroid has some measure of influence on some intestinal parasites. Hypothyroidism induced by thiouracil did not materially change the resistance of chickens to *Eimeria tenella* (Wheeler, Hoffman, and Barber, 1948), nor to *Ascaridia galli* or *Heterakis gallinae* (Todd, 1949), but the *Heterakis* specimens recovered from mildly hypothyroid birds were on an average longer than those obtained from controls. Hypothyroidism did not significantly change the resistance of young mice to *Hymenolepis nana* var. *fraterna* (Larsh, 1950). Whitlock (1949), on the other hand, reported some observations indicating that hypothyroidism, both naturally occurring or thiouracil induced, may be important in *Trichostrongylus* infections of lambs. Hypothyroid animals developed trichostrongylidosis more readily than normal ones.

Artificially induced hyperthyroidism did not markedly alter the resistance of chickens to *Ascaridia galli* or *Heterakis gallinae*, but *Ascaridia* attained in hyperthyroid birds a greater length than in controls (Todd, 1949). Daily feeding of 3.3 mg thyroid extract to old mice, on the contrary, largely eliminated their resistance to *Hymenolepis nana*. In the treated animals more cysticercoids developed than in young mice of the most susceptible age (Larsh, 1950).

The mechanism responsible for the observed effects is at present rather obscure. Some possibilities, discussed by Larsh (1950) and Read (1950), are vitamin deficiency induced by hyperthyroidism in mice, lowering of the mucous anthelminthic factor in chickens, or changes in absorption rate of carbohydrates and fats. It does seem probable, on the whole, that only indirect influences are at work. It may, however, be worthwhile to study experimentally the question of whether or not the thyroid hormone has a direct influence on parasites. In this connection it should be recalled that very definite effects on the metabolism of some free-living invertebrates (*Lymnaea*, eggs of echinoderms, molluscs, and crustacea), as well as on the metamorphosis of tunicates have been reported (Duscova, 1932; Ashbel, 1935; Weiss, 1928; further literature in Koller, 1938).

## C. Prothoracic Glands

Cleveland (1947a) reported that the molting hormone produced by the prothoracic glands of *Cryptocercus punctulatus* induces the sexual cycle of the polymastigote and hypermastigote flagellates inhabiting its intestine. In a remarkable series of papers (Cleveland, 1947b, 1949, 1950a, b, c, d) he worked out the details of the sexual cycles of the genera *Trichonympha*, *Oxymonas*, *Saccinobacculus*, *Eucomonympha*, and *Notila*. Only a few of his observations that have a direct bearing on the question under consideration can be reviewed here. The evidence that the molting hormone actually induces the cycle rests on the finding that any treatment of the roaches slowing or stopping molting has an exactly identical influence on the cycle of the protozoa and conversely any treatment inducing more frequent molting induces the protozoa to undergo sexual development. One could of course object that a treatment of the host influencing its molting could also directly influence the protozoa. For one type of treatment at least this objection has been met in a most convincing way. Exposure to heat prevents molting, but if the entire roach is exposed to heat, obviously the flagellates are also. However, Cleveland was able to prevent molting and the sexual cycle of the protozoa by exposing only the head of the roaches to heat, in other words by an experimental procedure which prevented the heat from reaching the parasites.

Cleveland points out that the molting hormone reaches the parasites when the chitinous intima becomes eroded, if not earlier, and he assumes that its action is a direct one. Another very interesting observation is that gametogenesis of *Eucomonympha*, *Oxymonas*, *Saccinobacculus*, and *Notila* requires only 24 hours, while the process lasts 4 to 5 days in *Trichonympha*. Only the latter species undergoes development in the encysted state and it is assumed that the molting hormone diffuses only slowly through the cyst membrane while it reaches the other species freely. Despite this difference, however, the entire sexual cycle requires about the same time in all species. This is due to the fact that the species undergoing rapid gametogenesis have a resting period before the final phase of the cycle begins, that is, before meiosis sets in. "This perhaps means that the change in environment which is responsible for initiating meiosis in *Eucomonympha* does not occur until some time after fertilization is completed" (Cleveland, 1950d).

## D. Miscellaneous Observations

According to Andrews and Landsberg's (1937) observation the intestinal trichomonads of a diabetic increased in number each time that glycosuria occurred. This probably was not related to a susceptibility of the flagellates to insulin, but rather to an indirect effect, possibly a better availability of sugar, or changes in water metabolism of the host.

Occasionally, however, parasites are found that seem to be affected directly by insulin. Harvey (1948) reported a curious effect of zinc insulin on *Trypanosoma hippicum* kept *in vitro*. He found that it increased the aerobic oxygen consumption and pyruvate production but reduced materially the glucose consumption. Anaerobically, pyruvate production was more strongly inhibited than glucose consumption. The mechanism involved in these changes is not yet understood.

Adrenocorticotropic hormone and cortisone proved to be without effect on the oxygen consumption of the blood stream form of *Trypanosoma equiperdum* and the culture form of *Trypanosoma cruzi* and they did not change the rate of sugar consumption of the former species. Both hormones failed to influence the parasitemia due to *Trypanosoma equiperdum* in rats (von Brand, Tobie, and Mehlman, 1951). The tissue form of *Trypanosoma cruzi* does not seem to be materially affected by ACTH, although a beneficial effect of the hormone on the clinical picture of infected dogs has been described (Robles Gil and Perrin, 1950). The internal secretions of the adrenals are probably also without effect on *Trichinella* larvae. An indirect sign to this effect is the observation made by Larsh and Nichols (1949) that adrenalectomy does not materially change the eosinophil response of infected rats. Administration of cortical hormone to nonadrenalectomized trichinous rats did not reduce the circulating eosinophils markedly. A similar response was elicited by epinephrine and urethane (Stein, 1949).

## LITERATURE

Ackert, J. E., and Dewhirst, L. W. (1950). *J. Parasitol.* **36** Suppl.: 16.
Addis, C. J. (1946). *J. Parasitol.* **32:** 574–580.
Addis, C. J., and Chandler, A. C. (1944). *J. Parasitol.* **30:** 229–236.
Andrews, J., and Landsberg, J. W. (1937). *Am. J. Hyg.* **26:** 416–421.
Andrews, J., and Miller, F. W. (1936). *Am. J. Hyg.* **24:** 433–438.
Ashbel, R. (1935). *Nature* **135:** 343.
Baffoni, G. M. (1947). *Pubbl. staz. zool. Napoli* **21:** 36–49.
Baffoni, G. M. (1948). *Pubbl. staz. zool. Napoli* **21:** 132–147.
Baffoni, G. M. (1949). *Pubbl. staz. zool. Napoli* **21:** 236–254.
Baffoni, G. M. (1950). *Arch. zool. ital.* **35:** 289–295.
Beard, R. L. (1940). *J. Econ. Entomol.* **33:** 269–272.
Beck, J. W., and Chandler, A. C. (1950). *J. Parasitol.* **36** Suppl.: 44.
Bennison, B. E., and Coatney, G. R. (1948). *Science* **107:** 147–148.
Biedl, A. (1913). Innere Sekretion. 2nd Edition, Urban and Schwarzenberg Berlin.
Bieniarz, J. (1950). *Nature* **165:** 650–651.
Bovien, P. (1937). *Videnskab. Medd. Dansk Naturhist. Foren.* **101:** 1–114.
von Brand, T. Tobie, E. J., and Mehlman, B. (1951). *Am. J. Hyg.* **54:** 76–81.
Braun, M., and Seifert, O. (1926). Die tierischen Parasiten des Menschen. Kabitzch, Leipzig.
Brinkmann, A. (1936). *Bergens Museums Skrift.* No. 18: 1–111.
Buchner, P. (1925). *Z. Morph. Ökol. Tiere* **4:** 88–245.
von Buddenbrock, W. (1950). Vergleichende Physiologie. Vol. IV, Birkhäuser, Basel.
Burtt, E. (1946). *Ann. Trop. Med. Parasitol.* **40:** 74–79.
Callan, H. G. (1940). *J. Exptl. Biol.* **17:** 168–179.
Campbell, D. H. (1939). *Science* **89:** 415–416.
Campbell, D. H., and Melcher, L. R. (1940). *J. Infectious Diseases* **66:** 184–188.
Chagas, C. (1911). *Mem. inst. Oswaldo Cruz* **3:** 219–275.
Chagas, C. (1916). *Mem. inst. Oswaldo Cruz* **8:** 37–60.
Chandler, A. C. (1943). *Am. J. Hyg.* **37:** 121–130.
Chang, K., and Tong, W. K. (1949). *Am. J. Hyg. Monogr. Ser.* **19:** 58–78.

Chernin, E. (1950). *J. Parasitol.* **36** Suppl. 22-23.

Christie, J. R. (1936). *J. Agr. Research* **52:** 161–198.

Christie, J. R. (1937). *J. Agr. Research* **55:** 353–364.

Clapham, P. A. (1939). *J. Helminthol.* **17:** 192–194.

Cleveland, L. R. (1947a). *Science* **105:** 287–289.

Cleveland, L. R. (1947b). *Science* **105:** 16–17.

Cleveland, L. R. (1949). *J. Morphol.* **85:** 197–296.

Cleveland, L. R. (1950a). *J. Morphol.* **86:** 185–214.

Cleveland, L. R. (1950b). *J. Morphol.* **86:** 215–228.

Cleveland, L. R. (1950c). *J. Morphol.* **87:** 317–348.

Cleveland, L. R. (1950d). *J. Morphol.* **87:** 349–368.

Cort, W. W., McMullen, D. B., Olivier, L., and Brackett, S. (1940). *Am. J. Hyg.* **32** Sect. D: 33–69.

Currie, G. A. (1937). *Proc. Linnean Soc. N.S. Wales* **62:** 147–174.

Curtis, M. R., Dunning, W. F., and Bullock, F. D. (1933). *Am. J. Cancer* **17:** 894–923.

Dudgeon, L. S., and Clarke, C. (1917). *Lancet* **193:** 153–156.

Duke, H. L. (1930). *Ann. Trop. Med. Parasitol.* **24:** 95–96.

Duke, H. L. (1933). *Ann. Trop. Med. Parasitol.* **27:** 355–356.

Duscova, V. (1932). *Spisy Lékaťske Fakulty. Masarykovy Univ.* **11** (not seen).

Fage, L. (1940). *Compt. rend.* **211:** 335–337.

Forsman, B. (1938). *Zool. Bidrag Uppsala* **18:** 1–161.

Garnault, P. (1889). *Bull. sci. France Belg.* **20:** 137–142.

Gerdjikoff, I. (1939). *Klin. Wochschr.* **18:** 1214–1217.

Giard, A. (1886). *Compt. rend.* **103:** 84–86.

Giard, A. (1887). *Compt. rend.* **104:** 1113–1115.

Gösswald, K. (1929). *Zool. Anz.* **84:** 202–204.

Gösswald, K. (1930). *Zool. Anz.* **90:** 13–27.

Gösswald, K. (1938). *Z. Parasitenk.* **10:** 138–152.

Goldschmidt, R. (1931). Die sexuellen Zwischenstufen. Springer, Berlin.

Goodey, T. (1931). *J. Helminthol.* **9:** 157–174.

Haemmerli-Boveri, V. (1926). *Z. vergleich. Physiol.* **4:** 668–698.

Harvey, S. C. (1948). *Proc. Soc. Exptl. Biol. Med.* **69:** 555–557.

Hashimoto, S. (1939). *Trans. Soc. Path. Japan* **29:** 534–537 (not seen).

Hauschka, T. S. (1947). *J. Parasitol.* **33:** 399–404.

Hermann, R. G. (1934). *Berlin. Tierärztl. Wochschr.* **50:** 81–84.

Hungerford, H. B. (1919). *J. Parasitol.* **5:** 186–192.

Hurst, C. T. (1927). *Univ. Calif. (Berkeley) Pubs. Zool.* **29:** 321–404.

Ihm, P. (1951). *Vie et milieu* **1:** 279–283.

Josephson, E. S., Taylor, D. J., Greenberg, J., and Nadel, E. M. (1949). *J. Natl. Malaria Soc.* **8:** 132–136.

Junior, P., and Brandao, P. P. (1937). *Brasil Medico* **51:** 1047–1058.

Kean, B. H., and Taylor, C. E. (1946). *Am. J. Trop. Med.* **26:** 209–219.

Kloft, W. (1949). *Z. Parasitenk.* **14:** 390–422.

Koller, G. (1938). Hormone bei wirbellosen Tieren. Akademische Verlagsgesellschaft, Leipzig.

Kornhauser, S. I. (1919). *J. Morphol.* **32:** 531–636.

Kotlan, A., and Chandler, W. L. (1925). *J. Am. Med. Assoc.* **67:** 756–763.

Kraus, R. (1926). *Wien. klin. Wochschr.* **39:** 378–382.

Krull, H. (1935). *Zool. Jahrb. Abt. Anat.* **60:** 399–464.

Larsh, J. E. (1950). *J. Parasitol.* **36:** 473–478.

Larsh, J. E., and Nichols, J. (1949). *Proc. Soc. Exptl. Biol. Med.* **71**: 652–654.

Le Roux, M. L. (1931a). *Compt. rend.* **192**: 889–891.

Le Roux, M. L. (1931b). *Compt. rend.* **193**: 885–887.

Linke, O. (1934). *Zool. Anz.* **36** Suppl. 7: 164–175.

Lipschütz, A. (1924). The Internal Secretions of the Sex Glands. Williams and Wilkins, Baltimore.

Lysaght, A. M. (1943). *Parasitology* **35**: 17–22.

Macy, R. W. (1940). *J. Parasitol.* **26**: 158.

Maegraith, B. (1948). Pathological Processes in Malaria and Blackwater Fever. Charles C Thomas, Springfield, Ill.

Marañon, G. (1939). *Brasil Medico* **53**: 93–95.

McKee, R. W., Cobbey, T. S., and Geiman, Q. M. (1947). *Federation Proc.* **6**: 276.

McKee, R. W., and Geiman, Q. M. (1946). *Proc. Soc. Exptl. Biol. Med.* **63**: 313–315.

Nadel, E. M., Taylor D. J., Greenberg, J., and Josephson E. S. (1949). *J. Natl. Malaria Soc.* **8**: 70–79.

Natali, C. (1934). *Arch. Schiffs-u. Tropen-Hyg.* **38**: 243–249.

Neuhaus, W. (1940). *Z. Parasitenk.* **12**: 65–77.

Neuhaus, W. (1949). *Z. Parasitenk.* **14**: 300–319.

Nilsson-Cantell, C. A. (1926). *Arkiv Zool.* **18** A: 1–21.

Nouvel, H., and Nouvel, L. (1935). *Bull. soc. zool. France* **59**: 516–521.

Nyden, S. J. (1948). *Proc. Soc. Exptl. Biol. Med.* **69**: 206–210.

Okada, K., and Miyashita, Y. (1935). *Mem. Coll. Sci. Kyoto Imp. Univ. Ser.* **B10**: 169–208.

van Oordt, G. J. (1928). *Zool. Anz.* **76**: 306–310.

Paisseau, G., and Lemaire, H. (1916). *Presse méd.* **24**: 545–547.

Pérez, C. (1927). *Bull. soc. zool. France* **53**: 523–526.

Pérez, C. (1931a). *Bull. soc. zool. France* **56**: 509–512.

Pérez, C. (1931b). *Compt. rend.* **192**: 1274–1276.

Pérez, J. (1886). *Acta soc. Linnéenne Bordeaux* **40**: 21–60.

Potts, F. A. (1906). *Quart. J. Microscop. Sci.* **50**: 599–621.

Pratt, I., and Barton, G. D. (1941). *J. Parasitol.* **27**: 283–288.

Rabaud, J., and Millot, J. (1929). *Arch. anat. microscop.* **25**: 280–293.

Read, C. P. (1950). *Rice Inst. Pamphlet* **37** No. 2: 1–94.

Reinhard, E. G. (1942). *Biol. Bull.* **83**: 401–415.

Reinhard, E. G. (1950). *Biol. Bull.* **98**: 277–288.

Reinhard, E. G., and Buckeridge, F. W. (1950). *J. Parasitol.* **36**: 131–138.

Rempel, J. G. (1940). *J. Exptl. Zool.* **84**: 261–289.

Reverberi, G. (1944/45). *Rend. ist. lombardo sci.* **78**: 217–246.

Rigdon, R. H. (1942). *Am. J. Hyg.* **36**: 269–275.

Rigdon, R. H., and Stratman-Thomas, W. K. (1942). *Am. J. Trop. Med.* **22**: 329–339.

Risbec, M. J. (1930). *Bull. muséum natl. hist. nat. Paris* [2] **2**: 660–664.

Robles Gil, J., and Perrin, M. (1950). *Arch. inst. cardiol. Mex.* **20**: 314–326.

Rothschild, A., and Rothschild, M. (1939). *Novit. Zool.* **41**: 240–247.

Rothschild, M. (1936). *J. Marine Biol. Assoc. United Kingdom* **20**: 537–546.

Rothschild, M. (1938). *Novit. Zool.* **41**: 84–102.

Rothschild, M. (1941). *J. Marine Biol. Assoc. United Kingdom* **25**: 69–80.

Sadun, E. H. (1948). *J. Parasitol.* **34** Suppl.: 18.

Salt, G. (1927). *J. Exptl. Zool.* **48**: 223–319.

Salt, G. (1931). *J. Exptl. Zool.* **59**: 133–166.

Shiino, S. M. (1931). *Mem. Coll. Sci. Kyoto Imp. Univ.* **B7**: 63–101 (not seen).

Smith, G. (1905). *Mitt. zool. Station Neapel* **17**: 406–409.

Smith, G. (1911). *Quart. J. Microscop. Sci.* **57**: 251–265.

Smith, G. (1913). *Quart. J. Microscop. Sci.* **59**: 267–295.

Smith, G., and Hamm, A. H. (1914). *Quart. J. Microscop. Sci.* **60**: 435–461.

Sollas, I. B. J. (1911). *Ann. Mag. Natl. Hist.* [8] **7**: 335–337.

Sorce, S., and Mutolo, V. (1946). *Boll. soc. ital. biol. sper.* **22**: 399–400.

Steidle, H. (1930). *Arch. exptl. Path. Pharmakol.* **157**: 89.

Stein, K. F. (1949). *Proc. Soc. Exptl. Biol. Med.* **71**: 225–226.

Szidat, L. (1924). *Zool. Anz.* **58**: 299–314.

Szidat, L. (1941). *Z. Parasitenk.* **12**: 251 (not seen).

Thompson, M. T. (1901). *Bull. U. S. Fish. Comm.* **21**: 53–56.

Todd, A. C. (1949). *J. Parasitol.* **35**: 255–260.

Trager, W. (1948). *J. Parasitol.* **34**: 389–393.

Trager, W., and McGhee, R. B. (1950). *J. Exptl. Med.* **91**: 365–379.

Trager, W., Stauber, L. A., and BenHarel, S. (1950). *Proc. Soc. Exptl. Biol. Med.* **75**: 766–771.

Vandel, A. (1930). *Compt. rend.* **190**: 770–772.

Vandel, A. (1933). *Bull. biol. France Belg.* **67**: 125–134.

Vandel, A. (1934). *Ann. sci. nat. zool.* [10] **17**: 47–58.

Varley, G. C., and Butler, C. G. (1933). *Parasitology* **25**: 263–268.

Veillet, A. (1945). *Ann. inst. océanogr. Paris.* **22**: 193–341.

Wehr, E. E., and Christensen, J. F. (1942). *U. S. Dept. Agr. 1942 Yearbook* 1007–1040.

Weiss, P. (1928). *Biol. Zentr.* **48**: 69–79.

Wesenberg-Lund, C. (1931). *Kgl. Danske Videnskab. Selskab Skrifter Naturvidenskab. math. Afdel.* [9] **4**: 89–142.

Wesenberg-Lund, C. (1934). *Kgl. Danske Videnskab. Selskabs Skrifter Naturvidenskab. math. Afdel.* [9] **5** No. 3: 1–223.

Wheeler, R. S., Hoffman, E., and Barber, C. W. (1948). *J. Am. Vet. Med. Assoc.* **112**: 473–474.

Wheeler, W. M. (1928). *J. Exptl. Zool.* **50**: 165–237.

Whitlock, J. H. (1949). *J. Parasitol.* **35** Suppl.: 12–13.

Whitlock, S. C. (1937). *J. Parasitol.* **23**: 426.

Wozonig, H. (1945). *Z. Immunitätsforsch.* **105**: 411–416.

Yorke, W. (1937). *Trop. Diseases Bull.* **34**: 275–300.

# CHAPTER 20

# PARASITE PHYSIOLOGY AND CHEMOTHERAPY

## I. The Physiological Basis of Chemotherapy

### A. Introductory Remarks

Chemotherapy, in its endeavor to find parasiticidal drugs, has used and is still using, since its inception, an empirical approach almost exclusively. This is not surprising. The pressing task of finding active drugs was the overriding consideration. If the synthesis and the screening of thousands and thousands of inactive compounds required an incalculable number of man hours, the finding of such drugs as tryparsamide, Bayer 205, and many others has clearly demonstrated the merits of this approach and there can be little doubt that many chemotherapists will favor it for a long time to come.

There are, however, indications that a second approach, based on physiological research, will become a rival of empirical chemotherapy. It has been strongly advocated in recent years by Wright (1946), Rogers (1946), Work and Work (1948), and Bueding (1950b). There is of course general agreement that the elucidation of the mechanism of drug action which can be solved only by physiological and biochemical studies, is not only of academic interest, but also of the greatest practical significance. It sheds light, for example, on the often obscure questions of whether a given drug acts directly on a parasite, whether it is first changed in the body of the host to a more active compound, or whether it acts primarily by enhancing the defense mechanisms of the host.

Most proponents of the "rational approach" have still greater expectations. They assume that a knowledge of the biochemical activities of the parasites should yield important clues as to what types of compounds may have therapeutic value; in other words they hope that physiological studies may open a way obviating the necessity of screening compounds indiscriminately. The fulfillment of these expectations rests on the ingenuity of the biochemist and chemotherapist of the future. At present it is possible to point out two instances in which physiological thinking has led to encouraging results in the field of parasite chemotherapy.

The first instance, admittedly, is not too good an example because the original theoretical assumption turned out to be wrong. Starting from the assumption that the terminal hypoglycemia of trypanosome-infected animals was due to the sugar consumption of the parasites and was harmful to them, Schern and Artagaveytia-Allende (1935, 1936) and von Jancsó and von Jancsó (1935) independently tried to damage the flagellates by producing hypoglycemia in experimental animals by means of synthalin. Both groups obtained good trypanocidal results with this treatment, but the subsequent analysis by Lourie and Yorke (1937) showed that the compound had a direct lethal influence on the parasites. An immediate result of this finding was the introduction of diamidines into practical chemotherapy and one may well be justified in asking how much time would have elapsed before the empirical approach would have led to the same group of compounds.

The second example concerns a segment of the large field of malaria chemotherapy. Trager (1943) had observed that calcium pantothenate favored the survival of *Plasmodium lophurae in vitro*. This observation induced a group of investigators (Mead *et al.*, 1946) to synthesize analogs of pantothenic acid hoping that they would act as antagonists of that substance and thus damage the parasites. Marshall's (1946) experiments then showed that some of the compounds indeed had definite anti-malarial activity. While this particular line has not yet yielded drugs of real practical importance, there is no denying that the general type of approach is feasible and it is hardly overenthusiastic to hope that future research may yield results of definite practical value.

An attempt will be made to summarize briefly in the following sections our knowledge concerning the mechanism of parasiticidal drug activity. The presentation will be strictly limited to this aspect of the problem; it is not intended to give an introduction to the chemotherapy of parasitic diseases. Many drugs of the greatest practical importance will hence not even be mentioned because their mode of action has not yet been studied.

## B. Mode of Action of Antiprotozoal Drugs

The analysis of antiprotozoal drugs is limited essentially so far to some compounds active against blood flagellates and malarial parasites and these two groups of parasites alone will be considered here.

Arsenicals are very useful in African trypanosomiasis and their action has been studied frequently both *in vitro* and *in vivo*. It has been found that trivalent arsenicals have *in vitro* much greater trypanocidal powers than pentavalent compounds, the latter requiring from 60,000 to 120,000 times greater concentrations than the former in order to kill the flagellates at the same rate (Yorke and Murgatroyd, 1930). In chemotherapeutic praxis, however, the pentavalent arsenicals are highly effective and are safer to use than the trivalent compounds. In contrast to trivalent arsenicals they penetrate into the central nervous system and are thus effective in the late stages of African trypanosomiasis. It is generally assumed that their relatively low toxicity to vertebrates and their pronounced trypanocidal effectiveness *in vivo* is due to a conversion, within the body of the host, to trivalent compounds, only the latter actually killing the parasites (Ehrlich, 1909; Voegtlin *et al.*, 1923, 1924; Voegtlin, 1925; Crawford and Levvy, 1947).

Quantitative and qualitative determinations have definitely shown that arsenicals penetrate the bodies of trypanosomes (Levaditi and von Knaffl-Lenz, 1909; Singer and Fischl, 1934; Singer, Kotrba, and Fischl, 1934; Yorke and Murgatroyd, 1930). The extent to which they are fixed in the bodies of the flagellates seems to depend essentially on the following factors: The nature of the drug (Reiner, Leonard, and Chao, 1932a), the physico-chemical constitution, for example the pH, of the medium (Eagle, 1945b), and the species of trypanosome employed (Pedlow and Reiner, 1935). The demonstration that the drugs actually enter into the parasites is important since it represents a rather clear indication that their chemotherapeutic activity is related to the combination of arsenic with some cell constituent. The question then is what precisely is the cell constituent involved? Ehrlich's (1909) side chain theory has in this connection only historical interest and will not be considered. We shall review in the following paragraphs only the more recent viewpoints.

Voegtlin, Dyer, and Leonard (1923) pointed out that arsenoxide reacts readily with sulfhydryl compounds. They found within the body of *Trypanosoma equiperdum* a compound which may have been glutathione, giving sulfhydryl reactions. They furthermore observed that an excess of sulfhydryl compounds protected trypanosomes both *in vivo* and *in vitro* against the toxic action of arsenicals and that, of course within certain limits, the effects of arsenic poisoning could be reversed by such compounds as glutathione or cysteine (Voegtlin, Rosenthal, and Johnson, 1931). Essentially on the strength of these findings, Voegtlin developed the theory that arsenoxide reacts within the body of the flagellates with glutathione (or a similar sulfhydryl compound), a reaction followed by a disruption of the cellular oxidation-reduction processes which in turn would be lethal to the trypanosomes.

The view of a central position of glutathione in the picture of arsenic poisoning has been abandoned in recent years. It has been recognized that many of the cellular enzymes responsible for the utilization of carbohydrate and protein depend for their activity on the presence of intact sulfhydryl groups (Rapkine, 1938; Hopkins, Morgan, and Lutwak-Mann, 1938; Hellerman, Chinard, and Deitz, 1943; Barron and Singer, 1945; and others). These enzymes then are inactivated by compounds which combine with their essential sulfhydryl groups, and arsenicals are one group of compounds which do just that. It is clear that Voegtlin's concept is rather rigid and that on its basis the differential toxicity between parasite and host, as well as the different susceptibility of various species of parasites can be explained only by invoking unproven auxiliary hypotheses, such as differences in the amount of glutathione present in different types of cells. The enzyme theory, on the other hand, is much more flexible and plausible, since it is a well established fact that the enzymes of various organisms, even if they perform the same function, can be chemically different and it can hence very readily be visualized that they react differently to drugs.

In so far as trypanosomes specifically are concerned, Chen (1948) and Marshall (1948a) respectively have shown that the hexokinase of *Trypanosoma equiperdum* and *Trypanosoma evansi* is very sensitive to trivalent arsenicals. If it is blocked, the utilization of carbohydrate is effectively interrupted. The African trypanosomes, however, are absolutely dependent for their energy requirements on glycolytic processes. It seems likely, therefore, or at least possible, that the inhibition of this enzyme lies at the root of the trypanocidal activity of arsenicals. Suggestive in this connection also is the observation that *Trypanosoma cruzi* does not respond at all to chemotherapeutic measures based on the administration of arsenicals. It has been found that this species is relatively insensitive to arsenicals, and other sulfhydryl inhibitors during *in vitro* experiments, suggesting that its intracellular enzyme complex is quite different from that of the African species. Furthermore it has been found that *Trypanosoma cruzi* (blood stream form) consumes practically no sugar (von Brand *et al.*, 1949, 1950). Hence, even if the organism has hexokinase and even if the enzyme is blocked by arsenicals, this may not be fatal simply because *Trypanosoma cruzi* primarily uses substances other than carbohydrates in its metabolism and the required enzymes may not have essential sulfhydryl groups. It must be admitted, however, that whether or not arsenicals enter this parasite as freely as they do the African species has not yet been solved.

Antimonials are useful especially against leishmanias, but they also have trypanocidal powers. Both trivalent and pentavalent compounds are used. Although studied less than arsenicals, it appears possible, but by no means certain, that the mode of action of both is fundamentally similar. On the basis of Voegtlin and Smith's (1920) experiments it can be assumed that the pentavalent antimonials are transformed into trivalent compounds within the host's body. This view has been strengthened by Chen and Geiling's (1945) observation that pentavalent antimonials are much less effective *in vitro* in inhibiting the glucose consumption of *Trypanosoma equiperdum* and by Fulton and Joyner's (1949) report of a similar difference with respect to the influence on the oxygen consumption of both culture and tissue stages of *Leishmania donovani*. The pentavalent sodium stibogluconate indeed had no inhibitory influence whatsoever on the latter para-site. In so far as the specific enzymes inhibited by trivalent compounds are concerned, it does appear that they are identical with those inhibited by arsenicals (Chen, Geiling, and MacHatton, 1945; Chen, 1948) and again it may be justified to attribute the lethal action, at least tentatively, to the inhibition of hexokinase. However, these findings cannot be generalized. Bueding (personal communication) found that the hexokinase of schisto-somes, an SH-enzyme, is inhibited completely by low concentrations of trivalent arsenicals, but is not inhibited even by high concentrations of trivalent or pentavalent antimonials.

The mode of action of diamidines, used both in trypanosomiasis and leishmaniasis, is less obvious since apparently considerable differences be-tween different compounds exist. Marshall (1948a) found that undecane diamidine, a straight chain compound, but slightly reduced the oxygen consumption of *Trypanosoma evansi*. It stimulated the glucose consumption slightly and had no apparent influence on the intermediates of glucose metabolism, but decreased pyruvate production. The drug is thought to attack somewhere in the dehydrogenase system. Stilbamidine, an aromatic compound, did not interfere with the glucose and oxygen consumption of the flagellates, nor with the production of pyruvic acid, but it did change the levels of phophorylated intermediates. Marshall (1948a) assumes that the compound acts by inhibiting protein synthesis and hence growth by preventing pyruvic acid from being drawn into the cycle of protein syn-thesis. It should be remembered, however, that stilbamidine produced a denaturation of nucleoproteins and a dissociation of nucleic acid from pro-teins with other material (Kopac, 1947; Bichowsky, 1944), an effect that also would result in suppression of growth if it were realized in trypano-somes. The mechanism of leishmanicidal action of diamidines is still less known. Fulton and Joyner (1949) found that fairly high concentrations of stilbamidine and propamidine were required to inhibit materially the oxy-gen consumption of the culture form of *Leishmania donovani*, while the Leishman-Donovan bodies were still more resistant in this respect.

Bayer 205 (suramin) strongly inhibits such enzyme systems as fumarase (Quastel, 1931), hyaluronidase (Beiler and Martin, 1948), trypsin (Town and Wormall, 1949), yeast hexokinase and carboxylase (Wills and Wormall, 1949), and the view has been expressed that it eliminates trypanosomes by interference with some of their metabolic enzymes (Town, Wills, and Wor-mall, 1949). It is curious, however, and quite in contrast to the facts re-viewed above concerning trivalent arsenicals, that during short time ex-posure to suramin *in vitro* neither the respiration nor the glycolysis of pathogenic trypanosomes is affected markedly (von Fenyvessy and Reiner, 1928; von Issekutz, 1933a, b). Similarly, normal metabolic reactions were observed when trypanosomes were studied which had been exposed, prior to the determinations, to the compound *in vivo* for 30 minutes. If the parasites were subjected for longer periods to the drug, however, respiration and glycolysis were reduced and, in contrast to untreated controls, glycerol accumulated in anaerobic incubates (Glowazky, 1937). In view of these results it appears somewhat doubtful that the hexokinase of trypanosomes can be as sensitive to Bayer 205 as that of yeast or that this drug inhibits it as strongly as do arsenicals. The possibility of slow penetration or change to a more active compound within the host's body may have to be taken into account; according to Wills and Wormall (1949) suramin almost certainly cannot penetrate through the cell wall of yeast.

Quinine probably has a direct lethal action on malarial parasites since it suppresses the growth of *Plasmodium knowlesi* in culture at concentrations comparable to those attained in a treated host (Ball, 1946; Geiman, 1948). *In vitro* analysis has shown that the drug inhibits to some extent the oxygen consumption of *Plasmodium gallinaceum* at approximately therapeutic concentrations ($6 \times 10^{-6}$ $M$), but not its glycolysis. At higher concentrations ($10^{-3}$ $M$), however, both aerobic and anaerobic glycolysis are also affected (Silverman *et al.*, 1944). Subsequent investigation of parasites taken from chickens previously treated with quinine (Moulder, 1948, 1949) showed that the compound inhibits strongly the oxidation of pyruvate. It was found that both the complete oxidation of pyruvic acid *via* the tricarboxylic acid cycle and the incomplete oxidation to acetate were affected. Since both pathways have only one step in common, Moulder (1949) suggests that "quinine inhibits pyruvate oxidation in free parasites by irreversibly removing some unknown factor necessary for conversion of pyruvate into a reactive two-carbon particle." This mechanism is possibly not the only point of attack, however. Marshall (1948b) found, besides inhibition of pyruvate oxidation, an inhibitory effect of quinine on the hexokinase, phosphoglyceraldehyde dehydrogenase, and lactic dehydrogenase of *Plasmodium gallinaceum*. He points out that trivalent arsenicals which inhibit only one type of enzyme, the sulfhydryl enzymes, are inactive against malarial parasites probably because alternate metabolic pathways exist or because various substrates can be used. Quinine, on the other hand, can in his opinion interrupt the metabolic pathways at various points and is therefore active also against metabolically versatile organisms.

Of the newer antimalarial drugs, atabrine (quinacrine, mepacrine) has received most attention. It was found that it inhibits enzymes which have flavin as prosthetic groups or as coenzymes (Wright and Sabine, 1944; Haas, 1944; Bovarnick, Lindsay, and Hellerman, 1946a, b), but that its inhibitory action is not limited to flavo enzymes, some nonflavo enzymes being affected markedly also (Bovarnick, Lindsay, and Hellerman, 1946b).

It has been suggested (Haas, 1944) that atabrine affects malarial parasites by competitive inhibition of flavo enzymes, an assumption which is none too probable because, among other reasons reviewed by Bueding (1950b), the concentration required to inhibit these enzymes is appreciably higher than that producing antimalarial effects *in vivo*. A more probable possibility is that the synthesis of an essential flavine may be inhibited (Ball *et al.*, 1948). It is hardly likely, however, that this is the only mechanism of atabrine action. *In vitro* experiments have led to the tentative assumption that atabrine interferes with some phosphorylation reaction. The drug seems to belong to a class of compounds capable of combining with proteins. It might, therefore, combine with the proteins of enzymes, but the result on the metabolism of the parasites would depend upon whether the affected moiety of the enzyme is essential or nonessential for its activity (Bovarnick, Lindsay, and Hellerman, 1946b; Hellerman, Bovarnick, and Porter, 1946). Specifically, it has been shown that the compound strongly inhibits the hexokinase of *Plasmodium gallinaceum*, its phosphoglyceraldehyde dehydrogenase moderately, and that it probably also interferes with its pyruvate oxidation (Marshall, 1948b).

While quinine certainly and atabrine possibly exert a direct lethal action on malarial parasites, indications exist that other antimalarial drugs become essentially active after having undergone changes within the body of the host. This, for example, is probable in the case of chlorguanide (paludrine). The active compound has not yet been identified, but interesting suggestions concerning its mode of action have been made. Greenberg, Boyd, and Josephson (1948) observed that the antimalarial activity of chlorguanide is potentiated by sulfadiazine. Its effectiveness is not inhibited by *p*-aminobenzoic acid (PABA) but the amount of PABA necessary to inhibit sulfadiazine, a PABA competitor, is increased by simultaneous use of chlorguanide. Greenberg (1949) pointed out that paludrine can hardly be a PABA competitor, but that it is, nevertheless, probably involved in some way in the PABA metabolism. He thinks it might interfere with the synthesis or utilization of pteroylglutamic acid which is one of the endproducts of PABA metabolism.

A last group of potential antimalarials, the naphthoquinones, may be mentioned briefly, although they are of no practical value in human malaria therapy. It has been shown that some members of the group, especially hydroxynaphthoquinones, strongly inhibit the respiration of malarial plasmodia *in vitro* (Wendel, 1946; Fieser and Heyman, 1948). Their activity is due chiefly to an inhibition of succinic dehydrogenase brought about by an interference with the interaction of cytochrome B with cytochrome C (Ball, Anfinsen, and Cooper, 1947). *In vivo*, however, the activity of naphthoquinones varies greatly from host species to host species. They are thus quite active in ducks, moderately so in chickens, but essentially inactive in man. This is due to a differential affinity of the serum albumin of various mammalian species for hydroxynaphthoquinones (Heyman and Fieser, 1948). It may be added that a similar inactivating action of serum on the effectiveness of naphthoquinones as inhibitors of the glycolysis of schistosomes recently has been described by Bueding and Peters (1951).

## C. Mode of Action of Anthelminthic Drugs

The fundamental approach to the analysis of antiprotozoal drugs has so far been only biochemical. In contrast, results of considerable interest have been obtained with anthelminthic drugs by means of purely physiological methods which cannot be applied to protozoa due to their small size. Some use has thus been made of kymographic methods which, essentially, show what influence a given compound has on the nervous and muscular system of an organism. Tapeworms (Betham, 1946), liver flukes (Chance and Mansour, 1949), roundworms (Rico, 1926a, b; Baldwin, 1943), and acanthocephala (Rebello and Rico, 1926) have been used in this way. To exemplify the results obtained, the most comprehensive study may be used, that of Chance and Mansour (1949) on *Fasciola hepatica*. They could distinguish between four types of reaction depending upon the nature and, in some cases, the concentration of the drugs. Stimulating drugs were, among others, carbon tetrachloride, tetrachlorethylene, hexachlorethane, and amphetamine. Paralysis occurred under the influence of low concentrations of oil of chenopodium, of santonin, and other compounds. Directly lethal drugs were oil of chenopodium at higher concentrations, extractum filis mas, gentian violet, hexylresorcinol, and others. Entirely inactive on the preparations were, besides many other compounds, the well known anthelminthic phenothiazine, as well as emetine and penicillin.

An interesting line of research was also followed by Trim (1949). He studied two questions that are of prime importance in practical chemotherapy: The power of penetration of anthelminthic drugs into *Ascaris* and the influence of the environment on the rate of penetration. He reached the conclusion that a thin outer lipid layer of the cuticle is the main barrier and that essentially three processes are involved in determining the rate of penetration of organic substances: Traube capillary effects, interfacial diffusion, and lipid-water partition. Of environmental factors, surface active substances may be important since certain detergents greatly increased the action of nicotine, probably in part at least by changing the permeability of the cuticle. Bile salts, however, completely inhibited the entry of hexylresorcinol through the *Ascaris* cuticle (Trim, 1943) and sodium taurocholate drastically reduced its efficiency against *Nippostrongylus muris* (Rogers, 1944), demonstrations of the undisputed fact that compounds quite active *in vitro* cannot always be expected to act in an exactly similar manner *in vivo*. In order to be of practical value every prospective anthelminthicum must pass the acid test of how the parasites react to it *in vivo*.

There has been relatively little analysis so far on the biochemical mode of action of anthelminthic drugs. It is clear, however, that at least two types of action occur. One group of drugs consists of proteolytic enzymes of vegetable origin, such as papain, bromellin, or ficin, which destroy nematodes by digesting their tissues (Berger and Ansenjo, 1939, 1940; Robbins, 1930; Walti, 1937, 1938; Andrews and Cornatzer, 1942). Leche de higueron used against *Trichuris* contains ficin as the active principle.

The other group of anthelminthics, or potential anthelminthics, exerts its action by inhibiting certain metabolic reactions. It has thus been shown that the antimonial fuadin primarily inhibits the oxygen uptake of schistosomes while its effect on glycolysis is only moderate (Bueding, Peters, and Welch, 1947; Bueding and Oliver-Gonzalez, 1948; Bueding, 1950a). This is an interesting observation since it explains why fuadin has to be given to infected humans in doses approaching the toxic level in order to be effective against the worms. The reason is simply that the schistosomes are not fatally injured by even a drastic reduction of their aerobic metabolism; in order to kill them the anaerobic glycolytic processes must be interfered with and, as explained above, fuadin does this only at relatively high concentrations (Bueding, 1950b). It is probable that the action of the drug is due to an interference with sulfhydryl enzymes, as indicated by the fact that BAL reverses its inhibitory effects (Bueding, 1949a).

The antischistosome mechanism of the newer drug miracil is not yet known. It has no significant inhibitory effect on the oxygen consumption, glycolysis, or nucleoprotein metabolism of the worms (Bueding *et al.*, 1947). This latter observation is rather curious since miracil seems to be a poison attacking the nuclei, especially those of the reproductive glands. Histological studies showed that it inhibits mitosis (Goennert, 1947).

Cyanines possess a considerable chemotherapeutic effect against *Litomosoides carinii* (Welch *et al.*, 1947; Wright *et al.*, 1947; Peters *et al.*, 1949a, b). They act by interfering with the oxidative metabolism of the worms. Reduction of their rate of oxygen consumption has been shown to occur both after exposure to the dyes *in vivo* and *in vitro* (Bueding, 1949b). A compensatory increase in glycolysis occurred, but the anaerobic faculties of the worms are not pronounced enough to keep them alive for longer periods of time once the aerobic metabolic chain is interrupted. It is important to note that the cyanines are inactive *in vivo* against *Dirofilaria immitis* and *Wuchereria bancrofti* (Santiago-Stevenson *et al.*, no date; Peters and Welch, no date). Since the drugs in these experiments were injected into the vascular system of the hosts, they certainly must have reached *Dirofilaria* at least in high concentrations and it is clear that the different response must have been due to differences in metabolism. (Bueding, 1950b). This is a significant observation indicating that the screening of potential anthelminthics with another worm as the one against which they are to be used in praxis, may give a quite misleading picture. From the metabolic standpoint it would appear that those worm species endowed with anaerobic faculties potent enough to keep them alive after elimination of a large part of the aerobic mechanism will not be affected adversely by the cyanines. This is rather clearly indicated by the observation that the compounds have marked chemotherapeutic value against dog hookworms and whipworms (Hales and Welch, 1947; Welch and Hales, personal communication), which are probably able to secure significant amounts of oxygen under natural conditions. The compounds are inactive against tapeworms (Welch and Hales, personal communication), parasites usually assumed to be primarily anaerobic organisms, and against *Schistosoma mansoni* (Bueding, Peters, and Welch, 1947; Bueding and Oliver-Gonzalez, 1948). The schistosomes rely primarily on anaerobic processes for their energy production (Bueding, 1950a) and they are actually the best example of worms that are not adversely affected by the cyanines due to good anaerobic faculties, since it has been shown that the cyanines markedly reduce their oxygen consumption regardless of whether they were exposed *in vivo* or *in vitro*. Their rate of glycolysis was not significantly changed, since it already proceeds at maximal rate under normal conditions and the worms were not damaged by the drugs. Some caution against generalizations is, however, indicated, since the cyanines are quite effective against dog ascarids (Welch and Hales, personal communication) and only moderately effective against *Necator americanus* (Oliver-Gonzalez, personal communication). *In situ* the former worms probably lead a primarily anaerobic life while the latter presumably do not.

The mode of action of phenothiazine, used in praxis extensively against roundworms but also against other parasites, is not exactly known, although it may well be active *via* enzyme inhibition. It has been shown to inhibit markedly such enzymes as catalase, cytochrome oxidase, lactic dehydrogenase, or cholinesterase (Collier, 1940; Collier and Allen, 1942a, b). All tests were carried out, however, with enzymes derived from mammalian tissues and no study of the drug's influence on the metabolism of helminths is available.

## II. The Problem of Drug Resistance

### A. Introductory Remarks

Drug resistant strains of parasitic protozoa are a serious problem for the practitioner of tropical medicine, especially in dealing with African sleeping sickness and malaria. The ability to develop drug fastness is not peculiar to these two groups of parasites; it has been produced experimentally also with *Babesia canis* and with *Endamoeba histolytica*. It can be assumed that many other protozoa would become resistant under the right set of circumstances. It is also well known that strains of DDT-resistant flies and mosquitoes have appeared in recent years. In view of this widespread occurrence of the phenomenon and the fact that anthelminthic measures have been carried out intensively over many years, it appears rather singular that so far no evidence has been reported of helminths becoming drug resistant.

## B. Origin of Drug Resistance

One of the most widely used methods of procuring drug resistant parasites is the injection of subcurative doses of a given drug into infected experimental animals, as shown first in Ehrlich's laboratory with pathogenic trypanosomes (Ehrlich, 1907). In this case, where the infection has an acute character leading in a rather short time to the death of the host, it is necessary to expose the parasites in successive animal passages to the drug, increasing the dosage as required to achieve a temporary disappearance of the parasites from the peripheral blood. Where the infection follows a more chronic course, drug fastness can be developed by prolonged treatment of one and the same host with subcurative doses. This latter procedure, for example, was used by Hawking and Perry (1948) with *Plasmodium knowlesi* maintained in baboons.

Drug fastness can also be achieved by exposing parasites to the drugs *in vitro*. Yorke, Murgatroyd, and Hawking (1931) used this procedure successfully with trypanosomes. They exposed the flagellates for short periods to arsenicals, or other drugs *in vitro*, injected them into experimental animals and repeated this procedure either with the same or, more efficiently, with increasing drug concentrations until the maximum of resistance had developed. Protozoa that can be cultivated continuously *in vitro* need not to be passed through animals. Some resistance against sulfanilamide and aureomycin was produced in *Endamoeba histolytica* by subjecting successive culture transfers to the drugs (Rodaniche and Kirsner, 1942; Watt and VandeGrift, 1950).

A third possibility is the spontaneous development of drug resistance which so far has been reported only for *Trypanosoma equiperdum* (Eagle and Magnuson, 1944).

It is clear that the question of how drug fastness comes about actually involves two separate problems. The first concerns biochemical or physicochemical mechanisms while the second comprises the biological mechanism.

In so far as the former are concerned, mainly trypanosomes have been studied. Essentially, two possibilities exist: Metabolic adaptations or changes in permeability. Voegtlin, Dyer, and Miller (1924) assumed that arsenic resistance would develop in trypanosomes by the acquisition of an additional amount of sulfhydryl compounds above the normal, which would enable the flagellates to detoxify more of the poison. This theory is not tenable, however, since Harvey (1948) could not find a significant increase in sulfhydryl content of arsenic-resistant trypanosomes. Also, it has not yet been possible to demonstrate definite metabolic differences between normal and arsenic-resistant trypanosomes (Harvey, 1949), but the possibility that some metabolic by-pass may develop cannot be ruled out completely. On the other hand, some evidence has been produced to the effect that altered permeability is of great importance. It is true that some investigators have reported an identical arsenic fixation by resistant and nonresistant strains (Reiner, Leonard, and Chao, 1932b; Pedlow and Reiner, 1935). However, Yorke, Murgatroyd, and Hawking (1931) and Hawking (1937) have demonstrated with a considerable degree of precision that the amount of arsenic fixed by resistant flagellates is much smaller than that taken up by normal specimens. A very thought provoking observation is Hawking's (1938) finding that the actual intracellular arsenic concentration required to kill resistant trypanosomes is smaller than that necessary in the case of normal ones. As to the exact mechanism responsible for the assumed changes in permeability, no definite information is available. Changes in the isoelectric points of some protoplasmic constituents may be involved (Schueler, 1947). Only circumstantial evidence is available for malarial parasites. Since paludrine-resistant *Plasmodium gallinaceum* strains do not show resistance to pyrimidine precursors of the drug, it is thought that in that case also the uptake of the drug is primarily involved (Williamson and Lourie, 1947).

The biological mechanism of drug resistance has given rise to some specutions, but no actual experimental analysis has taken place. It is obvious that low grade resistance can be explained theoretically by selection. That is, one can assume that only those individual parasites survive and are able to multiply that are, for unknown reasons, more resistant to a given drug than the average. This has been emphasized as a possibility both for trypanosomes and malarial parasites (Voegtlin, Dyer, and Miller, 1924; Knoppers, 1949). It is clear, however, and generally conceded that a more pronounced drug resistance cannot originate in this way. Any resistance to a drug concentration higher than* what kills all the individuals of the original strain is necessarily indicative of some fundamental change. In trypanosomes, for instance, a five-hundred fold increase in tolerance to arsenicals has been developed (Yorke, Murgatroyd, and Hawking, 1931), and in *Plasmodium cynomolgi* even a thousand fold increase to paludrine (Hawking and Perry, 1948). The most generally accepted explanation is that in such cases a genetic change, a mutation, has taken place (Yorke, Murgatroyd, and Hawking, 1931; Eagle and Magnuson, 1944). It would seem, however, that at least one other possibility exists. According to Sonneborn (1949) the development of drug fastness could be due to plasmatic inheritance. This possibility will be difficult to test with trypanosomes since they do not show fusion phenomena, but it may be open to analysis with malarial parasites.

### C. Stability of Drug Resistance

The speed with which drug resistance can be developed in parasitic protozoa varies both with the species of parasites and the drugs employed. In general it appears less difficult to procure resistant trypanosomes than malarial parasites. In the former, drug resistance is readily and relatively rapidly induced with organic arsenicals, antimonials, or acriflavine, while the process is much more laborious when Bayer 205 or diamidines are employed. Resistance against tartar emetic cannot be produced at all by exposing normal trypanosomes to the drug, but is readily produced if one starts from a strain previously made resistant to arsenic, antimony, or acriflavine (Lourie and Yorke, 1938). In malarial parasites, resistance to paludrine can be produced without undue difficulty (Hawking and Perry, 1948; Seaton and Adams, 1949). The same is true for plasmoquine resistance of *Plasmodium knowlesi* (Nauck, 1934; Fulton and Yorke, 1941a, 1943), while, on the contrary, *Plasmodium gallinaceum* proved refractory in this respect (Fulton, 1942). It is quite difficult to develop quinine resistance of malarial parasites experimentally and, as a matter of fact, Lourie (1935) and Williamson, Bertram, and Lourie (1947) were unable to do so despite a great amount of work. More recently, however, Knoppers (1949) reported a twofold increase in quinine resistance of *Plasmodium gallinaceum*, a small increase when compared to the thousand fold increase in paludrine resistance reported for *Plasmodium cynomolgi*, but nevertheless an apparently significant one.

The stability of experimentally induced drug fastness has been tested in two ways. On the one hand, drug resistant parasites have been propagated in successive series of experimental animals by syringe passage without being reexposed to the drug. It was found in this way that the character is often quite stable. Arsenic resistance was maintained by trypanosomes for many years, the maximum tested being 12 years and 6 months (Fulton and Yorke, 1941b). The resistance against synthalin and diamidines was somewhat less stable, being completely lost after 3 years and 6 months. No general statement is possible in the case of Bayer 205 since rather pronounced differences between strains of trypanosomes seem to exist (Fulton and Yorke, 1941b). Less information is available concerning this point for malarial parasites. However, Knoppers (1949) found that *Plasmodium gallinaceum* maintained its quinine resistance for at least 26 weeks. Finally, Fulton and Yorke (1941c) found the resistance of *Babesia canis* to 4:4'-diamidinostilbene to persist at least 28 months.

The second way to test the stability of drug resistance is to inquire

whether or not the character survives passage through the normal intermediate host, that is, whether it is influenced by cyclical development. It
has been found that arsenic resistance of trypanosomes was not changed by
a tsetse fly passage (Murgatroyd and Yorke, 1937; Fulton and Yorke,
1941b) while conflicting evidence has been presented for Bayer 205. According to Murgatroyd and Yorke (1937) the Bayer 205 resistance of
*Trypanosoma brucei* was not changed by a passage through *Glossina morsitans*, but van Hoof, Henrard, and Peel (1938) found a loss of resistance
after passing *Trypanosoma gambiense* through *Glossina palpalis*. The resistance of *Plasmodium falciparum* to paludrine (Seaton and Adams, 1949)
and that of *Plasmodium gallinaceum* to quinine (Knoppers, 1949) or paludrine (Bishop and Birkett, 1949) was not changed materially by mosquito
transmission.

### D. Specificity of Drug Resistance

It became evident very soon after the phenomenon of drug resistance had
become known, that it was not entirely specific. A trypanosome strain made
resistant to a certain drug proved to be resistant also to other compounds
which, frequently, were not even closely allied to the former. Ehrlich (1907,
1909) distinguished between resistance to arsenicals, basic triphenylmeth-
ane dyes, and azo dyes. Some of the newer findings are summarized in Table
42.

In so far as arsenic resistance is concerned, the term does not refer to all
arsenical compounds indiscriminately. Atoxyl resistant strains of trypanosomes are thus susceptible to arsenophenylglycine (Roehl, 1909) and sodium arsenite (Yorke and Murgatroyd, 1930), and strains resistant to
amino- and amide-substituted arsenicals are readily influenced by $\gamma$-($p$-ar-
senophenyl) butyric acid (Eagle, 1945a). In general, identical results are
obtained, within groups of compounds, regardless of the particular one to
which resistance has been developed. That is, a strain made resistant to
tryparsamide is resistant to acriflavine, and conversely, a strain rendered
resistant to acriflavine will be resistant also to tryparsamide. Exceptions to
this rule occur, however. It has been found that *Trypanosoma rhodesiense*
made resistant to nonacid substituted phenylarsonates and arsenoxides and
to acridines was sensitive to melaminyl substituted phenylarsonates and
arsenoxides (Lourie and Yorke, 1938), but the reverse is apparently not
true. A melarsen resistant strain was resistant to such drugs as tryparsamide, mapharside, and acriflavine (Rollo and Williamson, 1951). These and
similar observations are best explained on the assumption that "arsenic"
resistance is no true resistance to arsenic proper, but that it is directed
against one or more other groups of the drug molecule, the degree and
specificity of resistance being determined by the mechanisms by which the

drugs enter the body of the parasites (Yorke and Murgatroyd, 1930; King and Strangeways, 1942; King, 1943; Rollo and Williamson, 1951).

Only few data concerning the question of the specificity of drug resistance are available for malarial parasites. The findings are fundamentally similar to those reviewed concerning trypanosomes, the specificity not being absolute. Paludrine resistant strains of *Plasmodium gallinaceum* were found to be normally sensitive to quinine, mepacrine, pamaquine, and sulfadiazine, but resistant to drug No. 4430, a methyl homolog of paludrine (Williamson, Bertram, and Lourie, 1947; Bishop and Birkett, 1949). A quinine resistant strain of the same parasite was also resistant to cinchonidine, normally sensitive to atabrine, chloroquine, chlorguanide, and sulfamerazine and it was, surprisingly, oversensitive to such 8-aminoquinolines as plasmoquine, pentaquine, and isopentaquine (Knoppers, 1949).

TABLE 42. Specificity of drug resistance in trypanosomes (after data from Lourie and Yorke, 1938)

| MADE RESISTANT TO | SENSITIVITY TO (+ = RESISTANT; − = NONRESISTANT) | | | | | | |
|---|---|---|---|---|---|---|---|
| | Aromatic arsenicals | Aromatic antimonials | Acri-flavine | Tartar emetic | Bayer 205 | Ami-dines | Guani-dines |
| Aromatic arsenicals.. | + | + | + | − | − | − | − |
| Aromatic antimonials.............. | + | + | + | − | − | − | − |
| Acriflavine.......... | + | + | + | − | − | − | − |
| Bayer 205........... | − | − | − | − | + | − | − |
| Amidines............ | − | − | − | − | − | + | + |
| Guanidines......... | − | − | − | − | − | + | + |

LITERATURE

Andrews, J. C., and Cornatzer, W. E. (1942). *J. Pharmacol. Exptl. Therap.* **74:** 129–133.
Baldwin, E. (1943). *Parasitology* **35:** 89–111.
Ball, E. G. (1946). *Federation Proc.* **5:** 397–399.
Ball, E. G., Anfinsen, C. B., and Cooper, O. (1947). *J. Biol. Chem.* **168:** 257–270.
Ball, E. G., McKee, R. W., Anfinsen, C. B., Cruz, W. O., and Geiman, Q. M. (1948). *J. Biol. Chem.* **175:** 547–571.
Barron, E. S. G., and Singer, T. P. (1945). *J. Biol. Chem.* **157:** 221–240.
Beiler, J. M., and Martin, C. J. (1948). *J. Biol. Chem.* **174:** 31–35.
Berger, J., and Ansenjo, C. F. (1939). *Science* **90:** 299–300.
Berger, J., and Ansenjo, C. F. (1940). *Science* **91:** 387–388.
Betham, E. J. (1946). *Parasitology* **37:** 185–191.
Bichowsky, L. (1944). *Proc. Soc. Exptl. Biol. Med.* **57:** 163–164.
Bishop, A., and Birkett, B. (1949). *Parasitology* **39:** 125–137.
Bovarnick, M. R., Lindsay, A., and Hellerman, L. (1946a). *J. Biol. Chem.* **163:** 523–533.
Bovarnick, M. R., Lindsay, A., and Hellerman, L. (1946b). *J. Biol. Chem.* **163:** 535–551.

von Brand, T., Tobie, E. J., Kissling, R. E., and Adams, G. (1949). *J. Infectious Diseases* **85**: 5–16.

von Brand, T., Tobie, E. J., and Mehlman, B. (1950). *J. Cellular Comp. Physiol.* **35**: 273–300.

Bueding, E. (1949a). *Federation Proc.* **8**: 188–189.

Bueding, E. (1949b). *J. Exptl. Med.* **89**: 107–130.

Bueding, E. (1950a). *J. Gen. Physiol.* **33**: 475–495.

Bueding, E. (1950b). *J. Parasitol.* **36**: 201–210.

Bueding, E., Higashi, A., Peters, L., and Valk, A. D. (1947). *Federation Proc.* **6**: 313.

Bueding, E., and Oliver-Gonzalez, J. (1948). *Proc. Intern. Congr. Trop. Med. Malaria 4th Congr. Wash. D. C.* **2**: 1025–1033.

Bueding, E., and Peters, L. (1951). *J. Pharmacol. Exptl. Therap.* **101**: 210–229.

Bueding, E., Peters, L., and Welch, A. D. (1947). *Federation Proc.* **6**: 313.

Chance, M. R. A., and Mansour, T. E. (1949). *Brit. J. Pharmacol.* **4**: 7–13.

Chen, G. (1948). *J. Infectious Diseases* **82**: 226–230.

Chen, G., and Geiling, E. M. K. (1945). *J. Infectious Diseases* **77**: 139–143.

Chen, G., Geiling, E. M. K., and MacHatton, R. M. (1945). *J. Infectious Diseases* **76**: 152–154.

Collier, H. B. (1940). *Can. J. Research* **B18**: 345–350.

Collier, H. B., and Allen, D. E. (1942a). *Can. J. Research* **B20**: 189–193.

Collier, H. B., and Allen, D. E. (1942b). *Can. J. Research* **B20**: 284–290.

Crawford, T. B. B., and Levvy, G. A. (1947). *Biochem. J.* **41**: 333–336.

Eagle, H. (1945a). *Science* **101**: 69–71.

Eagle, H. (1945b). *J. Pharmacol. Exptl. Therap.* **85**: 265–282.

Eagle, H., and Magnuson, H. J. (1944). *J. Pharmacol. Exptl. Therap.* **82**: 137–151.

Ehrlich, P. (1907). *Berlin. klin. Wochschr.* **44**: 233–236, 280–283, 311–314, 341–344.

Ehrlich, P. (1909). *Ber.* **42**: 17–47.

von Fenyvessy, B., and Reiner, L. (1928). *Biochem. Z.* **202**: 75–80.

Fieser, L. F., and Heyman, H. (1948). *J. Biol. Chem.* **176**: 1363–1370.

Fulton, J. D. (1942). *Ann. Trop. Med. Parasitol.* **36**: 75–81.

Fulton, J. D., and Joyner, L. P. (1949). *Trans. Roy. Soc. Trop. Med. Hyg.* **43**: 273–286.

Fulton, J. D., and Yorke, W. (1941a). *Ann. Trop. Med. Parasitol.* **35**: 233–239.

Fulton, J. D., and Yorke, W. (1941b). *Ann. Trop. Med. Parasitol.* **35**: 221–227.

Fulton, J. D., and Yorke, W. (1941c). *Ann. Trop. Med. Parasitol.* **35**: 229–232.

Fulton, J. D., and Yorke, W. (1943). *Ann. Trop. Med. Parasitol.* **37**: 41–47.

Geiman, Q. M. (1948). *Proc. Intern. Congr. Trop. Med. Malaria 4th Congr. Wash. D. C.* **1**: 618–628.

Glowazky, F. (1937). *Z. Hyg. Infektionskrankh.* **119**: 741–752.

Goennert, R. (1947). *Naturwissenschaften* **34**: 347.

Greenberg, J. (1949). *J. Pharmacol. Exptl. Therap.* **97**: 238–242.

Greenberg, J., Boyd, B. L., and Josephson, E. S. (1948). *J. Pharmacol. Exptl. Therap.* **94**: 60–64.

Haas, E. (1944). *J. Biol. Chem.* **155**: 321–331.

Hales, D. R., and Welch, A. D. (1947). *Federation Proc.* **6**: 335–336.

Harvey, S. C. (1948). *Proc. Soc. Exptl. Biol. Med.* **67**: 269–272.

Harvey, S. C. (1949). *J. Biol. Chem.* **179**: 435–453.

Hawking, F. (1937). *J. Pharmacol. Exptl. Therap.* **59**: 123–156.

Hawking, F. (1938). *Ann. Trop. Med. Parasitol.* **32**: 313–331.

Hawking, F., and Perry, W. L. M. (1948). *Lancet* **255**: 850.

Hellerman, L., Bovarnick, M. R., and Porter, C. C. (1946). *Federation Proc.* **5**: 400–405.

Hellerman, L., Chinard F. P., and Deitz, V. R. (1943). *J. Biol. Chem.* **147**: 443–462.

Heyman, H., and Fieser, L. F. (1948). *J. Pharmacol. Exptl. Therap.* **94**: 97–111.

van Hoof, L., Henrard, C., and Peel, E. (1938). *Trans. Roy. Soc. Trop. Med. Hyg.* **32**: 197–208.

Hopkins, F. G., Morgan, E. J., and Lutwak-Mann, C. (1938). *Biochem. J.* **32**: 1829–1848.

von Issekutz, B. (1933a). *Arch. exptl. Path. Pharmakol.* **173**: 479–498.

von Issekutz, B. (1933b). *Arch. exptl. Path. Pharmakol.* **173**: 499–507.

von Jancsó, N., and von Jancsó, H. (1935). *Z. Immunitätsforsch.* **86**: 1–30.

King, H. (1943). *Trans. Faraday Soc.* **39**: 383–389.

King, H., and Strangeways, W. I. (1942). *Ann. Trop. Med. Parasitol.* **36**: 47–53.

Knoppers, A. T. (1949). *Doc. Neerland. Indones. Morbis Trop.* **1**: 55–60.

Kopac, M. J. (1947). *Cancer Research* **7**: 44–46.

Levaditi, C., and von Knaffl-Lenz (1909). *Bull. soc. path. exotique* **2**: 405–409.

Lourie, E. M. (1935). *Ann. Trop. Med. Parasitol.* **29**: 421–433.

Lourie, E. M., and Yorke, W. (1937). *Ann. Trop. Med. Parasitol.* **31**: 435–445.

Lourie, E. M., and Yorke, W. (1938). *Ann. Trop. Med. Parasitol.* **32**: 201–213.

Marshall, E. K. (1946). *Federation Proc.* **5**: 298–304.

Marshall, P. B. (1948a). *Brit. J. Pharmacol.* **3**: 8–14.

Marshall, P. B. (1948b). *Brit. J. Pharmacol.* **3**: 1–7.

Mead, J. F., Rapport, M. M., Senear, A. E., Maynard, J. T., and Koepfli, J. B. (1946). *J. Biol. Chem.* **163**: 465–473.

Moulder, J. W. (1948). *J. Infectious Diseases* **83**: 262–270.

Moulder, J. W. (1949). *J. Infectious Diseases* **85**: 195–204.

Murgatroyd, F., and Yorke, W. (1937). *Ann. Trop. Med. Parasitol.* **31**: 165–172.

Nauck, E. G. (1934). *Arch. Schiffs-u. Tropen-Hyg.* **38**: 313–326.

Oliver-Gonzalez, J., and Welch, A. D. (no date). Unpublished experiments quoted in Bueding, E. (1950b).

Pedlow, J. T., and Reiner, L. (1935). *J. Pharmacol. Exptl. Therap.* **55**: 179–199.

Peters, L., Bueding, E., Valk, A., Higashi, A., and Welch, A. D. (1949a). *J. Pharmacol. Exptl. Therap.* **95**: 212–239.

Peters, L., Higashi, A., and Welch, A. D. (1949b). *J. Pharmacol. Exptl. Therap.* **96**: 460–471.

Peters, L., and Welch, A. D. (no date). Unpublished experiments quoted in Bueding, E. (1950b).

Quastel, J. H. (1931). *Biochem. J.* **25**: 1121–1127.

Rapkine, L. (1938). *Biochem. J.* **32**: 1729–1739.

Rebello, S., and Rico, J. T. (1926). *Compt. rend. soc. biol.* **94**: 915–918.

Reiner, L., Leonard, C. S., and Chao, S. S. (1932a). *Arch. intern. pharmacodynamie* **43**: 186–198.

Reiner, L., Leonard, C. S., and Chao, S. S. (1932b). *Arch. intern. pharmacodynamie* **43**: 199–208.

Rico, J. T. (1926a). *Compt. rend. soc. biol.* **94**: 918–920.

Rico, J. T. (1926b). *Compt. rend. soc. biol.* **94**: 921–923.

Robbins, B. H. (1930). *J. Biol. Chem.* **87**: 251–257.

Rodaniche, E. C., and Kirsner, J. B. (1942). *J. Parasitol.* **28**: 441–449.

Roehl, W. (1909). *Z. Immunitätsforsch.* **1**: 633–649.

Rogers, W. P. (1944). *Parasitology* **36**: 98–109.

Rogers, W. P. (1946). *Australian J. Sci.* **9**: 55–59.

Rollo, I. M., and Williamson, J. (1951). *Nature* **167**: 147–148.

Santiago-Stevenson, D., Oliver-Gonzalez, J., Peters, L., and Welch, A. D. (no date). Quoted in Bueding, E. (1950b).

Schern, K., and Artagaveytia-Allende, R. (1935). *Arch. soc. biol. Montevideo* **6**: 244.

Schern, K., and Artagaveytia-Allende, R. (1936). *Z. Immunitätsforsch.* **89**: 21–63.

Schueler, F. W. (1947). *J. Infectious Diseases* **81**: 139–146.

Seaton, D. R., and Adams, A. R. D. (1949). *Lancet* **257**: 323–324.

Silverman, M., Ceithaml, J., Taliaferro, L. G., and Evans, E. A. (1944). *J. Infectious Diseases* **75**: 212–230.

Singer, E., and Fischl, V. (1934). *Z. Hyg. Infektionskrankh.* **116**: 36–40.

Singer, E., Kotrba, J., and Fischl, V. (1934). *Z. Hyg. Infektionskrankh.* **116**: 133–137.

Sonneborn, T. M. (1949). *Am. Scientist* **37**: 33–59.

Town, B. W., and Wormall, A. (1949). *Biochem. J.* **44**: XXXVIII.

Town, B. W., Wills, E. D., and Wormall, A. (1949). *Nature* **163**: 735–736.

Trager, W. (1943). *J. Exptl. Med.* **77**: 411–420.

Trim, A. R. (1943). *Parasitology* **35**: 209–219.

Trim, A. R. (1949). *Parasitology* **39**: 281–290.

Voegtlin, C. (1925). *Physiol. Revs.* **5**: 63–94.

Voegtlin, C., Dyer, H. A., and Leonard, C. S. (1923). *U. S. Pub. Health Service Pub. Health Repts.* **38**: 1882–1912.

Voegtlin, C., Dyer, H. A., and Miller, D. W. (1924). *J. Pharmacol. Exptl. Therap.* **23**: 55–86.

Voegtlin, C., Rosenthal, S. M., and Johnson, J. M. (1931). *U. S. Pub. Health Service Pub. Health Repts.* **46**: 339–354.

Voegtlin, C., and Smith, H. W. (1920). *U. S. Pub. Health Service Pub. Health Repts.* **35**: 2264–2273.

Walti, A. J. (1937). *J. Biol. Chem.* **119**: CI.

Walti, A. (1938). *J. Am. Chem. Soc.* **60**: 493.

Watt, J. Y. C., and VandeGrift, W. B. (1950). *J. Lab. Clin. Med.* **36**: 741–746.

Welch, A. D., Peters, L., Bueding, E., Valk, A., and Higashi, A. (1947). *Science* **105**: 486–488.

Wendel, W. B. (1946). *Federation Proc.* **5**: 406–407.

Williamson, J., Bertram, D. S., and Lourie, E. M. (1947). *Nature* **159**: 885–886.

Williamson, J., and Lourie, E. M. (1947). *Ann. Trop. Med. Parasitol.* **41**: 278–291.

Wills, E. D., and Wormall, A. (1949). *Biochem. J.* **44**: XXXIX.

Work, T. S., and Work, E. (1948). The Basis of Chemotherapy. Interscience Publishers, New York.

Wright, C. I., and Sabine, J. C. (1944). *J. Biol. Chem.* **155**: 315–320.

Wright, H. N., Cuckler, A. C., Cranston, E. M., and Bieter, R. N. (1947). *Federation Proc.* **6**: 387–388.

Wright, W. H. (1946). *In* Powers, Advancing Fronts in Chemistry. Vol. 2, Reinhold, New York, pp. 105–146.

Yorke, W., and Murgatroyd, F. (1930). *Ann. Trop. Med. Parasitol.* **24**: 449–476.

Yorke, W., Murgatroyd, F., and Hawking, F. (1931). *Ann. Trop. Med. Parasitol.* **25**: 521-544.

# AUTHOR INDEX

Numbers in italics refer to the page on which the reference is listed in the bibliography at the end of each chapter.

## A

Abdel-Akher, M., 13, *21*
Abderhalden, E., 136, *143*
Abrams, E., 8, *9*
Achard, C., 260, *262*
Ackert, J. E., 208, *211*, 218, 222, 225, *231*, *234*, 280, *283*
Ada, G., 255, 257, 260, *262*
Adam, W., 146, 147, 151, 172, *173*
Adams, A. R. D., 96, *125*, 299, 300, *304*
Adams, G., 94, *122*, 139, *144*, 250, *262*, 290, *302*
Adcock, E. M., 76, *84*
Addis, C. J., 132, *143*, 226, 227, *231*, 279, *283*
Adler, S., 148, *173*, 180, *191*, 197, *211*
Aducco, V., 56, 57, *61*
Aitken, T., 248, 251, 256, *265*
Albanese, G., 67, *71*
Allen, D. E., 296, *302*
Almasy, F., 59, *62*
Alsterberg, G., 190, *191*
Alt, H. L., 110, *121*, 146, 150, 152, *173*
Alton, C. H., 210, *212*
Amy, A. C., 238, *243*
Anderson, H. H., 135, *143*, 199, *211*
Anderson, R. J., 6, *10*, 12, 16, *23*, 25, 26, 28, *35*, 37, 38, *43*, 141, *145*
Anderson, W. A. D., 61, *62*, 66, *71*, *73*, 237, *245*
Andrade, S. O., 70, *73*
Andrew, B. J., 216, *231*
Andrews, J., 65, *71*, 96, 106, *121*, 180, *191*, 238, 239, 241, *243*, *244*, 278, 282, *283*
Andrews, J. C., 295, *301*
Andrews, J. S., 228, 230, *231*, 240, 241, *243*, 247, *262*
Andriadse, N., 246, *262*
Anfinsen, C. B., 93, 96, 97, 108, 117, *121*, *123*, 131, *131*, 134, 138, 140, *144*, *145*,

157, 160, 164, 165, 167, *173*, *174*, 181, 185, *191*, *193*, 199, 203, *211*, *212*, 225, *231*, 246, 247, *265*, 293, *301*
Angolotti, E., 252, *262*
Ansenjo, C. F., 295, *301*
Armer, J. M., 14, 18, *21*, 30, *34*, 101, *121*, 127, *131*, 218, 221, *231*
Arndt, W., 31, *34*
Artagaveytia-Allende, R., 249, *265*, 288, *304*
Artemov, N. M., 47, *50*
Ascoli, V., 60, *61*
Ashbel, R., 148, *173*, 281, *283*
Ashcroft, L. S., 69, *71*
Askanazy, M., 3, *9*, 60, *61*
Augustine, D. L., 133, *144*, 251, 254, *262*
Auricchio, L., 250, *262*
Axmann, M. C., 15, 19, *22*
Axtmayer, J. H., 226, *233*

## B

Bacq, Z. M., 47, *50*
Baer, J. G., 59, *62*, 150, 152, 156, 160, 161, 165, 168, *173*, 204, *213*
Baernstein, H. D., 59, *61*, 93, 106, *122*, 166, *173*, 199, *213*
Baffoni, G. M., 270, 271, 273, *283*
Bahler, T. L., 248, 261, *266*
Bailenger, J., 69, *73*
Baker, M., 224, *232*
Balbiani, E. G., 181, *191*
Baldwin, E., 13, 21, *22*, 47, *50*, 113, *121*, 134, 142, *144*, 294, *301*
Balian, B., 248, 251, 261, *262*, *266*
Ball, E. G., 93, 96, 97, 108, 117, *121*, *123*, 130, *131*, 134, 138, 140, *144*, *145*, 157, 160, 164, 165, 167, *173*, *174*, 181, 185, *191*, *193*, 199, 203, *211*, *212*, 225, *231*, 246, 247, *265*, 292, 293, *301*
Ball, G. H., 134, *145*, 200, *214*, 224, *234*

305

Fischl, V., 289, *304*
Fisher, M. L., 225, *231*
Fleisher, M. S., 137, *145*
Fleming, E. M., 236, *245*
Flössner, O., 110, *123*, 141, *144*
Florkin, M., 143, *144*, 178, *192*
Flosi, A. Z., 246, *263*
Flury, F., 4, 5, 6, 7, *9*, *10*, 16, 17, *22*, 26, 27, 28, 29, 31, *34*, *35*, 38, 40, 41, *43*, 56, *62*, 67, 70, *72*, 99, 110, 112, *123*, 136, 141, 142, *144*, 259, *263*
Fodor, O., 251, *263*
Foote, M., 248, 251, 256, 261, *263*
Forbes, H. S., 178, *191*
Ford, W. W., 238, *244*
Forsman, B., 270, 273, *284*
Foster, A. O., 220, *232*, 240, 241, *244*
Foster, M., 12, *22*
Foury, P. J. J., 241, *244*
Foy, H., 236, 237, *244*
Fraipont, J., 3, *10*
Frank, L. L., 251, *263*
Franklin, M. C., 248, *263*
Fraser, A. H., 220, *233*
Fraser, L. A., 14, *22*
Fredericq, L., 68, *72*, 178, *192*, 230, *233*
Freeman, E. A., 225, *231*
Frei, W., 59, *62*
French, M. H., 250, 252, 258, 260, *263*, *266*
Friedheim, E. A. H., 59, *62*, 150, 152, 156, 160, 161, 165, 168, *173*
Friedmann, E., 237, *245*
Frye, W. W., 197, 198, 199, *213*, *214*
Fülleborn, F., 208, *212*, 241, *244*
Fuhrmeister, C., 223 *232*
Fujii, H., 69, 70, *73*
Fulton, J. D., 4, *9*, 60, 61, *62*, 94, 96, 106, 108, 109, 114, *122*, *123*, 140, 141, *144*, 147, 148, 149, 152, 166, 167, *173*, 250, 253, 255, 257, 260, *262*, *263*, 290, 291, 299, 300, *302*

## G

Gall, E. A., 247, 250, *263*
Gammel, J. A., 258, 260, *263*
Garin, C. P., 236, *244*
Garnault, P., 269, *284*
Gatin-Gruzewska, Z., 13, *22*
Gear, J., 236, 237, *244*

Geiger, A., 65, *72*, 96, 107, *123*, 238, 239, *244*
Geiling, E. M. K., 96, 117, *122*, 290, 291, *302*
Geiman, Q. M., 66, *72*, 93, 96, 97, 108, 117, *121*, *123*, 131, *131*, 134, 137, 138, 140, *144*, *145*, 157, 160, 164, 165, 167, *173*, *174*, 181, 185, *191*, *193*, 199, 203, *211*, *212*, *213*, 225, *231*, *234*, 246, 247, *265*, 268, *285*, 292, 293, *301*, *302*
Gelfand, M., 227, *233*
Gellhorn, A., 260, *263*
Gerdjikoff, I., 268, *284*
Gettier, A., 83, *84*, 211, *212*
Ghalioungi, P., 254, *263*
Ghosh, B. M., 255, *264*
Ghosh, B. N., 60, *62*, *63*, 260, *263*
Giard, A., 270, 271, *284*
Gilbert, G. B., 178, *194*
Gilmour, D., 106, *123*, 180, *193*
Giovannola, A., 14, 15, 18, 19, *22*, 33, *35*, 130, *131*
Giraud, P., 260, *263*
Giroud, A., 46, *50*
Girth, H. B., 208, *212*
Giusti, L., 68, *72*
Glaessner, K., 98, *123*, 236, *243*
Glaser, R. W., 197, 198, 207, 208, 209, 210, *212*
Glenn, P. M., 260, *263*
Glick, D., 46, *50*
Glowazky, F., 108, *123*, 292, *302*
Goennert, R., 295, *302*
Gösswald, K., 274, *284*
Goldfisher, R., 19, *24*
Goldschmidt, R., 69, *72*, 272, *284*
Golubeva, N. A., 188, *193*
Gonzalez, M. D. P., 160, *173*
Goodey, T., 274, 280, *284*
Gordon, H. H., 253, *264*
Gordon, H. McL., 220, *233*, 248, *263*
Gordon, R. M., 53, *61*, 101, *121*, 127, *131*, 137, *144*, 184, *191*
Gourevitch, M. A., 59, 60, *62*
Grana, A., 69, 70, *73*
Granovsky, A. A., 216, *233*
Grass, H., 178, *193*
Grassé, P., 15, *22*
Grassi, G. B., 70, *72*
Greeff, R., 53, *62*

Green, A. A., 48, *50*
Green, N. K., 68, *74*, 133, *145*, 205, *212*, 242, *245*
Greenberg, J., 222, *233*, *234*, 268, *284*, *285*, 293, *302*
Greig, E. D. W., 255, *263*
Griffin, A. M., 197, 199, *214*
Gritti, P., 98, *122*, 127, *131*
Groll, H., 259, *263*
Guerrini, G., 67, *72*
Gundel, M. E., 224, *234*
Gurtner, H., 5, *10*, 70, *72*
Gurwitsch, B. M., 30, *35*
Gutfreund, H., 13, *22*
Guthrie, R., 200, *212*
György, P., 223, *232*

## H

Haas, E., 292, 293, *302*
Hackett, L. W., 219, *233*
Haemmerli-Boveri, V., 273, *284*
Hager, A., 222, 226, *233*
Hahn, P. F., 240, *244*
Hale, M. W., 238, 239, *245*
Hales, D. R., 296, *302*
Hall, M. C., 205, *212*, 229, *233*
Hall, R. P., 126, *131*
Hall, S. R., 216, 220, *232*
Halsall, T. G., 13, *22*
Hamann, O., 33, *35*
Hamill, J. M., 230, *233*
Hamm, A. H., 275, *286*
Hansen, E. L., 135, *143*, 199, *211*
Harned, B. K., 230, *233*
Harnisch, O., 93, 107, *123*, 147, 150, 161, 162, 163, 169, 172, *174*, 182, *193*
Harris, M. M., 197, *211*
Harrison, H. C., 178, *192*
Harrison, W. T., 69, *73*
Harrop, G., 178, *191*
Hartman, E., 248, 251, 256, 261, *263*, *265*
Hartog, M., 75, *84*
Harvey, S. C., 48, *50*, 59, *62*, 93, 94, 106, 108, 109, 117, 119, 121, *123*, 126, 130, *131*, 149, 167, *174*, 186, *193*, 229, *233*, 282, *284*, 298, *302*
Harwood, P. D., 66, *72*, 188, *193*, 241, *244*, 251, 262, *263*
Hashimoto, S., 267, *284*
Hassan, A., 259, 260, *264*

Hastings, E. G., 217, *233*
Hatieganu, J., 251, *263*
Hauschka, T. S., 65, *72*, 278, *284*
Hausen, C., 8, *11*
Hausmann, L., 182, *193*
Havens, L. C., 178, *194*
Hawking, F., 203, *212*, 297, 298, 299, *302*, 304
Hegner, R., 218, 221, 223, *233*
Heim, J. W., 259, *263*
Heise, R., 136, *143*
Helander, E. V., 241, 242, *243*, *244*
Hellerman, L., 92 119, *121*, *123*, 140, *144*, 165, 167, *173*, 289, 292, 293, *301*, *302*, 303
Helmy, M., 133, *144*
Hendee, E. C., 216, *233*
Hendry, E. B., 255, *263*
Henrard, C., 201, *211*, 300, *303*
Henry, A. F. X., 257, *263*
Herfs, A., 75, 78, 79, *84*
Hermann, R. G., 277, *284*
Herrick, C. A., 14, *22*, 149, 155, *175*, 248, 261, *266*
Hesselbrock, W. B., 253, 254, *264*
Heyman, H., 293, 294, *302*, *303*
Hickman, H. R. B., 178, *192*
Hicks, D. O., 184, *192*
Higashi, A., 189, *194*, *195*, 295, *302*, *303*, 304
Highman, B., 222, *234*
Hill, A. W., 241, *244*
Hill, C. H., 222, *234*
Hill, G. R., 46, *50*, *51*
Hill, K. R., 258, *263*
Hill, T. S., 236, *245*, 246, 260, *265*
Hinshaw, H. C., 176, 180, *193*
Hiraishi, T., 226, *233*
Hiromoto, T., 248, 256, 261, *264*
Hirsch, G. C., 8, *10*, 19, *22*, 33, *35*, 129, *131*
Hirst, E. L., 13, *22*
Hirvonen, M., 248, *264*
Hoare, C. A., 170, *174*
Hobson, —, 1, 6, 7, *10*, 81, *84*, 89, 90, *91*
Hobson, A. D., 181, *193*, 204, *212*
Hoeppli, R., 15, *24*, 68, *72*, 136, 137, *144*, 204, 205, 208, *212*
Hoffenreich, F., 251, *264*
Hoffman, E., 281, *286*
Hoffman, W. A., 133, *144*, 226, *233*

# SUBJECT INDEX

## A

Acanthocephala (see also various genera of acanthocephala)
  chemical composition
    dry substance, 5, 6
    enzymes, 50
    inorganic substances, 5, 7
    lipids, 26–28, 31, 33, 34
    pigments, 52, 53
    polysaccharides, 13, 18–20
    proteins, 38, 42
    toxic substances, 70
  growth requirements, 211
  influence of host nutrition on, 219
    on endocrine glands, 273
  metabolism of
    carbohydrates, 103, 105
    lipids, 127, 129
  water exchange, 82, 83
*Acanthocephalus* spp., 52, 127, 129
*Acanthocheilonema perstans*, 15
Acetaldehyde, 113
Acetic acid, 107, 108, 110, 113, 115, 121, 126, 215, 292.
Acetylcholine, 47, 48
Acetylmethyl carbinol, 112, 113
*cis*-Aconitic acid, 119
Acriflavine, 299, 300, 301
Adenosinetriphosphatase, 48
Adenosinetriphosphate, 87, 140, 204
Adenylic acid, 102, 140, 204
Adrenocorticotropic hormone, 268, 283
*Agamermis decaudata*, 42, 274
Age, influence on respiration, 147, 152, 153
*Aggregata eberthi*, 46, 273
Alanine, 40, 140
Albumin, 38, 257, 259, 260, 294
Albumoses, 38, 70, 141, 241
Aldolase, 116
Allantoicase, 143
Allantoin, 259
Allantoinase, 143

*Allassostoma magnum*, 56, 59
*Allocreadium transversale*, 54
Aluminum, 6, 7
*Amallocystis fasciatus*, 273
Amidines, 301
Amine bases, 141
Amino acid oxidase, 142
Amino acids
  as metabolic endproducts, 141, 142, 259
  essential, 134, 200
  in parasite cultures, 199, 203, 207
*p*-Aminobenzoic acid, 203, 293
Ammonia, 77, 139, 140, 141, 142, 143, 259
Amphetamine, 294
Amygdalin, 95
Amylase, 98, 99, 100, 101, 102
Anaerobic life (see also oxygen lack)
  occurrence of, 128, 188, 189, 190
  origin of, 190, 191
*Anaplasma*, 236, 238, 239
*Ancylostoma braziliense*, 209
*Anyclostoma caninum*
  anticoagulants in, 137
  chemical composition, 14, 16
  diet of host and, 220
  influence on host, 240, 251
  *in vitro* survival, 182, 208, 209
  metabolism, 130, 156, 157, 188
*Ancylostoma duodenale*, 79, 133, 209
Ancylostomiasis
  anemia in, 240, 241
  blood lipids in, 256
  blood proteins in, 258, 259
  carbohydrates in, 251, 254
  edema in, 259
Anemia, origin of, in
  coccidiosis, 240
  *Diphyllobothrium* infections, 67, 68, 241–243
  hookworm infections, 240, 241
  malaria, 236, 237, 258
  trypanosomiasis, 238, 239
*Angusticaecum* sp., 82

4:4′-Diamidinostilbene, 299

*Dicrocoelium lanceatum*, 32, 56

Diet of host
  deficient diet and parasites, 219–220, 279
  influencing hookworm anemia, 241
  influence of single components, 223–227
  one-sided diet and parasites, 221–222

Digestion coefficients, 228

Dihydrosphingosine, 28

Dihydroxyacetone phosphate, 116

Dinitrophenol, 165, 170

*Dioctophyme renale*, 42, 55, 56, 57, 141, 143

Dipeptidase, 135, 136

*Dipetalonema gracilis*, 17

*Diphyllobothrium latum*
  chemical composition, 4, 16, 26–29, 38, 59
  cause of anemia, 67–68, 241–243
  digestive enzymes, 135
  growth, 133
  influence on minerals of host, 248
  osmotic relationships, 80, 90
  respiration, 150, 152, 156, 159, 160, 161, 165, 168
  survival *in vitro*, 205

*Diplodinium maggii*, 99

*Diplospinifer serpenticola*, 55

*Diplostomum flexicaudum*, 135, 197, 206, 269

*Dipylidium caninum*, 4, 31, 47, 135

*Dirofilaria immitis*, 5, 17, 68, 205, 267, 295

*Distomum globiporum*, 79

*Dracunculus insignis*, 93, 97, 105, 109, 111, 151, 169

*Drepanidotaenia*, 277

Drug resistance
  origin, 297–299
  specificity, 300–301
  stability, 299–300

Dry matter, 1, 4, 5, 6

Dulcite, 95

## E

Ecdysis of nematodes, 209, 210

*Echinobothrium* spp., 54

*Echinococcus granulosus*
  chemical composition, 1, 3, 7, 12
  enzymes, 136

  localization in innersecretory glands, 267
  metabolic endproducts, 31, 110, 141
  oxygen relationships, 189
  survival *in vitro*, 204
  toxic substances, 67, 68

*Echinorhynchus* spp., 33, 50, 52, 55

*Echinostoma revolutum*, 54, 226, 251

Edema, 258, 259

*Eimeria nieschulzi*, 223

*Eimeria stiedae*, 52, 254

*Eimeria tenella*, 149, 155, 247, 250, 253, 281

Elastin, 38, 41

Elephantiasis, filarial, 259

Embden-Meyerhof sequence, 113, 114, 116, 117

Emetine, 294

*Endamoeba blattae*, 127, 218, 221

*Endamoeba histolytica*
  cyst wall, 41
  drug resistance, 297
  enzymes, 50, 98, 135, 136
  glycogen, 18, 101, 103
  growth requirements, 198–199
  infectivity and host diet, 222
  oxygen relationships, 180, 198
  sterile specimens, 196, 197

*Endamoeba invadens*, 199

*Endolimax* spp., 41, 218

Endotoxins in trypanosomes, 65

*Endotrypanum schaudinni*, 21

*Enterobius vermicularis*, 184, 226

*Enteromonas*, 221

*Entodinium*, 77, 99

Enzymes of
  acanthocephala, 50
  arthropods, 101, 135, 137
  cestodes, 47, 49, 50, 116, 135, 136, 143, 186
  nematodes, 47, 48, 50, 99–101, 127, 136, 137, 186, 230
  protozoa, 48, 50, 59, 98, 99, 116, 117, 135, 136, 230
  trematodes, 47, 49, 116, 135–137, 143, 186, 230

*Epidinium*, 77

Ergosterol, 8

Erythrite, 95

Estradiol, 280

**H**

mechanism of anemia, 238
respiration of host, 239
suprarenal involvement, 268
toxic influences, 65, 252
Tryparsamide, 300
Tryptophane, 200
Tumors
and cestodes, 68
and *Trypanosoma cruzi*, 65
*Tylenchinema oscinellae*, 274, 280
Tyrosinase, 56
Tyrosine, 40, 41, 53

**U**

Undecane diamidine, 291
Urea, 77, 141–143, 258–260
Urease, 143
Urethane, 168, 169, 283
Uric acid, 77, 141–143, 259

**V**

*Vahlkampfia calkensis*, 76
Valeric acid, 107, 110, 112, 113
Valine, 40, 134, 140, 200

Vitamins
occurrence in parasites, 45–46, 217
of host diet influencing helminths, 220, 225–227
influencing protozoa, 216, 223, 224
role in parasite cultures, 199, 207, 210
question of withdrawal, 230, 242
Vitelline membrane, 33
Volutin, 42, 86

**W**

Water metabolism of
arthropods, 83, 84
helminths, 79–83
protozoa, 75–78
*Watsonius watsoni*, 67
*Wuchereria bancrofti*, 205, 295

**X**

Xylose, 95, 98

**Z**

Zinc, 6
*Zoogonus vividus*, 54